The VANISHING VILLAGE

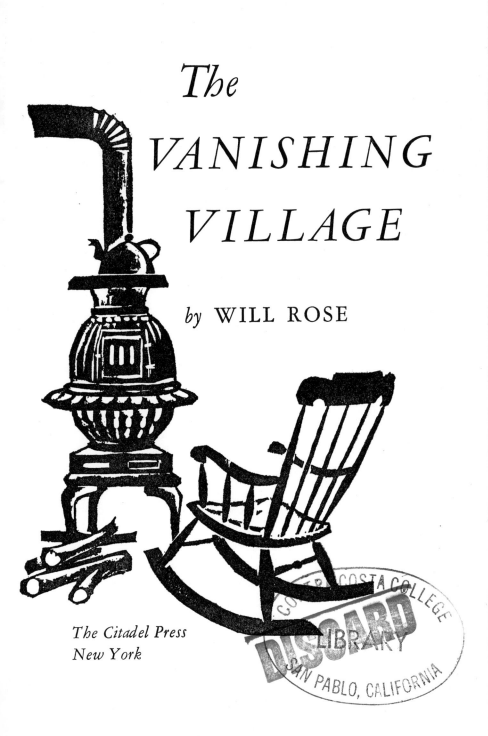

The
VANISHING
VILLAGE

by WILL ROSE

The Citadel Press
New York

For Louise Lamberson Rose

Contents

HISTORICAL NOTE

Artists of all types began to discover the beauty and seclusion of Woodstock Valley, New York, around 1901. From then on, the characteristics and customs of the Holland Dutch who had inhabited the Valley almost exclusively since 1770 were submerged by the new inhabitants and lost forever. This book is set in the period between 1896 and 1903.

Alice! a childish story take
And with a gentle hand
Lay it where childhood's dreams are
Twined
In memory's mystic band.

LEWIS CARROLL

✻ Around the White-Bellied Stove

. . . and the rumor that the artists are coming

My father says that I am the best little overhearer in the business and that it is a bad business to get into. You can't tell much about a horse by his tail, he says. "My life would be a lot easier if you would stick to safe subjects for young minds," he says.

"We are not talking about any old horse's tail," I say. But, of course, I know what he means. I am about through with the eighth grade in district school because I started in when I was four years old and I have what Linnie Jewel, our hired girl who lives with us, calls a sponge in my head. So I know my father was making what Elijah T. Bovee, who teaches district school, calls a metaphor. He does not mean a tail, but a tale; and it is just like Linnie says—you can't tell much from a tale but you can tell something.

My father acts like his patience is strained because I stick around in my father's general merchandise store in Woodstock to overhear the men talking around the white-bellied stove. So I know a lot of things they don't teach you in district school because they are not in the schoolbooks. Maybe some of them are things that a boy has no business to know, like the night Jim Plass was telling how that young Suffern woman from New York who was boarding with the Vandenbergs got Pete Vandenberg, who is only fifteen but big, to climb up in the haymow with her. But when Jim Plass tells it, you take it with a grain of salt anyway. Jim Plass is what they call barnyard and always trying to get attention with some kind of tale, and you would do better to let it go in one ear and out the other.

My father's store is a big one. On the ground floor and along past the middle, from the front door, there is a big open space with a big, white-bellied stove in the middle. A long bench and a lot of chairs are around the stove and the men come in at night and sit there. They smoke and knock their pipes out in the spittoons, and in winter they spit against the hot sides of the white-bellied stove, where it sizzles. This has been going on, I guess, from before I was born because the white belly of the stove is all stained and spotted with burned tobacco juice.

I have overheard my mother say that it is a nest and ought to be cleaned out, but my father says it is good for business because they get to feel friendly with our store and it is a kind of club. Mostly, it is the good men of the village who come in and sit there. Once in awhile a man who is drunk wanders in, but if he does not go to sleep the men take him out the front door and start him on his way. There are only two other places for the men to go at night, and they are the barrooms in the Woodstock Hotel at the bend in the road through the village, and the old hotel, which is Sam Elwyn's Hotel, up by the Methodist Church; and so men who do not drink, or not very often, are likely to come and sit in my father's store.

The talk I hear in the store is interesting and it helps my knowledge, but it has not been earth-shaking until lately. They are saying that our old Holland Dutch village is going to pass out of the picture. They say that they hear men by the names of Whitehead or White or Brown or something like that have bought up half the side of the Overlook Mountain below Mead's Mountain House and that they are going to change Woodstock into an art colony. If this is so, it is terrible.

Of course, I don't know what an art colony is. But it seemed like a safe subject, and so just as soon as I could get any attention at breakfast I asked my father. He said he does not rightly know himself. The talk and guesses of the men at the store, he says, make him think that a lot of cabins are going to be built on the side of the mountain in the woods, and that they will be rented to folks who call themselves artists. Or maybe some of them have enough money to buy cabins. He is not acquainted with artists, he said, and so he does not know much about them. But he has heard or read that they are Bohemian. I asked what that was and he said a kind of freethinking. At the same time, he said, he didn't know as that had ought to bother Woodstock much because all thinking is pretty free so far as he knows.

About all he knows about artists is that they paint pictures, he said. Some of them are not very strong in the church, or so he has heard, and some of the pictures they paint don't look like anything anybody has ever seen but sometimes turn out to be worth thousands and thousands of dollars. That's about a hundred years or so later, he said, after somebody has discovered something about them that nobody has noticed before. All in all, he said, he wasn't taking the art colony as seriously as some were, and he guessed they would get along all right in Woodstock if they behaved themselves.

I think what my father meant by this is that Woodstock is pretty religious and pretty strict. Our backbone is Holland Dutch. The Riseleys, Harders, Longyears, Shufeldts, Roses (that's us), the Herricks, Winnies, Lowns, Wurtses, Van Ettens, Bovees, Mowers, Van Kurens, Shorts, and Hogans are all Dutch Reformed Church folks.

Of course my father is strong in the Dutch Reformed Church, but he is quite a joker sometimes about the Church and the way some people who are very strict sometimes act. When he gets a twinkle in his eye about religion I can see that my mother does not like it. She says there are no two ways about it and that everybody can be good if they want to. Excuses don't go, she says.

But I have heard my father say that it is easier for some to be good than for others. Sometimes, he says, when a bad man is good he deserves more credit than a camel going through the eye of a needle. Just the same, my father is so strong in the Dutch Reformed Church that he is what they call Presiding Elder and he goes to what they call Classis for our church. When we needed a new minister he got him, and the minister lived with us until his family came. My father looks after making church ends meet, too.

Come to think of it, my mother is a pretty strong Dutch Reformed, too. She is very pretty and she sings in the choir, and she is strong in the Ladies' Aid. When I was younger, I went to choir practice with her and noticed that they seemed to have a lot of fun, but the thing that interested me then was Vernon Lown's Adam's apple. He is a tall, bony bachelor who leads the choir, and the women josh him all the time even when they sing "Jesus Lover of my Soul." Vern sings base. Old Elijah T. Bovee, who taught district school until he was kicked out for raising so many welts on Delancy Boice, said that base is spelled bass, the same as a fish. There are big-mouth bass and small-mouth bass, and maybe that is why. When Vern is dressed up in a Prince Albert on Sunday, he wears a wing collar too big for his neck so that his throat can have full play, my father says, and when he stands up in front of the congregation and sings a solo, his Adam's apple moves up and down about four inches. I am always on the edge of the pew for fear it will go too far. But he certainly can sing bass like a deep roar, and folks say he missed his calling behind a plow. He has three brothers who can sing, too, but they are not all bass.

My mother is a little different from my father about church. She used to be a Methodist, and that is why she is more strict. Somehow she seems to know exactly what she knows, but my father is not always so sure. I asked her once why she is in the Dutch Reformed Church when there is a Methodist church right here in Woodstock and she used to be in a Methodist one, but all she said was, "Didn't you ever hear about Ruth?" I said, "Ruth who?" but she was on her way to the pump for a pail of drinking water and went right on, and when she came back I wasn't there. Her father was Methodist, too, I guess. He died before I was born, but there is a picture on our wall of him and he looks pretty strict. It is a bigger picture in a frame smeared with black paint that my mother dusts every day. He has a long beard and lots of hair all wild on his head like pictures of prophets in the Bible. I saw my father looking at the picture one day and I overheard him say to himself, "I wonder why she wants to keep that around. The old gentleman wasn't the way that looks." So maybe my mother's father wasn't so strict. I don't know.

My father's first name is Abram. He says it is the same as Abraham, like in Abraham Lincoln when my father was born, but it is more up-to-date. It was so favored when Abraham Lincoln was shot, he says, that we have dozens of Abrams around here and in Kingston. I do know that one of my uncles is Abram Palen in Kingston. They are all called Abe—Abe this and Abe that. My father's middle name is DuBois. I have heard him say that our name, Rose, is English by way of Holland. That's low Dutch, he says. And DuBois is Huguenot from France. They wanted to believe in God to suit themselves, he says, and so they protested, and that's why we are called Protestants. My mother says, "Oh, Abe, don't be like that."

My mother's name was Mary Palen. She says the Palen used to be Vanderpalen away back in Holland when ink was cheap and there was lots of time to write out long names. But this is America, where my father says time is of the essence. It must be, the way he rushes even through his meals because he has to get back to the store. Whether ink is cheaper I don't know. Anyway, Vanderpalen has been shortened down to Palen. So, being Holland Dutch, we go to the Dutch Reformed Church.

The chances are that the artists will find it tough to get used to

Sunday in Woodstock. It is not right to say so, I know, but Sunday is a pretty dull day. We have to get all dressed up early, and we go to Sunday School at half-past nine and stay to church at half-past ten and get free when Dominie Park wakes up and remembers to look at his watch. When church starts, our family walks in, single file, like Indians in the *Leather Stocking Tales*. My father is first and carries Alvarez, who is our baby and about two years old. My mother is second, Harry third, I am fourth, and Clifford is fifth. When we get to our pew, way down front, my father stands aside and my mother goes to the inside and Varse next to her, Clifford next, Harry next, and I am beside my father when we sit down. This is to keep order with Harry, who is supposed to be big enough to help out with Varse and Clifford. Folks watch us come in every Sunday, and they say it is a remarkable family sight. Maybe it is, and if going in was all there was to it, it would be fine. But then you have to sit there for an hour and a half if the Dominie is kind and lets us out on time. Dominie Park is a wonderful man and he is kind except when he forgets to stop. When we succeed in reaching the halfway point in church my mother goes up into the choir, and Alvarez and Clifford start to get pretty bad with nobody alongside them but Harry to keep them in line. My father says he can keep track of our ages by the condition of the hymn books and he will have to get the fourth set soon.

The artists won't be able to make a weekday out of Sunday. You have to stay dressed up and stay clean. You can't fish. You can't go swimming. You can't hunt sap or chestnuts or walnuts. You can't skate in winter or ride downhill or hook onto bobs. After church comes dinner, and after that you are up against it. It is all right to read and rest. No Nick Carter or Frank Merriwell or Buffalo Bill, though. You have to stick to *Youth's Companion, Oliver Optic, Mister Cooper* and so forth, and the big folks read *The Ram's Horn* and *Innocents Abroad*. Stuff like that.

I do not understand what my father means when he says the

artists will not be attracted to the church, if he means the Dutch Reformed Church. You would think that artists, if they know so much about beautiful things, would be just as strong for it as my father and mother are because I have heard my father say that it has Greek columns in front all the way to the roof and all across a wide porch of Ulster County bluestone. And look at the simple shape of the church like in pictures of old Greece. My father says that altogether it is the purest Greek influence anywhere around here except maybe the Greek restaurant in Kingston.

They say that the coming of the artists will change Woodstock; but then my father says that when folks say, "They say," fact flies out the window. Linnie Jewel, who is quite old, about twenty-two, and experienced, says it would not be the worst thing in the world if Woodstock changes. It may bring some life into the town, she says, and it may be all the year like July and August when our boarding houses fill up with boarders from New York City. Right away my mother said that the devil always walks about and that there is no call for flirting with sin more than can be avoided. My father said well, then all the life there is, is right here now.

But it will be too bad if the artists come swarming down off the mountain and wreck us with sin. That's what Brook Romer said, and then he made up a song about it to sing to us boys. Brook is our best friend, well the most interesting, anyway. He was only a little drunk this afternoon after school. Brook drinks more than is good for him, Jack Moran says, and Jack knows because he drinks quite a lot himself.

But I guess we might as well get ready for mighty changes. That's what Dominie Park was telling some men in front of the store when the mule stage from West Hurley came in with the mail. What he said was too much for me, but my friend Brook Romer was there, and he understands everything, and afterwards I got Brook to write it down for me. The Dominie started out serious. "Customs change," he said, "as the years and centuries change and our beloved haunts creep into the foggy past as the future rolls in upon us. Fires and new demands will consume our traditions, and the chisel and the saw will orchestrate their symphony." The men standing around seemed to know that Dominie was saying something, but they looked as if they didn't know exactly what. And so right about then the Dominie seemed to come to himself like the prodigal son in the Bible did and realize that he was trying to be too intellectual to be understood. That's what Brook said. The Dominie glanced around and tried to smother it with a change, Brook said. "Behold, gentlemen," the Dominie went on, "the handiwork of the cobbler and blacksmith will vanish, new emporiums will arise, dust will turn to paving." But he wasn't getting there yet, Brook said, and he knew it. So he waved his hand and said, "And don't be surprised if clothes change, too, and hairy legs are exposed in a free and informal, and shall I say artful, way of life." Then he made a bow and left everybody laughing while he went into the store to get his mail.

Maybe when you can't do anything about something, it is best to joke about it. But a change in Woodstock won't be funny to me. I know there are such things as progress. There are hard streets and gas lights and these new-fangled streetcars that move without a horse ahead or behind in Kingston, where I have been lately. But give me our hard-coal heater and an Oliver Optic and our beautiful oil lamps for dark winter nights when you know there will be buckwheat cakes and headcheese and vinegar for breakfast. Give me the smells of our horses and sweaty leather and hot iron in Henry Pepper's blacksmith shop in summer. Give me the smell of smoke and maple syrup and melting snowbanks in spring. Give me the air full of ripe apples and plums and pears and grapes in fall. And, yes, even the horse manure and the dust in our roads. Give me the dust, especially in March when you see the first patches in roads. Give it to me in summer when you can go barefoot and plop your feet in it and it squeezes up between your toes.

❧ The Village in 1900

. . . where it is and the best way to get there

The geography says that Woodstock is a valley between the Overlook Mountain and the Ohio Mountain. But that is not enough to tell so you won't miss it. The geography could go on and say it is ten miles back in the Catskills from Kingston, and from Rondout. It is Rondout where the Rondout Creek is the end of the Delaware and Hudson Canal and goes into the Hudson River. It is where the mules can rest after they have towed the barges filled with coal through the canal all the way up from Pennsylvania. This Rondout has a harbor that is filled with awfully big piles of coal, tugboats, big river steamers, and ferries, and the air is filled with the noise of mallets, building barges, and boats in many boat yards. You can't miss Rondout on the map, and if you run your finger just a little bit to the west, it comes to Woodstock.

Woodstock is full of fine farms, and the men say that this is because so many little streams of pure water come down from the mountains. These streams go through the farms and into the Sawkill that runs through the valley. The men say it tumbles through, and that certainly is right. We call it the Sawkill because *kill* is a Dutch word that means creek, and there are sawmills on it. It rushes over big stones that it has worn flat, and once in awhile, when the clear water seems to want to rest up, it stops in big deep pools. Then it goes on tumbling again.

Now here's how you get to Woodstock. The best way is to come in summer on the Hudson River Dayboats, and most people do. One boat is called the *New York* and the other one is called the *Albany.* When one goes up the river from New York to Albany in one day, the other is coming down from Albany to New York. They are mighty big boats with deep whistles and bells and great big paddle wheels on the sides and three decks and two big tall smokestacks and crowded with people all dressed up in their Sunday best, the men with straw sailors with colored hatbands and the women with floppy hats pinned to their hair with fancy pins about a foot long. These boats land at Kingston Point Park. The one from Albany lands at twelve o'clock and the one from New York City about two o'clock. Kingston Point Park is on the river outside Rondout.

Of course you can come right to Rondout on the famous *Mary Powell* that goes down to New York and back every day. Or you can come in on night boats with their searchlights that skip along the shores all along. But the night boats are mostly freight and folks seem to like the dayboats better.

Hundreds and hundreds of folks who have a picnic at Kingston Point Park stand on the long pier and watch the dayboats come in. About the time the boats land, you turn around and see the dayboat trains to and from the Catskills backing toward the pier on a long trestle built right through Rondout Harbor. The engine snorts and whistles and rings the bell, the boats bark their deep whistles, the Park band plays a lively piece in its round stand covered with colored lights out in what they call a lagoon, and the crowds shout and surge. The kids run and jump around, the men pushing the baggage trucks swear and cuss at the crowd, trying to get through without hurting anybody, and the black porters in white coats stand by their parlor cars calling out the towns in the mountains their parlor cars go to. It's wonderful, and you certainly know you are on your way to Woodstock or wherever.

You have to get on the train if you are going to Woodstock. After it has stopped at Rondout and at the Union Station in Kingston with its West Shore and Walkill Valley Railroads, and after

the train has sort of snaked along the rocks and sides of the foot-
hills through Stoney Hollow, you get off at West Hurley.

Then you take the stage of Johnny Saxe with his mule team
for the five miles to Woodstock.

When you get to the valley you see the Overlook Mountain
House way up on top of the Overlook Mountain. It looks like a
wonderful place to get to but that is all there is into it because
it is not running. The men say it was a pipe dream of a man with
more money than brains. The road he built has too many steep
places and the storms cut it to pieces. Just below it is a big gash
in the mountain that is the California Quarry where Ulster County
bluestone comes from. And off to the left and farther down the
mountain is a nice-looking group of white buildings that is
Mead's. It is just Mead's Mountain House and a chapel that they
call Episcopalen, or something, but it runs and it has a good road
to it but full of thank-you-ma'ams between the steep pitches. It is
run by Will Mead, who says he is a high private in the front ranks
of the busted. He means he is not getting rich when folks accuse
him of it.

But while you are in Woodstock, you miss something if you do
not make your way somehow to the Overlook Mountain House
for the view. We do that about once a year with whatever part of
my uncles and aunts and cousins are visiting us. We have lots of
them in Kingston, Calicoon Hook, St. Remy, Montgomery, Rondout, and so forth. We take a picnic and drive to Mead's, where
we leave the rig. Then we climb the rest of the way to the Overlook. It's rough going, and the old people are slow, and you are
ahead, and you get awfully tired because after just so long you
expect to see the Mountain House around the next turn at the
top of the next climb on the rocky road, and it isn't. But when you
do get there, you can look right down all over the valley. The
long Hudson River is like a snake down there, and you see away
over into New England. If you jumped, you would sail down

two thousand feet, they say, before you struck anything and even then, it would be only part of the way. I looked Overlook Mountain up and it is 3,150 feet high, but there is another mountain right close called Mink and it is 3,810. If you know your measurement tables in school, there are 5,280 feet in a mile, so that's pretty high.

Now remember, you are coming into Woodstock in the mule stage. The first thing you see is the iron bridge over Sawkill Falls. A lot of flat rocks on all sides lead down to a big pool there, and you will see a lot of summer boarders in swimming or lying on the flat rocks in the sun. They look like slick seals I saw once in New York City. I mean in a zoo.

Across the bridge is Aaron Riseley's big boarding house with lawns and big red barns. The barnyard there is in plain sight of the road and that's where the bull of Woodstock Valley is that they take the cows to. But it is surrounded by a high board fence so that you can't see in, because everybody would, of course.

This is where the road from Saugerties comes in, and there on your right side is the grist mill of Hugo Dish with its big wooden water wheel.

Next on the right, going up to the center of the Village, is the home of Celia and Jimmie Lasher. Celia is Jim's wife and the same age. Folks call her Ceil. She is slim and pretty and says jolly things so that she always has everybody laughing.

A little farther on you see a lane between rows of maple trees leading to the stone house of Cornelius Hogan. They call him K'Neal. Just about there on the left of the road is the district school with its little room and its big room. It is stone, too, and in a corner of the old stone wall we have our den.

Next to it is the old sawmill of Eulie Boice. He has a new sawmill over on the Sawkill, but this old sawmill has some timbers left and big piles of sawdust, and some of the timbers stick out over the piles. That is where we have our dare. Every boy must make the jump from the end of an old timber to a pile of sawdust across a gulley if he ever wants to be in on things.

Now you are at the foot of a long grade leading up to the center of the Village. Half way up, first on the right, is Henry Pepper's house where Willie and Johnny Pepper live, and Mr. Pepper's blacksmith shop next. Then comes the big barn of the Woodstock Hotel of Jake Wurts who has two beautiful grown-up daughters, and they drive around with their own pretty bay mare and rubber-tired runabout. Next to the barn is the Woodstock Hotel and the bar where they buy all the empty whiskey bottles we find. On the left is the harness shop, then the new Lutheran Church, then the home of Eulie Boice, where Egbert and Delancy Boice live, and then the oldest big store in Woodstock. It belongs to Ed Snyder, but his son Byd Snyder runs it because Mr. Snyder is getting pretty old. Byd is the only one short of West Hurley who can do telegraph, and he has the Western Union.

From Ed Snyder's store you go round the green, and you will see the burned ruins of Will Elwyn's store. Next comes my father's store except that Will Longyear is partners with my father, and Will Elwyn used to be. Then there's Mower's ice cream parlor with homemade ice cream, the old Dutch Reformed Church, the New England brick home of Ed and Byd Snyder, and the parsonage of our Dominie, where little Nelson Park died because he was such a delicate child. And then you are back at the Woodstock Hotel and Ed Snyder's store.

Down a lane past the parsonage are the Dutch Reformed sheds for tying up rigs and the big windmill of Ed Snyder to pump water to his home. I have climbed to the top of that windmill many times.

From the village green you can go three ways out of town besides the one from West Hurley you have just come in on. One is up toward the base of the Overlook Mountain and clear up to

Mead's. It goes past Elick Longyear's, the cemetery, the farm, barn, barnyard, and blacksmith shop of Cal Short where Harry Short lives; next is the home of pretty Salo Shultis; and on up to the farm of Levi Harder where Roy and his grown-up brother Ed live. You are now at what they call Rock City, but it is only two more farmhouses. But there are a lot of rocks, and maybe they thought it would be a city sometime.

If you take the road to Bearsville, Shady, and Mink Hollow from the village green, you pass our home on the right. My father says our house is 100 years old with expensive changes. It has a big Dutch oven in the old part of the cellar but we don't use it. Our home is white and has a long, white picket fence and it is surrounded with big weeping willow and locust trees. Across from us is the home of Mr. and Mrs. Lown before Mrs. Lown was found dead in their home, Mr. Lown's cobbler shop, and the home of Mr. and Mrs. Larry Elwyn, where Norm, Orville, and Fred Elwyn live. Orville saved Clifford, Fred, and me from drowning in the Big Deep when big boys tipped the raft to scare us. This Elwyn home stands where Dr. Smith's boarding house was before it burned down. Fred Elwyn runs with us. Larry Elwyn is the town barber and has his shop in part of his barn. On this road you cross an iron bridge over Tannery Creek and the pond that used to make power for the tannery, but the tannery is gone. As you go on up this road, you pass the home of Hyp Bovee and his big barn across the road. Hyp Bovee is working up a trade as an undertaker. Then you come to another bridge over a small brook with no name to it, but it has snakes and eels in it. And then comes the bigger undertaking place of Frank Lasher where Victor Lasher lives. Cooper's Meat Market and butchering place is across the way. It is terrible to watch them butcher, but we watch it just the same.

Then you go on up toward Bearsville past Dr. Downer, the Methodist Church and Hall, the Old Hotel and Bar of Sam

Elwyn, the Ran Johnsons, where Addie Johnson, who is big and beautiful for a schoolgirl, lives, the cider mill, and up past the farms of Chris Winnie whose father-in-law always calls him "my sonerlaw, Chris Winner," and Peter Lewis Harder. His grandson, Lewis Harder, comes down to the village to visit me, and we have great fun. He stutters.

The third road from the village green leads down past the home of Minnie Whispel who is grown-up, and the folks call her the belle of the village; then past Mr. Herrick, who makes tintypes and has a son named Bruce about eighteen years old, who writes poetry. Then over a little bridge over the lower part of Tannery Creek you come to Aaron Riseley's pine grove, where church picnics and night square dances are held; and then the Big Deep, where Tannery Creek empties into the Sawkill and we swim; and then another bridge across the Sawkill.

Above this bridge is Eulie Boice's new sawmill with its long race. Its iron water wheel is smaller than Hugo Dish's wooden one, because the water falls a long distance on it from the top of a tower where the race ends. This sawmill has a long track running up to the second story to haul logs to the big saws, and we sometimes go there with Delancy Boice to ride the log trucks down the grade after Mr. Boice and his men have gone home. They warn us that we are risking life and limb, but after they go home they don't know it.

Now you can go in one direction, the other side of the Sawkill, past Aaron Riseley's big apple orchard where he has piles of red Spitzenbergs, Baldwins, and Snow apples, and Yellow Pippins, and green Greenings, and red and white Woodstock Jonathans, and brown Rusty Coats in the fall before they put them in barrels. The colored piles are pretty and make your mouth water. This way takes you round to the Kingston road.

Or after the bridge by Eulie Boice's sawmill, you can go the other way past the homes of Jack Moran, redheaded George

Riseley, and the farms of Charley Riseley where Libby and Ophelia live. They are sisters of George and Charley, and Libby teaches the class for little folks in the Dutch Reformed Sunday School. My father says Libby is the salt of the earth, and he is right. She has a running laugh whenever she talks, and she talks fast all the time. She never got married. If you follow this road, you get to the top of Ohio Mountain where Washington Riseley has a yoke of beautiful white oxen. But you don't have to go all the way up there to see the oxen, because Wash Riseley "Gees" and "Haws" them down to the Village about every week.

Anybody who owns a farm in Woodstock Valley is rich, my father says, but maybe not in cash. But they have everything. Even ice houses for lemonade and ice cream. They make enough sausage and headcheese and they smoke enough hams and bacon and beef and put down enough salt pork and corned beef to last all winter and to sell some. The sausage is in long tubes of muslin about three inches thick, and the headcheese is in big flat pans and covered with lard.

You can eat in our dining room and look out at the fields on the side of Ohio Mountain and see the gusts of wind move across the tops of the big fields of grain. It's like a big crazy quilt of greens, yellows, and blacks, because about every fifth field is buckwheat that turns black and makes the air sweet when it is ripe, and you know it will soon be winter.

Most farms have a sugar bush of soft maples for boiling down syrup and sugar for buckwheat cakes. Buckwheat batter is started in the fall. It is stirred and added to every night, and it ferments all winter long. We eat these cakes very thin, from a hot griddle, with maple syrup, all winter, along with sausage and eggs for breakfast. Sometimes a thick mixture of hot headcheese and vinegar is used on the cakes for a change. My mother or Linnie stands at the stove and bakes them one at a time because buckwheat cakes are no good unless they are crisp and hot. My father says it is foolish but they won't have it any other way. And of course, you can gather chestnuts and walnuts on the farms. Sometimes the farmers don't care and sometimes they do, but if you know how you can get them anyway. If you get enough of them, my father will send them to New York City and pay you what they bring.

I think all this is good and can't be beat. Maybe the coming of the artists will change it like the men say in their talk, but I hope not. I told my father this, and he said I am too young to be so serious, but the way I look at it somebody has got to be serious or nobody would ever think about anything. He said he guessed he couldn't quarrel with that but that Providence has quite a lot to do with things, too. Providence, he said, is leaving a few things to the Lord and having faith that He knows best.

Take himself, he said. He took very sick when he was a mere slip of a man and with a business and a wife and children on his hands. The doctor ordered him to the Woodstock Valley. He had to close out his grocery store in Rondout and start all over again —small.

He was very discouraged, he said, and he certainly wouldn't have tried to plan it that way. But Providence took a hand. The mountain air and water brought his health back. His business has grown to be the second biggest general merchandise store in Ulster County. The biggest one, he said, is D. L. Mathews in Shokan, but it is on the U & D, and a railroad in a town is a big help, my father says. He has helped the farmers, and they have helped him, he says. He barters eggs and butter and anything else the farmers have extra, even cordwood. Most of it he takes to Kingston. He does their banking for them, too. Some of the eggs are too old, and some of the butter is pretty bad, he says, but he gives trade or cash for them anyway, and it all seems to work out. And besides, there's his health.

Health is the first consideration, my father says. A man's business or his work is next, because if he does not buckle to it and make that go, nothing else will go. Next comes his family and then church and then a man's town. All along the line there is the United States, of course, he says, but the United States won't amount to much if everybody is a bust with the others.

Anyway that's the way it is in Woodstock, he says, and that's why it is a pretty fine place. But don't get too serious about it, he says.

I told him I will try not to get too serious for a boy. But I don't want to lose and forget Woodstock and my life before artists. I told him that it is not my fault if the coming of the artists has called my attention to myself and to Woodstock. So I am going to write it down.

"These things make you think," I said.

My father squinted his eyes and thought about that, and then he said "Yes, I guess they do."

❧ The Birth of Reason

*. . . and saving the chamber pots from Dr. Smith's
fire*

The first time my attention was called to me and that I am in Woodstock was when they tried to save the big pitchers and big bowls and chamber pots from the bedrooms in Dr. Smith's boarding house. I know now that I was alive before that, but I do not remember anything before. Just like little puppies or little kittens, I suppose, who just go bouncing around and would not know what they are doing if you asked them. They don't even know what they have done two seconds later. Ask them where they were yesterday and you might as well ask a chunk of wood in our woodshed. A chunk of wood don't know or care when you pick it up in the woodshed and carry it to the woodbox back of our kitchen. It don't know nothing, and that was like I was before the chamber pots, and so forth, in Dr. Smith's bedrooms.

It was them that started me to thinking. I thought the men who were saving the chamber pots were very silly. Then I looked around and noticed where I was and why. I asked my father what happened to me, and he said something about the birth of reason. In a small way, of course, he said. When I told him about the pitchers and chamber pots he said I had it about right. The men were silly. But he pointed out that the men were beside themselves with excitement.

The excitement was that Dr. Smith's boarding house was afire. Not just a lamp exploding and maybe catching a window curtain or two. Then you just bat out the curtains and throw the lamp outdoors and things go on the same.

Dr. Smith's boarding house was a big place, three stories and attic. It was big sideways, too. Dr. Smith was a real doctor, but folks said he liked to make a penny or two on the side. So he built on and built on, and up and up, for more and more boarders in the summertime. Not all sick ones. Some healthy.

The boarding house was right across the dusty road from our house. It was between Mr. Lown's cobbler shop and Dr. Smith's barn. A path was in front of it, but there was not much lawn to the front porch. Between the path and the road was a big stone horse block for people to step on when they got out of surreys. It is still there but Larry Elwyn bought the burnt foundation and built a home for his wife, Mehalie Elwyn, and his boys and girls. The horse block is high, and I have jumped off it into the road many times.

This night of the fire, which was long ago before Alvarez was born, I was asleep with my brothers Harry and Clifford in a little bedroom with a low ceiling upstairs. It had two little windows out onto our front porch roof, and these windows looked right across the road to Dr. Smith's boarding house. I was dreaming. We had a big jigsaw puzzle of a New York City fire engine going to a fire. I was putting it together, and when I got it all together and could look at the horses running full gallop, and the smoke bursting out of the smokestack, and the firemen hanging on and yelling, it was certainly going some. I heard the noise of it. I heard the men yelling, and the fire crackling under the smoke, and all the to-do. But the crackling did not seem right, and I could hear people running and that was not in the fire engine puzzle. Then the puzzle changed to Vesuvius and Pompeii, and people running because Vesuvius was erupting. That was on one of the picture cards in Libby Riseley's Sunday School class for little folks. It was not a nice dream. I was scared.

Then I heard my mother's voice, although I did not know what she said. Then I heard my father's voice and I did know what he said. He said, "You had better get the children up and be sure to get them dressed." But it wasn't a command. His voice sounded patient and sad.

I opened my eyes. It was the middle of the night but the bedroom was as light as day. It wasn't the white light from the lamp. It was a red light, and it chased around on the walls. It didn't seem as if the big maple tree in the front yard and the night were keeping the room dark at all. The crackling and the noise and the shouting and the running went on.

I ran to the window, and there it was.

My mother came running into the room. "Get up and dress fast," she said, "and go down to the kitchen and out the kitchen door into the side yard under the willows. Don't go out the front door. Don't go into the barns. Dr. Smith's rooming house is burning down. Go down under the willows and stay there, so I'll know where you are if I have to get you quick." She shook Harry and Clifford and told them the same thing, but, of course, she had to dress Clifford who was still in dresses. I do not remember dressing, nor what Harry and Clifford did, nor where they went. They were probably with me all the time. But soon I was standing by the pump in the side yard under the willows and holding on to it. I looked through the locust trees in the lower yard next to the road and watched all the running and shouting and the fire.

So far, the fire was back in the kitchens. They were blazing, and you never would believe the amount of smoke. It was going in puffs and clouds up into the sky. Men and bigger boys were coming a-running from all directions. Women and children were staying back. Some were on the bridge and on the other side of the tannery pond. Most of the men had pails, and when they came running up they joined a line of men down to the pond and started passing on buckets of water. At the head of the line the men were throwing the water up against the side of Dr. Smith's barn because that was nearest to the fire. They had horse blankets and quilts nailed on the side of the barn, to soak. But later, when the fire had finished the kitchens and was going into the main building, the men started on Mr. Lown's boot shop. Then I heard a man calling for water for the front of our house. "Gettin' hot as hell here," he yelled. "Paint's blisterin'." Two or three men ran to him with buckets of water, and he sloshed them on our house. Men who did not have buckets were carrying furniture out of the ground floor. Some of it was coming into our lower yard and some of it was going into Lown's yard.

Then the silly thing happened. My friend Brook Romer was standing near the horse block, and he was leaning against the stout tie post and smoking a cigar just as if no fire was going on at all. Since that night I have heard my father say that Brook is unaccountable at times, and so this must have been one of the times. It could be that he had been drinking and had been asleep in the hotel barn or some haymow and just didn't realize what was going on.

Just then one of the men in an upstairs window called to Brook. Brook nodded his head and stepped forward and held up his hands. The man in the window threw a big water pitcher from one of the bedrooms down to Brook. Brook caught it and was just setting it down at his feet when the man threw out a big bowl he had in his other hand. Brook dropped the pitcher on the grass and caught the bowl, but then another man came to the window with two pots, one in each hand, and threw them out, one after another. To catch one of the pots, Brook hollered at a man just passing back of him and tossed the bowl over his shoulder for the man to catch. The man caught it, set it down, and then moved on.

Brook must have thought the man stayed there, because he kept catching the pots, pitchers, and bowls and tossing them back over his shoulder. The fire was growing, and the men in the rooms were running back and forth to the window, and the pots and so forth were coming pretty fast. The trouble was that when Brook tossed them to the man back of him who wasn't there, they hit the horse block and smashed into a thousand pieces. I watched this go on, I will bet you, for ten minutes, with the fire roaring bigger and bigger and the black smoke roaring up into the sky in big black bursts and the men throwing out the pots faster all the time and Brook catching and smashing them on the horse block to keep up with them. Every time a pot or a pitcher smashed, I held onto the pump harder and shut my eyes. I tried to holler to Brook but he couldn't hear me. I could have run across the road and grabbed his coattails, but I was as scared as anybody else, and I had been told to stay there.

But it came to an end. By this time the fire had a good hold on the back part of the main building and was growing fast. Right at the building, it was clear fire and a little redder than the top of the flame in an oil lamp. But when it gained speed, shooting up into the sky, heavy smoke began, and then it seemed to be a race between the smoke and the fire to get to the sky first. The fire was roaring but the smoke began to get angry too, and it got so big and black that the fire gave up, and you couldn't see it at all except for millions of flying sparks. The smoke went on getting bigger all the time, and then it slowed down and made a big umbrella in the sky.

Just before the whole building burst into fire the men upstairs ran down and out the side door. They ran into Dr. Smith there, and I heard them shout that they had got out all the crockery. I saw Dr. Smith pat them on the back. They acted like they thought they had done a good job, and then they ran to help with the water buckets.

Brook turned. He saw the smashed crockery and stood and looked at it a minute. Then he shoved his hat lower on his forehead and walked away.

✸ The Honorary Backslider

. . . and the mystery of who is Brook Romer

There is a mystery about Brook Romer, who is the man in Woodstock who is with us boys so much that we know him best. I never heard anybody say where he came from. He does not seem to have any father or wife or anything, and I don't know where his home ever was. But I do know that he has slept in the barn of the Woodstock Hotel and some farmers' barns.

The first thing you notice about Brook is that he always seems happy. He has a smile on his round face, and his eyes are soft and quiet except when something pretty tough happens, of course. Maybe his ears are too big but you don't notice that because he has hair only on the sides of his head and it is always too long and looks almost white. I notice, when we are in swimming, that he has a big stomach and his body does not amount to much. His nose is red. Of course, when you find him drunk and asleep, all you can think of is an old wet mop that smells.

We have a lot of men and women in Woodstock that the world would call important, but none of the grown-up folks seem to think that Brook is one of them. I don't suppose you can blame the grown-up folks. Brook gets too drunk, and he works only when he feels like it or needs some money. He don't care anything about his clothes and, of course, he does not go to church.

Going to church makes folks think better of you. There is Frank Hudler who is rich enough to have two hired men, and his family looks after his farm and home. He hangs out most of the time in the bar of the Woodstock Hotel, but the bar is closed on Sundays, so he goes to church. He is in politics, and I hear folks talk about how he will go to the Legislature.

Brook hangs around mostly with us boys. He takes us fishing in a rowboat over in Yankeetown Pond for bullheads. Just at dusk the bullheads bite so fast you just yank them up with a short pole, and they fall off the hook into the boat. Brook shows us how to make willow whistles and carve wood. He recites famous speeches to us and tells us stories of gods and goddesses who, he says, had Greece and Rome by the ears. He teaches us how to run races and make the longest and highest jumps. And when he is what they call only three sheets in the wind, he sings ditties to us.

Brook helped us form two clubs. One is the Anti-Cigarette League. He writes almost as good as the Spencerian writing books in district school, and he can write a perfect business letter. He wrote somewhere and got us boys silver Anti-Cigarette badges. He does not smoke cigarettes that are called coffin nails, only cigars sometimes, so he is President of the club. Our other club is the Woodstock Temperance Club. Brook said we would have to elect our own officers of this club because he cannot be a member. We did not like that. We talked that over quite a while and then Brook said, well, if we wanted it that way, there was one office he would fit. Every organization has backsliders, he said. Maybe the best one in our club could have an office. We could call it Honorary Backslider, he said, so that is what we elected him. That gives him the right to be in our secret meetings and every time we have a meeting he gets up and gives a temperance lecture.

We used to ask Brook where he came from and who he is and how he got so much learning but he got us all mixed up because every time he just laughed and told us a lot of stuff that was different. Every time it is interesting, with a lot of adventures, but it does not get you anywhere. To hear him tell it he put spikes in Teddy Roosevelt's shoes so he wouldn't slip rushing up San Juan Hill. Or he was the secret son of the Prince of Whales and a barmaid in London. Or his grandfather was Daniel Boone. Or he was in California in the gold rush. Or he was a horseback preacher with the Mormons and ran away from fifteen wives. Or he was with a side show in Barnum's Circus. Or he was really the inventor of the safety bike. Or he taught history at Harvard University until he found out it did not do any good and got disgusted because folks go right on making the same mistakes Julius Caesar did.

After two or three of these Fred Elwyn, who is pretty brainy for a boy, would ask Brook "How long was you at that?" when Brook told a new one. Fred added it up and right now Brook is one hundred sixty-seven years old.

I asked my father about Brook and where he came from and he looked puzzled. He had never thought about it, he said. Brook was here already when he came to Woodstock, he said, and so maybe he was always here or somebody like him. A few days later he told me he had asked around but nobody seemed to know.

"Maybe he's an incarnation," he said. I asked him what that was and he said just someone you never get rid of.

One time when Brook was more than three sheets in the wind he stood on a little wooden bridge over Tannery Creek down back of the Dutch Reformed Church and he was having an argument with another drunk I did not know who was standing by the manure pile by our horse stables. I was snaring redfins in the brook and did not pay any attention. The other drunk threw his empty whiskey bottle at Brook without stopping to think that I was in the middle. The bottle smashed on my head and cut it open. Brook forgot all about the other drunk. He ran to me and picked me up and carried me to our house. He and Linnie stopped my crying and patched me up.

Another time Charley Riseley's team got scared and was running away in a dead gallop and Brook ran right out in front of them and grabbed a bridle and hung on and stopped them before they smashed themselves up. That is what broke his leg and gave him his limp.

And when Bent Bim, the hunchback, was killed in the woods by a falling tree and his wife needed money and the village took up a collection, Brook said he would give twelve dollars. They did not count on it, but Brook quit buying whiskey for a month and then came around with the money. It would have been all right if they had taken it, but by that time the collection was all over and they sort of laughed him off. So he used half of it to buy shoes for Bent Bim's kids and was about five sheets in the wind for two weeks with the rest.

People think it is like I heard Jack Moran say in the store one night. "If there ever was a man who didn't give a damn," he said, "Brook is it." But folks are wrong and they would know it if they would just put two and two together, or if they would be with us boys and Brook for awhile. He is a good man. All that is wrong with him is that he is a bum.

Brook is pretty good with a mouth organ, too. Lots of songs he sings are low and slow and sad and most of them tell a story. But once in a while he sings something comical and then teaches it to us. The best one of these is the one that Brook says is called "The Judge's Charge to the Jury." I learned it and it goes like this:

One morning in a courtroom
A boy stood up for trial
His father stood beside him
On his face there was a smile.
The old man told the jury
This is not my only son
For I have got three more like him
And I bring them one by one.

The boy was hard to handle
And he acted like a mule
He yanked a shooter from his belt
Like any silly fule.
And now there's thirteen funerals
For the jury men are dead.
The judge lived thirty minutes
And before he died he said:

"My boy you are a dandy
Now see what you have done.
No matter who your father was
You are your mother's son.
And if ever you get married
Just have one boy for fun.
But if he's a sport
Don't go to court
But kill the son of a gun."

Just because Brook is a bum, folks don't think he is all right otherwise. Brains, for instance. But he changed their minds one night around the white-bellied stove. Right at the time Brook was working for awhile, tending the big boiler of the steam sawmill of Chris Van Keuren up on the Sawkill. In the bunch around the stove was Jim Plass. He is about twenty-five years old and thinks he is very cute. He is good-looking like a Greek god would be in a lumberman's shirt and overalls, and he always talks as if he knows all about all kinds of girls and women and they are all after him. The trouble is that anybody who ever has anything to do with him finds themselves in hot water sooner or later. I do not think the men like him but it is like Larry Elwyn says—this is a free country. Anyway, he was there that night and Brook was, too.

Jim Plass is a sly kidder. If he wants to kid somebody he don't go at it straight to the one he wants to kid. This night I heard him say to Stanley Longyear that it takes real brains to tend a steam boiler in a sawmill. It can blow up and kill a body without brains, he said. For instance, he said to Stanley Longyear, "What would you do if you come into the boiler house and the blow-off valve was jammed and there was a heavy fire in the firebox and the gauge read about two thousand pounds?"

"Well, let me see," said Stanley. "I guess I would grab a sledge and knock off the blow-off valve."

"What would you do?" Jim Plass asked Larry Elwyn.

"I would remove the cause," said Larry. "I would grab a rake and rake the fire out of the firebox."

Jim Plass asked two or three others but they couldn't think of anything different. Some thought Stanley had it about right and some sided with Larry. You see, Jim Plass had made it so that all of them were trying to be brainy about it. All the time Brook sat without saying anything. He must have known that Jim Plass was up to his sly kidding and was trying to show him up.

But just then Jim turned to Brook. He put a smirk in his voice and said "Well, Brook, what would you do?" as if he expected Brook to flounder around about it.

"I would take one look and run like hell," said Brook, "and you would, too, if you had any brains." Then Brook got up and walked out of the store.

Nobody said anything for about a minute. Then Larry Elwyn said, "I guess all of us would, too, if we had Brook's brains. Even you, Jim."

That set Jim Plass back for fair. He colored up and stammered and swore some but it was quite a while before he got around to any more tricks.

The men talked about it some more. Before it was time for me to go home to bed I heard my father say, "Folks hadn't ought to discount Brook more than about twenty-five per cent. He's got a background somewhere."

And that is about it in a nutshell.

✻ The Dominies

. . . cash on the barrelhead and the New Testament arrives

Dominie Park is our Dominie. He came after Dominie Boggus. A good deal is told about both these Dominies by something very short my father said. He said that the end of Dominie Boggus and the beginning of Dominie Park was like the switch in the Bible from the Old Testament to the New Testament.

I never heard or overheard anything said about any wife of Dominie Boggus, and maybe that is the reason why the women of the church had to go into the parsonage and do a lot of work to get it ready for Dominie Park.

Dominie Park had a wife and they were from the city, and our Dutch women were not going to have her come into a parsonage that wasn't spic and span. You can bet on that.

I did hear and overhear this about Dominie Boggus. It was when he first came to Woodstock, and he called the men of the church together. I do not know who all was there, but I suppose Charley and George Riseley, Aaron Riseley, Levi and Peter Lewis Harder, K'Neal Hogan and some others. I know my father was there, because of what happened.

Dominie Boggus surprised them by saying that the old order changeth, and that a new one was taking hold right then in the Dutch Reformed Church. What he meant was that he wasn't going to look to donations of potatoes, apples, flour, turnips, clothing and other things from my father's store; preserves, hams, bacon, knitted stuff and fancy work and all such from the farm community; and depend for cash on pennies and nickels the church collections might bring in. He didn't want anything to do with that sort of an arrangement for his pay as Dominie, he said.

This was quite a shock to the men because that was the way it always had been. But Dominie Boggus said he did not want to stop their generosity, a ham or side of bacon, or a barrel of apples once in awhile, but he did not want to be dependent on it. What he wanted was cash paid every month, regular. That was the way it had to be, he said. It was a matter of dignity for the leader of the flock, he said, and they would pay more attention to him if they were paying for it in cold cash.

There was a lot of chewing about it, of course. It looked for awhile like the Dominie would have to find that kind of pasture somewhere else. The farmers said it was hard to get up with the cash regular, and there was only one, my father, who thought the

Dominie had a fair proposition. Then the Dominie took the floor again.

He was not expecting to slop a pig, he said, and he did not propose to run a canning factory. Nor keep a cow. The trouble with donations was that nobody knew what others were bringing in all at the same time. Gluts occurred. The Dominie could handle a quart of plums but what would he do with a dozen quarts of them? He could handle one barrel of apples, but what would he do with four or five barrels? And what would he do with a dozen bunches of radishes and so forth. There was waste. Waste was sin because big sections of the world were starving to death. Also the waste was the labor and sweat of the congregation to no good end, and he could not be a party to that. There was no sense, he said, in calling down the wrath of God on their heads. But on the other hand, you could be frugal with cash.

Well, my father saw that somebody would have to step forward in the name of the Lord. He said that, although he did not run a bank, he sort of acted as a little banker for the community. He would advance the Dominie's wages on the first of every month, and he would trust in the Lord and the congregation to see that it was made up to him except for his share. And no interest, he said.

So that was the way of it, and I have heard my father say that you could trust these Dutch farmers with your life. His share of the Dominie's wages seemed to run a little big sometimes, he said, but if he figured good will, which is what a merchant must have, he said, he didn't lose a cent.

I never heard how much cash Dominie Boggus got every month, but it wasn't the going rate for work. I heard the men at the store say that a dollar a day for hard work was a good job, and that dominies don't really work. So I suppose you could figure it was about twenty dollars a month.

Dominie Boggus must have come to an end in Woodstock,

or there never would have been any reason to find a new minister.
I have heard that finding a new minister is not easy to do. You
would almost think that the Lord would send one but that does
not seem to be the way of it.

When the men in the church did not get anywhere on their
own they decided that maybe somebody else could tell them how
to go about it. One of them thought of Dr. John G. Van Slyke of
Kingston, and they said if anybody knew how to get a new
minister he would be the one.

Dr. John G. Van Slyke (it is G. and for a name that sounds
like Guernsey to me) was the Dominie in the First Dutch Reformed Church in Kingston. My father says this church is about
two hundred fifty years old and a big one and so Dominie Van
Slyke, D.D., is a famous man and knows about everything or he
wouldn't be there. My father says he is a brother or some relation
of Van Slyke and Horton, who make the Peter Schuyler cigars
in Albany. When he means him he calls him Peter Schuyler Van
Slyke.

I have seen Dr. John G. He is not very tall but is very plump
and he dresses like a dominie most of the time. But my father says
that he sometimes rides a bicycle in Kingston and then he is
dressed in a round collar and black coat and what they call cloth
gaiters up to his knees like pictures I have seen of what they call
vicars in England. Nobody else is dressed like that, not when
riding a bicycle, and so he is very historic in everything he does.

The men said that my father could see him and ask him about
new ministers the next time he made his weekly trip to Kingston
with butter and eggs and to run errands.

Dr. Van Slyke told my father that the Valley of the Sawkill is
like the Garden of Eden. "But without Adam and Eve and the
snake, of course," my father told my mother and Linnie.

"Don't be too sure," said Linnie.

But my father did not pay any attention to her and said that
Dr. Van Slyke said that our church was small and the salary was

small and not many dominies would hear the call. And so he thought and thought while my father waited.

Pretty soon he said, "Mr. Rose, wasn't your health broken when you went to Woodstock?" My father said it was and that the mountain air and water had fixed him up. Then Dr. Van Slyke said that gave him an inspiration which might not be a true inspiration but was worth a try.

There is a Dominie Park at Millville, New Jersey, he said, who is in about the same shape you were when you went to Woodstock. You couldn't get him as a usual thing, but if you told him what the mountain air and water have done for you, maybe he would come.

Well, it turned out to be a true inspiration. And that's how Dominie Park came to Woodstock. His wife and little girl and little boy were not coming on for a couple of weeks, and the women did not have the parsonage ready, because this thing had happened quicker than anybody had dreamed of, and so Dominie Park came to our house to live until his wife came and the parsonage was ready.

I heard Linnie say to my mother, "My days, he is frail." He was a thin man and not very tall, but my father joined in and said, "You have to remember that Dr. Van Slyke said he is esthetic."

"And what does that mean?" asked Linnie.

"It means he tries to see everything in a beautiful way," said my father. "He is highly educated. He has studied Greek and Latin, and maybe the old Hebrew, so that he knows what the Bible really says. And he has studied poetry. He told me that the Psalms are poetry."

"They don't rhyme," said Linnie.

"He is refined and sweet," said my mother.

"He reads out loud," said my father. "Comical things. We will get him to read some comical things to us while he is here."

"We must remember that he has been through the Valley of the Shadow of Death," said my mother.

"But he got through and climbed up on the other side," said Linnie.

"We hope so," said my father. "The Valley is no fun, I can tell you. I've been there."

Dominie Park was quiet and he was no trouble. We did not see much of him when he stayed with us. He did not want any changes made in our living on his account, he said. He ate when we did, but Linnie said he didn't eat much. We had plain fare, my father said. My father did not like salads and dainty things like creams on vegetables and fancy desserts. Just pie or pound cake, and maybe cottage pudding once in awhile. He liked sharp cheese, the sharper the better. But Dominie Park did not complain and he didn't ask for anything else, not even toast for breakfast. We had plain homemade bread and butter, and fried eggs or poached salt mackerel in summer, when Dominie Park was there, and cereal and coffee with sweet condensed milk.

Dominie Park was with us only at meals. He read a lot in the living room. We could have let him in the parlor if we had thought, but the parlor was kept closed and dark except when we had company or Harry had to practice the piano. Mornings and afternoons he walked all over the Valley looking at the scenery and talking with the folks.

There was just one time when he kinda took my mother and Linnie by surprise. In the middle of one afternoon, my mother was passing through the living room when he was reading. She asked him if he was comfortable and if there was anything she could do for him. I suppose it was just in passing, to say something, and expecting the usual answer of No.

But he said he wondered if he could have a cup of tea. She said of course, but then she was up against it. The cup of tea was easy enough but she had read in books about afternoon tea and we didn't go in for that and she didn't know just what she was going to do about it.

She came down to the kitchen to Linnie all in a flutter and Linnie began to flutter, too. Nobody ever had any food served to them in our house. We would go years without anybody being sick enough to stay in bed over meal time. If they were that sick they didn't need to eat. We had no tray except one old battered one that all of us had played with when we were babies.

"What will we do?" my mother asked Linnie. "Stories tell of something they call a tea cart, and a silver tea service. A silver teapot to keep the tea hot, a silver cream pitcher, a silver bowl for sugar."

But Linnie had had time to think it over.

"Well, we certainly can't make them in a minute and we can't drag them out of the air," she said. "Besides, it's the tea he wants. He can't drink pitchers and pots."

"Oh, you don't understand," said my mother.

"I do understand," said Linnie. "You wish you could do this with a flourish, just as if you do it every day. Well, you don't. And don't you suppose Dominie Park knows it? Leave it to me."

She got out one of the big plates from the Haviland china, and a little pitcher for hot tea. She put on the can of sweetened condensed milk, so that no sugar was needed, and a spoon. Then she put a Haviland cup and saucer on the plate. "I'll take it to him," she said, after she had brewed some tea.

She came back to the kitchen with the condensed milk. "He takes it straight," she said. "He was very nice. Said it was just what he wanted. Said the tea was brewed just right, and how did I know how he liked it? And he thanked me over and over."

My mother worried about it a little more, but in the end Linnie put on an act about some high and mighty woman serving afternoon tea to several ladies she called Countess, Lady Priss, and Madame Snooty, and she soon had my mother laughing again.

My mother and Linnie, that first two weeks, never called Dominie Park by name. It was always he or him. He seemed like a stranger to them, but I guess they never thought about how strange we must have seemed to him.

After Dominie Park had lived at our house and the women had finished doing the parsonage, Mrs. Park and their little girl, Dorothy, and their very little boy, who was called Nelson, came on to Woodstock. Dominies sometimes don't have much furniture, but they had a lot, and my father sent the lumber wagon and the team over to West Hurley to cart it from the U & D Railroad. They got settled and Dominie Park preached and folks said they seemed like they had grown up right there in Woodstock Valley.

I was still very young and my father said I was not yet master of my short pants but I listened a lot and I watched a lot.

Mrs. Park was pretty. She had dark hair and she wore eyeglasses, but she was always smiling and talking perky. Little Nelson was still in dresses, but the women said he was a perfect cherub because he chuckled a lot and his eyes twinkled. But there was one thing wrong. He was very delicate. His hair was fair and his cheeks were red. He made me think of a tiny china doll that you can almost see through, because they were made that way and without clothes. We had two of them on the mantel in the parlor. They were ornaments, my mother said, and very delicate, and were not to be touched unless she handed us one to look at.

It turned out right away that Dominie Park was a Mason. This is a different Mason from the one who lays bricks and flat stones with mortar between them. This was the kind of a Mason who is a member of a lodge. The closest thing we have to that in Woodstock is the Odd Fellows and Red Indians in Bearsville.

I didn't know about this Mason business until one afternoon the hired men drove the rubber-tired runabout up in front of the store, and Dominie Park and my father came out of the store to get in it. They were all dressed up. Dominie Park had on an old soft hat but my father had a derby and I heard Dominie Park say that his old hat didn't look very good. But my father laughed and said that anything looked good on a handsome man.

I thought maybe they would take me and I tugged on my father's pants leg. But he said they were going to Kingston to introduce Dominie Park to old Kingston Number 10. Dominie Park is a Mason, he said, like the Odd Fellows in Bearsville. My father said he was a Mason, too, in the lodge they called Old Kingston Number 10. When you grow up you can be a Mason too, he said, but not today.

Somehow that Mason business seemed to make very close friends of the Parks and us. They were often at our house and we were often at the parsonage. Dominie Park would read comical things out loud. He and my father and Mrs. Park and my mother played what they called rounce with dominoes. Sometimes they played Authors. And sometimes Krokonole, and us little folks could help play that. Dominie Park said Authors was a good game for young folks, too, and so we sometimes got to play that, but it was hard to beat Dominie Park in Authors except sometimes when I thought he acted awful dumb. We could beat him then.

One night, about Christmas time, when the Parks were at our house, there was a heavy knocking on the front door. My father went to answer it and two of the worst-looking black men I ever saw walked in. They had big fat bellies and looked ragged and they carried paper sacks. My father asked them what they wanted and they said they were looking for good little boys. They scared me. Well, they said, they could see Harry and Clifford and Nelson Park, but didn't we have another little boy? And was he a good one?

My father said Willie is usually here and he must be around somewhere. Well, no matter, the men said. They just stopped by because they had red popcorn balls stuck together with syrup and sugar for all good little boys, and if Willie wasn't here they just guessed he wouldn't get one. I heard all this because I was right there. But when the men came in I was afraid, and so I had ducked in under the back of Dominie Park's long Prince Albert coat.

The men were not hurting anybody and I wanted a red popcorn

ball. So I came out from under the Prince Albert coattail of Dominie Park.

Dominie Park said no matter how young they are they all know who to go to for salvation. Everybody laughed. And then the black men took off their hats and showed their heads. One had red hair and the other didn't have any hair on the top of his head. You could see that they had covered their faces with something black and I knew who they were right away. The one with red hair was Jack Moran and the bald one was Brook Romer, my two best grown-up friends.

I got my red popcorn ball.

But everything with the Dominie and Mrs. Park and Nelson wasn't joyous like that. A very sad time was coming.

It was Nelson. The first thing was when he was in awful pain one night and couldn't stop crying. They asked him and asked him and he kept putting his little finger up his nose, and pretty soon he said he put something up there. Dr. Downer, who had come to Woodstock when Dr. Smith's boarding house had burned down and Dr. Smith had moved to Brooklyn to run a drugstore—he came but he said he would have to have the help of a Dr. Kemble in Kingston and so they got a rig and took Nelson to him. I overheard Dominie Park tell about it later. He said that Doctor Kemble turned out to be a rough man who said hell and damn a lot but he handled Nelson as tender as a delicate flower. He was a surgeon but he did not have to do an operation. He had a way of stopping the pain for Nelson, and then he got the thing out. It was a shoe button. Dominie Park said that when he was taking the button out the tears streamed down Doctor Kemble's face. I heard the men around the stove in the store say that God gives extra talents to men like Doctor Kemble in spite of their swearing.

Nelson got over the shoe button all right, but it wasn't long before he was taken real sick. They had to put him to bed. And then one morning we heard that he had died.

I tried hard not to believe it. I stood at the window in our living room while my father was combing and brushing his hair because there was a big mirror there and the light was best, and I looked out over the hobby horse on wheels on the porch, and past the big locust tree by the second gate, and over the white picket fence to the dust in the road, and I thought and I thought of some way it couldn't be true. Dominie Park was a fine man trying to do the work of the Lord. Mrs. Park tried to make everybody happy whereever she went. Nelson was a good little boy and a beautiful little boy in his curls and dresses. How could this have happened to them? I longed to see Nelson running toward us in the dusty road, through the gate and up to our door, and to know that it wasn't true.

But three days later they had his funeral. I saw him in a little white casket, and I had to believe it. My mother told me it must be that he was needed in Heaven to grow up to be an angel. That made me feel better.

𝄞 Memories at the Cemetery

. . . and three graves from black diphtheria in a month

Grove, the barn man, had our old horse, Dick, hitched up. Dick was a bay who was different from our team horses, Jim and Carrie. Dick knew so much that Grove would talk to him and he would make noises that talked back. We always drove Dick single and he was very gentle. My father said that Dick and he started in business together in Woodstock and had sprouted up from nothing and that nothing would ever be too good for Dick.

Grove drove out from under the feed room that connected the store and the barns. It made a perfect place to hitch up because it was always out of the weather. Grove turned Dick around and backed the wagon and him down the grade into the back yard under the big willows and across the stone walk that runs from the kitchen to the privy. He kept on backing right to the stone platform under the red and green pump. He got out and started pumping water into a pail and I noticed that he had a barrel in the wagon. I ran over to see what he was doing.

Grove always did things it was fun to do, and I knew him very well. He was different from the men in the store where there were my father and Will Longyear, who were partners, and Ed Harder, the head clerk, and Will Elwyn, the bookkeeper, and an extra young man who was learning and who could be some young fellow from the village or from away.

Right then he was Dickey Short. My father and Will Longyear were busy and serious when they were in the store and didn't care to have little boys around. Will Elwyn had a dimple and smiled a lot and he liked me around but not always as much as Grove did. Will sat on a high stool back of a high desk that had an iron grill around three sides of it. People could see you through the grill, but it seemed kind of cozy in there with Will Elwyn. His books looked pretty with black writing and perfect figures and blue and red lines, and he made his beautiful writing and perfect figures without clamping down tight with his fingers the way I have to do. Sometimes he lifted me up on the stool and stood beside me. I could wrap my legs around the stool and watch him make perfect little circles all the same in a straight line fast and easy as pie. And Ed Harder was always too busy joking with the customers. So except for Will Elwyn it was Grove for me most of the time.

Grove clerked in the store if he was needed but mostly he looked after the horses and barns and wagons, and delivered all over the Valley and the sides of the mountains. He would take me with him for the ride.

When he had pumped the pail full he climbed up on the hub of the wagon wheel and emptied the pail into the barrel. Then he came back and pumped the pail full again and kept on filling it and dumping it.

I didn't have to ask him if I could help him. There was another big pail in the wagon but it was too big for me. I ran into the washroom in the end of the woodshed and got my tin bucket there and when Grove was up on the wagon to empty his pail I hung mine over the pump spout and tried to turn the pump handle with both hands. But I couldn't turn it and so Grove came down and turned it for me. It filled with the first splash and I grabbed it and climbed up into the wagon and emptied it into the barrel. Grove laughed and from then on he filled my pail whenever I got around to the pump.

When we had the barrel half full he said that was enough and picked me up and plumped me up on the seat and we drove up to the front of the store.

My father came out and when he saw me he stopped. He looked at Grove and said, "Well, I don't know. He'll ask questions."

"He'll have to know sometime," said Grove and he looked at me with a soft light in his eyes. It was almost like my mother looked at me sometimes. "Why, he just helped me fill this barrel," he said.

"He did, eh?" said my father. "Well, Willie, you'll be a man before we know it." Then he climbed up on the seat with Grove and me and we drove off.

We turned into the road between the parsonage and the hotel and on past Longyears', and into the lane leading to the cemetery. I had been there on Decoration Day and the Fourth of July when Ed Harder always played the cornet in the band and everybody said he was fine, and after the band had played a piece and Ed had lifted his cornet up to the sky to make it loud and been red in the face, he always laughed and joked with folks and winked at the big girls. Folks were happy and were visiting these days, and after the band had played in the village green we all marched behind it up to the cemetery. Then people put little flags and flowers on the graves of war heroes and us boys played games.

The cemetery was different now. Nobody else was there. There wasn't any band and there wasn't any fresh flowers, only dead flowers, bent over and dried out, in jars half full of rusty water; and some of the jars had been blown over by the wind.

We drove around and in between all this and stopped at our family plot. It had a round marble pillar on a base with our name, Rose, carved on it. The plot had a curb of Ulster County bluestone around it and on the left-hand side of it were three little pieces of marble with names on them but I couldn't read the names. Back of these little pieces of marble were three places in the grass that looked like they had sunk down.

Grove and my father jumped down to the ground and stood and looked at the three places in the grass. They didn't say anything. My father walked around them and looked down at them and then went back to where he was at first. Grove had just stood still. Then he said "Well, we might as well get at it."

"I suppose," said my father. "I couldn't keep from remembering for a little."

They both got shovels out of the wagon and then they began to cut square pieces of the grass out of the places that were sunk down. They piled these pieces on the side. Then they went back to the wagon and I noticed what I hadn't noticed before. They had big bushel baskets filled with dirt in the wagon. They took these, one at a time, and dumped the dirt where they had cut out the grass and then they stomped the dirt down with their feet. Then they put the pieces of grass back and you wouldn't hardly know anything had been done.

"You get up on the wagon and hand the pails to me," said Grove.

My father got up in the wagon box and filled one of the pails and handed it down to Grove. Then Grove walked to the first spot and emptied the pail of water onto it easylike. They kept doing this on one spot after another. I climbed up in the wagon box to help, but I couldn't reach my tin pail far enough down in the barrel to get any water. So my father lifted me up by the arms and I filled my pail and he dropped me over the side of the wagon box onto the ground and then handed me my pail. I walked over and poured it onto one of the spots. Then I handed my pail to my father and he filled it again.

I helped like this for quite a while and then I stopped and thought. I put my fists on my hips and I said, "Say, what are we doing?"

Grove looked at my father and my father said, "We're watering the grass so that it will grow better."

"Then why don't we water it all over?" I asked.

Grove set down his pail and set himself down on the bluestone curb and picked a long grass from the path and began to chew on it. It was a hot day. My father took his handkerchief out of his hip pocket and wiped his face. He jumped out of the wagon box and came to me and laid his hand on my shoulder and we stood there looking down at the spots we dumped water on.

"Your brother and two sisters are buried here," he said.

"I've got brothers but I never had any sister," I said.

"They died when they were younger than you," said my father. "You never saw them. They have been here so long that their graves are sinking a little. I don't like to think it is anything but the dirt settling. So we are fixing them up."

"I didn't know I had another brother and two sisters," I said.

"I know," my father said.

"Older than Harry?"

"Yes. The first three."

My father was up in the wagon box now and had filled another pail. But Grove sat still on the curb and chewed the stem of grass and looked off toward Mead's on the side of the Overlook.

"Why did they die?" I asked. "It was like Nelson Park, wasn't it?"

"Yes. They all got too sick."

"They must have been awfully sick."

"Yes."

"Did they all die together?"

"Pretty near."

"Was it measles? Like I had the measles?"

"No. It was what they call black diphtheria."

"Did they all get sick together?"

"No. They got sick one after another. It took a month."

I thought about Nelson Park and I remembered how Dominie Park and Mrs. Park felt. Nelson was only one. I knew how my father and mother must have felt, and I looked at my father. But he was waiting with the pail full of water and was motioning to Grove.

They kept on until the barrel was empty, but I sat on the grass and looked at the graves. When they had finished they picked me up and put me on the seat of the wagon between them and Dick started us back to the barn.

When we turned out of the lane to the cemetery I looked back and thought how we had the band there and folks visiting and laughing and flags flying. It was a funny thing to do, I thought, because there was a lot more to a cemetery than that.

✻ The Sale of Grandfather's Picture

. . . and how imagination turns into reality

After dinner my mother and Linnie held up my father a
little bit from going right back to the store to wonder what they
would do about Clifford and me. Harry was older, they said, and
he would be all right anywhere around the village. But Clifford
was still in dresses and Willie wasn't much older even if he had
been in short pants for more than a year, they said. And did he
think they would be all right to be left alone while they drove to
the home of this dead Mister DuBois up by Bearsville and got into
the procession to the funeral at the Methodist Church?

"I suppose Linnie will have to go, too," my father said, "and
can't stay with the boys."

"Oh, I could," said Linnie. "I am not much for funerals anyway."

"No," my mother said. "Mister DuBois was Linnie's stepuncle
and very dear to her and always jounced her on his knee when she
was little. It is the least she can do for her stepuncle."

"Well, I suppose there is something into that," my father said.

"In the country, yes," my mother said. "There are not many
neighbors and relatives at best. Funerals count here."

My father looked at Clifford and me and said, "What about
it, boys? Will you be all right if we leave you here alone this afternoon for a couple of hours?"

We nodded our heads.

"Well, that's settled," my father said, and started for the store.

"Now wait," my mother said. "You are their father and you tell
them something else."

"What else?" he asked.

"You tell them they are not to go near the pond. I don't want Clifford falling off the bridge and just about drowning again. Brook Romer wouldn't be coming along this time to jump in and save him. They are not to play on the bridge. They are not to go into the barns or the house and get caught in a fire. They are to stay right here in the yard until we get back."

"You hear that, boys?" my father asked.

We both nodded.

My father went back to the store. My mother and Linnie went upstairs and got all dressed up and we went out to the barn to watch Grove get the rig ready. Being a businessman, my father was dressed all the time with his wing collar and necktie. All he had to do was to hitch on his starched cuffs and put on his coat, and he could do that at the store.

When they were ready we watched them drive off, and we went into the back yard under the weeping willow trees and sat down on the stone ledge around the pump and wondered what to do.

A while later Egbert and Delancy Boice showed up. They said their mother and father had gone to the funeral, too, but they had not been told they could not do anything. But you could understand that, because neither one of them was still in dresses like Clifford. So it was easy to see why I was caught and they weren't.

"I will sit down and think what we can do," Egbert said.

It was then he spied the two empty packing boxes under the feed room. They were not there as a rule but the men had unpacked them onto the hand elevator that went up into the feed room in the back of the store, instead of carrying everything all the way around to the front door. They did not have time yet to smash them up.

Egbert said we would drag them down under the weeping willow trees and play dog houses. It took a lot of tugging but we did it, and we got them outside the door into the little back hall where the wood box stood. You could go through this hall into the kitchen and dining room or you could turn left and go up three steps to a door with a latch on it and stick your head into an old storeroom where nobody ever went. It was where we kept the junk, my father said, and we would be wise if we never went in there.

Egbert crawled into one of the packing boxes and he got on his hands and knees and barked and growled. I crawled into the other packing box on my hands and knees and tried barking and growling, and then we barked and growled at each other.

I got out and ran into the woodshed that was past the pump and got a chain with a snap on one end of it and a ring on the other end that I knew was hanging there on a nail. Then I came back and fastened the snap on the collar of Egbert's blouse and slipped the ring end of the chain over a nail sticking out of the box. He waited until I did this and then he lunged out of the box until he felt the chain tighten, and then he growled and barked.

Lancy picked up a twig and stood just out of his reach and shook the twig in his face to make him do this. Clifford stood and watched. He never did what Egbert and Lancy and I did, but he watched and sometimes he laughed.

Lancy saw a board alongside the foundation of the house. He went over and lifted it and tugged it over to the boxes. He said we could make a Fourth of July lemonade stand like they had at the celebrations at the churches. This was a good idea, so we tugged the boxes into a line with a space between them. The board had some lumps of dirt and three angleworms and some bugs sticking to the under side. We picked the angleworms and bugs off but it was hard to get the dirt off with our hands. So I ran into the hall and got a broom and then we loosened the clumps of dirt with the end of the handle and swept the board clean.

We lifted the board up on top of the packing boxes and it made a fine counter. Then we got a pail and some glasses and filled the pail with water at the pump. We decided that little round stones would be nickels and we took turns at selling and buying and drinking the water like it was lemonade, until we were all filled up. We were about ready to think of something else to do when a young farmer drove his team under the shed and tied them and came walking down into the yard. He asked us what we were selling.

We just watched him and didn't say anything. He took a glass and tried some of the water and then he laughed and said we had ought to have something to sell and went away. That seemed like a foolish thing for him to say. Where would we get anything to sell? And so we stood with our elbows on the counter for a spell and thought about that. Running a store was a good idea but I wondered if we could sell something for real money. Lots of farmers came down to the shed to tie up their teams. If we had something to sell they might buy it.

Egbert said it didn't make any difference whether we had anything to sell. This was a great big store, he said, and people were coming in and going out all the time. Lancy said the store was all right and the people were all right but where was there anything to sell. Egbert pointed all around us. He showed us the candy and sugar. And the toys. And he turned around and pointed back of him and said the guns were there. Clifford looked everywhere Egbert pointed, but he didn't say anything and just watched.

Then I thought about the old storeroom. I said we could go in there and find things to sell maybe. We could, I said, if we dared to go in. So we went up the steps to the door and lifted the iron latch and looked in. It was dark in there. Some things were covered up. It was dusty. Some high things covered up with white sheets looked spooky.

But we went in a little farther and looked under the cloths. Nothing happened. And so we began looking at everything.

All of a sudden there was a terrible noise at the other end of the room and we rushed for the door and clear out into the yard.

But nothing followed us, so we crept back and looked into the room again. The room was lighter and didn't look spooky at all. Clifford was standing over by the window in the far end in his short dresses and staring at us and not saying anything. What had happened was that he had tugged at the window shade and it had jumped out of his hands and rushed up to the top.

Well, we looked around some more but we couldn't find anything much except broken furniture. There was nothing we could take out to our store and sell. When we were coming out I said there were some things in the house that I had heard my mother and father say they had ought to get rid of. We went into the house and I pointed them out.

There was a pair of ugly shoes of my mother's in a closet upstairs and I ran up and brought them down. There was the vinegar and salt and pepper holder in the center of the dining room table. And in the cupboard where we kept the eating dishes there was a little pile of sauce dishes painted with green and red colors that my father had bought from a woman visitor in the village one time to get rid of her. I knew my mother wouldn't care about these.

Egbert thought these would make good stocks for our store and he looked around and he said he thought there were a lot of other things that my mother and father had ought to want to get rid of. He pointed out a big oil lamp with a fringe dangling all around the edge of the shade. Then he came to the picture of my mother's Methodist father in the big paint-smeared frame and with wild hair and the long beard and fire in his eyes. Egbert looked at it for a spell and shook his head, and I said that I heard my father say once that he wanted to get rid of that. So Egbert lifted it down from the wall and took it out to our store. Then he came back in and pointed out one thing after another and it seemed that he was right about my mother and father wanting to get rid of them now that I looked at them close. So we took them out to sell.

We had so many things from our house that our one counter

store wasn't enough. Egbert sent Lancy and me to look for two more boxes and two more boards. We found them in the warehouse. Now we had a real store, like three sides of a square.

We had just fixed our stock when my father and my mother and Linnie drove down alongside of the store to the barn back from the funeral. I didn't see them until I heard my mother shriek. She had jumped out of the rig and was running down into the yard holding up her skirts and petticoats with both hands, along with her closed parasol. When she got to us she dropped her skirts and petticoats and swung her parasol like a club.

Egbert and Lancy took off fast around the corner by the pump and out of sight. Clifford just stood in his short dresses watching with his eyes big. I didn't know what to do. This store business had seemed all right as we went along, but now all of a sudden I knew that something was wrong about it.

My mother scolded, of course. But I knew she had a right to scold and so I didn't say anything. Then she picked up the big oil lamp with the fringe and started into the house. Linnie picked up some things, too, and followed her. Then they came out and got more.

My father had come down to our store now. At first he didn't say anything. He just went from one thing to another and picked them up and looked at them one at a time. He smiled at the red and green sauce dishes, and when he came to Grandpa Palen's wild picture he laughed, but my mother was in the house and didn't hear him.

Then he went and got the pair of ugly shoes and the holder for the vinegar and salt and pepper and Grandpa Palen's picture in the paint-smeared frame.

"How much are these?" he asked.

"I don't know," I said.

"I'll buy them," he said. "Then you can say you sold them. You don't need to say who bought them."

He opened his purse and laid down a nickel and a dime.

He smiled again and loaded these things into his arms. Then he walked out of the yard and up under the feed room and dumped them in an empty barrel standing there. Then he went into the cellar entrance and I suppose on up into the store.

Of course, this store business was quite a subject at the supper table that night. Clifford had forgotten all about it except for Egbert and me playing like dogs, and that was all he would talk about when my mother asked him questions. I knew enough to keep my mouth shut except to say that one thing led to another in our play and I guess we got carried away. I noticed that my mother and Linnie were doing all the talking and asking all the questions. My father did not say much and when my mother said she got about all the things back that she cared about except Grandfather Palen's picture and she wished I could remember who bought it I looked at my father and found that he was beading me with his eye. So I didn't let the cat out of the bag.

My mother worried about that old picture two or three days but then she forgot about it, so I guess it was just as well.

❦ The Mystery of the Tomcat

. . . and the end of Clifford's Santa Claus and Easter Bunny

The funny thing about Patchy was that he would drop his chest on the walk that ran from the barn to the pump with stop-offs by the kitchen door and the porch of the dining room. Then his hind legs looked like slanting props for his rump. Just the sort of slant that the prize stallion has on the calendar on the inside of the privy door. Then he would kick his back legs out behind him, first one and then the other, and meow.

Now this was a funny thing for a cat to do.

Patchy was a barn cat and we had not seen him for quite a while. We called him Patchy because he was full of patches of color. He was dark brown, but the dark brown was patched in so many places with white and tan and black that he looked as if his fur was made up of things left over. "His name had ought to be Joseph," my father said once. "A coat of many colors."

"Or a cat with many colored fathers," said Linnie.

Even his eyeballs were patched. They were part light brown and part black. He was a little scary and never walked. He always sort of sneaked to where he wanted to go with his body lowered a little so that you could see his shoulders and hips moving. He was different from Old Tom. Tom was gray and white and big and knew all about the chairs with cushions in them in the living room. Tom liked to doze and stand up and turn around and lie down and doze and stand up and stretch by the hour. He liked to be with people but Patchy didn't act as if he did.

I sat down on the step of the porch where Grove and Linnie sat and roughhoused a little in the dark sometimes when Grove came to the pump for water for the horses at night. I had my chin in my hand and was watching the funny way that Patchy was acting. Clifford came to watch, too. My mother came out of the kitchen door with the drinking pail to go to the pump. She did not notice us but she did see Patchy and the funny way he was acting. She turned and called back through the door to Linnie and Linnie came to the door. My mother pointed at Patchy and Linnie laughed.

"What's the matter, Patchy?" said my mother.

"Nothing that time and nature won't heal," said Linnie.

Then they saw us. And they said "Scat, Patchy, scat."

Linnie went back in the kitchen. My mother got her pail of water. She went back in the kitchen, too, and I heard her and Linnie giggling.

Just then Patchy sneaked off to the barn and Clifford and I went off up to the store to see if anything was going on up there.

But that night after Clifford got off his dresses and into his nightgown and had said his prayers on his knees with his head in my mother's lap he looked up at her.

"Why did Patchy act that way?" he asked.

My mother rubbed his head and smiled but did not say anything.

"Why did Patchy get down low and kick out his feet like that? He didn't hurt somewhere, did he? Tell me he didn't hurt," said Clifford.

"He didn't hurt," said my mother. "Why don't you just take my word for that and stop worrying about it? Just stop worrying about Patchy and go to bed and go to sleep like a good little boy."

Clifford stood up straight and asked her, "Would I be a better little boy to find out about what I am worrying about? Or would I be a better little boy to always go to bed and never care whether I found out?"

I heard a chuckle back of me and it was Linnie reading a book and she had her nose buried in it. She wasn't paying any attention to my mother and Clifford.

"It must be a good book," said my mother.

"It is," said Linnie. "All about the comical side of life."

"Well, life can be comical," said my mother. "Especially if you don't know all the answers to what little boys ask."

I was listening but I was beginning to have a hunch. I was pretty sure it was the thing that the men joked about around the stove in the store.

"Please don't talk with Linnie now," said Clifford. "You can talk with her after I am gone to bed. Talk to me now."

My mother smiled. "Well, of course I will."

"So. What about Patchy?" said Clifford.

"Well," my mother said. And then she stopped and she set her chin and her eyes narrowed and she looked across at Linnie.

Clifford saw it. "Did Linnie hurt Patchy?" he asked.

"Not I, Clifford, not I," said Linnie.

"No, no, of course not," said my mother. "It was, well, it was God. God has been speaking to Patchy."

"What?" said Clifford. "Does God talk with cats?"

"I suspect He does," said my mother. "But not the way it sounds. Patchy feels things. And that's really God talking to him. It's God that does lots of things. Like making the locust trees in the lower yard have such sweet and pretty blossoms in the spring."

"But what do the locust trees got to do with Patchy?" Clifford asked.

"It says here," said Linnie, "try to work that out note by note on your mandolin. And if too difficult, choose another tune."

"Mamma," said Clifford, "I wish you would make Linnie stop talking."

"Mamma," said Linnie, "I wish Clifford would go on to bed."

"I am afraid that Clifford would rather spoil the big surprise," said my mother.

"Oh, that would be a shame," said Linnie. She shook her head from side to side at Clifford. "I thought you liked surprises. Didn't you tell me that when it was your birthday and you didn't know it was your birthday—didn't you tell me then that you guessed a surprise was the best thing there is?"

"A surprise is fun," said Clifford, "What do you mean? A surprise? What is there about Patchy that's a surprise?"

"Now Clifford," said my mother, "you are a big enough boy to figure out that we can't tell you and still have it be a surprise."

"It's a real surprise? Like my birthday party?"

"I'll guarantee it," said Linnie.

We started for the door to go upstairs and to bed. When I turned in the door to close it, I saw my mother sigh and Linnie rub her fingers over her forehead and then shake them just like I have seen Henry Pepper do in the summer after he fitted a shoe on a horse and put it back in the fire. But Linnie wasn't shoeing a horse and I am sure she wasn't sweating and so I was sure my hunch was right. But I did not say anything to Clifford because I did not want to spoil his surprise, and he was too young anyway. He was still on the stork business. We went to sleep and the next day was another day.

The daffodils came and the locust trees were full of sweet flowers. The dirt roads turned to dust. I clear forgot about Patchy until one day Clifford and I were playing on the iron railings that run from a willow with a big hole in it to the end of the iron bridge. This was right at the end of our lower yard.

I had climbed up on the top rail and was leaning against the willow tree before trying to walk on the top rail, and I turned to make sure the tree was right behind me if I lost my balance. This brought my head even with the big hollow in the tree and I looked right into a pair of wild eyes in there. I was so scared I lost my balance and my arms went round in circles until I could grab the tree again.

I peeked closer, and then the face with the wild eyes said, "Meow."

"What's the matter?" cried Clifford who was standing down on the ground.

"Patchy's up here," I said.

"Well bring him down, ninny."

I tried to reach in and get hold of Patchy but he backed out of my reach. He didn't want to be helped down.

"Stand up on the lower rail," I said to Clifford, "and help boost me higher. I've got to get higher to reach in and get hold of Patchy."

Clifford found an old piece of plank that was higher than the top rail when he stood it against the willow tree. Then he pushed on my behind and I was almost up high enough to get hold of Patchy in the back of the hollow but I stopped. "My gosh," I said.

"What's the matter?" asked Clifford.

"Patchy's a she," I said.

"What?"

"Patchy's a she. She has two little bits of kittens up here in the hollow. One is tiger and one is blue and white."

"Throw them down and I'll catch them."

"Patchy won't let me. She hits at me with her paw every time I reach. She keeps meowing. She is trying to tell us something, I guess."

"Cat talk," said Clifford. "A lot of good that does."

"Well, let me down," I said. "We'll have to tell somebody."

My mother and Linnie acted excited when we told them.

"The surprise has arrived," said Linnie.

"What surprise?" said Clifford.

"Don't you remember when Patchy acted funny and you would not go to bed? And we promised you a surprise?" said my mother.

"You said it would be bigger and better than my birthday," said Clifford. "This is only kittens."

"Wait till you see them," I said. "Patchy acts like she is trying to tell us something and we are too dumb to understand," I told Linnie.

"She is and you are," said Linnie.

"The kittens don't have their eyes open yet," said my mother. "Patchy knows they will crawl around. The hollow was a good idea. Dry and covered. But now it is dangerous because the kittens could tumble out and kill themselves."

Linnie had been bustling around and not saying much. She had put on a pair of old gloves and she picked up a basket.

"Come on," she said. She went to the woodshed and picked up a little ladder and carried it out through the picket gate and to the willow tree. She set the ladder up against the tree and climbed up on it. Patchy was meowing and struck at her when she put her hand into the hollow. But Linnie paid no attention to her.

"You know a lot more about these things than I do, up to a certain point," she told Patchy. "But from here on I'll do the calling off."

She picked up the crying kittens one at a time and put them in the basket. Then Patchy was glad to be picked up and put in the basket, too. Linnie told Clifford and me to bring the ladder and she marched to the woodshed. She got a box and filled it with shavings and set it in a corner of the woodshed where next winter's wood for the kitchen stove was piled and wouldn't be touched. She put Patchy and the kittens in it.

"There, there, Patchy," she said, "there's your house and your home and your family all safe and sound."

For the rest of the day Clifford and I went in to see Patchy and the kittens every hour or so and we took Patchy milk and some sardines in cracker crumbs that Linnie fixed. Patchy stayed right with her babies and didn't let them out of her sight. That night we closed the door to the woodshed so that nothing could get in to hurt them.

We would have gone right to the woodshed the next morning, but it was the day the Italian came down out of the mountains with the trained bears. We forgot to go to see Patchy and the kittens. Then, when we did, they were gone.

We looked all over the woodshed and the washroom next to it. We called. But Patchy and her babies were not anywhere. So we ran into the house and asked Linnie and my mother, but they didn't know either and thought it was very queer.

"Maybe Patchy has moved them back into the willow tree," said my mother.

"If you were Patchy would you?" Linnie asked my mother.

"No, I guess not," said my mother.

But Clifford and I ran to the willow tree and climbed up to see. It was no use. They were not there.

It was all just too bad and we could kick ourselves for not keeping track of Patchy.

"You couldn't be blamed for wanting to see the trained bears," said Linnie.

My mother said not to worry. "They will turn up," she said. "Just now I wish you would worry about filling the woodbox."

I started to do it and Clifford came with me to carry his one stick, because he was still in dresses and I was in short pants. I got an armful of the dry wood that was a year old in the woodshed, and carried it past the dining room porch and the pump to the little hall back of the kitchen. I was just ready to let it go clattering into the woodbox when Clifford let out a yell. I couldn't see over the wood in my arms but I held on and looked over the side of the wood at Clifford and he was pointing into the woodbox and trying to speak before I let the wood go.

I put the wood down on the floor and looked in the box. And there was Patchy looking up at me and she had the kittens with her.

We called Linnie. Linnie told Patchy that was about the worst place she could pick. "Where is all the animal sense I have read about?" she asked Patchy. She got the basket again and took Patchy and the kittens back to the box in the woodshed. But it didn't do much good. Three times we found Patchy and the kittens in the woodbox and three times Linnie carried them back to the woodshed. It got so you did not dare to let an armful of wood drop without looking in the box first. It got to be a game between Linnie and Patchy, and my father laughed about it a lot.

But Linnie said she might not be any relation to General Grant but she had a lot of General Grant in her. I asked my father what she meant and he said General Grant never gave up.

"I'll show that cat that the human brain can beat an animal brain," said Linnie.

But my father said it was a question whether it did. Because after Linnie had put Patchy back in the woodshed six times we did not find her and the kittens in the woodbox any more. She was gone. And the kittens were, too. Clifford and I looked high and low outside, and Linnie helped us look all over the house and barn and woodshed and feed room and store, but we couldn't find her. In the end Linnie said, "Oh, the devil with it!" And that's where we had to leave it.

Then, one night at supper, my mother and Linnie were acting mighty cute and mysterious. I saw it and my father saw it and Harry saw it. Clifford saw it, too, because you had to be pretty young if you missed it. Harry and I were old enough to begin to be like my father when my mother and Linnie acted cute, and we made out like we didn't notice them at all. Harry and I glanced at my father and he glanced at us, and he winked when my mother and Linnie did not see him, and we just wouldn't ask questions. But Clifford was different. He couldn't stand it because his bump of curiosity was pretty big yet.

Linnie was saying very seriouslike, "Of course, animals have a way of survival."

"Yes," my mother said with a flat face, just as if they were talking science or something like schoolteachers do. "But," my mother said, "humans might survive better too by not weaning them so fast. No telling what humans might do if put to it."

"That's true," said Linnie. She raised her eyebrows and chewed on some dry bread that she did not know she was chewing because she was play-acting so hard. My father exploded in his plate, but made out it was a sneeze.

"What do you mean? What's weaned and who's weaned who?" Clifford asked.

"You win," said my father to Linnie and my mother, and then

we all laughed and laughed until we had to hold our sides and stop eating. All but Clifford, that is. He'd laugh a little as if he ought to and then he'd go sober and look at us with questions in his eyes and then laugh again.

My mother got up and put her arm around him and said, "Look, dear, it's just a little game we were playing. We wanted you to ask us a secret."

"Well, what is it?" asked Clifford going straight to business.

"You tell him, Linnie," said my mother. "You found them."

"No, you tell him," said Linnie.

"We found Patchy and the kittens," said my mother. "And where do you suppose they have been all this time? Down in the back of the old cellar that has not been used since Indian times. Where the old Dutch oven is. Linnie had to go back there this afternoon to see if she could find an old piece of tin to patch a mouse hole in the back hall. She lighted a lantern and took it down. When she was looking around she looked up to the top of the foundation at one place and saw four eyes that the light of the lantern was shining on. It came over her that it might be Patchy's kittens. So she followed them around and looked closer, and they were."

"Gosh," said Harry. "Down there all the time? How did she feed them, do you suppose?"

"Well, they're too big to be nursing yet," said Linnie.

"Patchy must have some way of getting in from the outside," said my mother. "She must carry food to them that way."

"No, I don't think so," said my father. "There isn't any opening that I know of unless that old chimney and that's impossible."

"Well, it's a mystery," said my mother. "But there they are. As lively and plump as can be, Linnie says. But they don't know humans and they are terribly wild, Linnie says."

"Let's get them," I said.

"No, now wait, Willie," said my mother. "You would have

to corner them and you can't do that in that old Dutch cellar. It's cluttered."

"They've got to get used to humans," said Linnie. "But you and Clifford can be the humans they get used to."

"That's the only way, we think," said my mother. "You and Clifford can take milk down to them every night. Just set it on the floor and stay there away from the dish, quiet for a little bit. At first you may not see them but they will see you. By and by they will come right out to you when you bring the milk. Then you can pick them up."

"Mornings or noontime," I said. "Not at night. It would be bad enough in that old cellar mornings or noontime."

"Well, noontime then," said my mother. "But, of course, that's foolishness—being afraid to go down into the old cellar at night."

"If you had your choice would you take night?" I asked.

"Bull's eye," said my father.

"Willie's right," said Linnie. "I wouldn't go down there at night. Not alone. When you think of all that's gone on down there in a hundred years. Folks who baked in that old Dutch oven and dead for years. I don't believe in ghosts but I have a mighty healthy imagination. Maybe somebody was killed there. And bats. Some folks say that bats are the same as ghosts."

"Linnie, stop that," said my mother. "There's no use making it worse than it is. And in front of the boys, too."

"I couldn't make it worse than it is," said Linnie. "But what's to be gained going down at night? Except goose flesh on the back of your neck. Noontime is better. That's when we have dinner and that's when we feed the other cats."

"Of course," said my mother. "I just thought that the boys would like to practice up on their courage a little."

"There's no need to rush them," said my father. "Everybody learns gradually. Now take this experience with Patchy and the kittens. The boys have learned that kittens and colts and calves and babies have to be born. There's no stork about it. And the way that gets started is . . ."

"Abe!" said my mother. "And right here before Linnie."

"Linnie knows the facts of life," said my father.

"Let's get back to feeding the kittens," said Linnie.

Clifford slid down off his chair and stood up strong. "Who's afraid?" he said. "Give me a lantern and some milk and I'll go down and feed them alone."

"You will not," said my mother. "You and Willie will go down together when you take milk down there. And tonight there has been so much silly talk about what's down there that all of us will go down with you right now. Even you, Abe."

My father opened his watch and looked at it. "Too late for me," he said. "I have to get back to the store."

Linnie laughed. "Mr. Rose doesn't have any hankering to mingle with the ghostly spirits summoned by memory and imagination," she said. "I read that in a book one time."

"Linnie," said my mother, "stop your fooling."

"And ghosts," Linnie went on.

"Cobwebs," said my mother.

"Dirt," said my father. "I'd have to change my clothes before I went back to the store."

"We're all going down," said my mother, real firm. "Get the lantern, Linnie."

Linnie got the lantern and lighted it. She handed it to my mother and my mother opened the cellar door and said, "Come on."

"Haven't you forgotten something?" asked my father.

"The milk," said Linnie. "Wait till I get the milk."

"Now we're ready," said my father. "One, two, three, four, five, six. Six of us with a lantern and a bowl of milk. Enough to scare a tiger, let alone two kittens brought up in the dark."

We crept down the steps into the front cellar where everything was as clean as a whistle. Flat stones fitted in the floor, everything painted white, and everything scrubbed clean. Because this was the food cellar and no junk around. Nobody worth his salt kept any junk in the food cellar. The apple barrels were empty this time of year because it was between storage seasons. And no sausage hanging in their white muslin tubes, or hams or bacon. The headcheese pans were empty and polished. There were no nubby ears of popcorn in the box. But the smell of all these things and the cold of the cellar were in the air.

We crossed the cellar and my mother held up the lantern. She loosened the leather strap on the upper half of the Dutch door to the old cellar. It let out a long squeak when she swung it back. You might as well have opened the door to a tomb, it was so pitch dark in there ahead of us. My mother lifted the lantern up over the lower half of the door and stuck it through into the darkness. Then she leaned over into the darkness and peered around.

She didn't seem to see anything and so she loosened the lower part of the Dutch door and stepped through. We crowded after her, except that Clifford and I hung onto my father's pants legs.

We stood there and waited, but nothing happened. We saw lots of junk in this old cellar.

"There might be antiques in here," said my father. "Why don't you women rustle these things out of here sometime and clean them up and we'd have a look?"

"Why don't you?" said my mother.

"You do it and I'll split fifty-fifty with you. Of course, I'll have to take out cost of repair and rent for the space in the store and so forth, first."

"If we do it we'll keep one hundred per cent," my mother said.

"Well, there's no cats here tonight," said my father.

We had been moving around a little to the edge of the lantern light and looking behind this and that. We had come in front of the old Dutch oven. It was big enough to crawl into and make

a bed. But there was nothing in the oven. It was about waist high
and all open in front. The light from the lantern did not reach
way back into it but you could see that most of it was clear. My
father bent over to look under the shelf of the oven where the old
Dutch settlers burned the wood to heat the oven, and just then
something happened. There was a kind of a swish and the biggest
cat I ever saw landed on my father's back from up somewhere and
then jumped into the oven. It was just one big streak.

My mother screamed. I couldn't breathe for a minute. The cat
half knocked my father down and he didn't see it at all. He got
up from the dust and dirt in front of the oven and started brushing himself off. "Damn," he said, "if I must say so. Who pushed
me?"

"It was a big cat," said Harry. "He landed on your back. He
jumped into the oven. Look in. Is he there?"

"I don't see him," said my father. "Was it Patchy?"

"No," said my mother.

"It was a great big cat," said Clifford. "None of ours. None
of anybody's. I know them all."

"You don't suppose it was a wildcat, do you?" asked my father.
"Look at my clothes. A wildcat. I wonder. Do you suppose?"

"I do," said Linnie. "And that explains the whole thing. I knew
Patchy was wild but I didn't know she was that wild."

"A wildcat," said my father. "Coming in through the chimney
of the old Dutch oven. The father of the kittens. Why, that's
how they've been fed. Sure. That big cat could have killed small
game. Birds. He could have climbed the big willows and come
over the roof. And down the Dutch chimney."

"What about water?" said my mother.

"A big cat like that could have carried the kittens out," said
Linnie. And even Patchy. Up the chimney and out on the roof.
Down the willows to the creek."

My mother stood there holding up the lantern. Our faces and

white part of our clothes stood out in the light but you couldn't
see the rest of us in the dark around us. It was spooky.

"Let's get out of here," said my mother. "That's all we can do
tonight. The kittens must be down here somewhere. Linnie saw
them this afternoon."

"But they are not here now," said Harry.

"They'll come arunning when the milk arrives," said my
mother.

"Yessir," said Linnie. "You can break down anybody, even
kittens, by giving them something they like."

"Linnie," said my father, "you have just said something wiser
than Confucius or even Solomon. If people only realized it they
could end all the trouble in the world. I knew a man once who
was a sucker for a piece of green-apple pie. The girls all tried to
land him. Some with spooning. Some with clothes. Some with
witty talk. Some with music. Some with wisdom. But he was
bulletproof. Then one tried green-apple pie and that was it. Find
out what a man wants and he is putty in your hands. For a kitten
either, I suppose. Now, some people are crazy about strawberry
ice cream for instance . . ."

"Oh, Abe, do be still," said my mother. "Look at your hands.
Black. And your face is smeared. Your great thoughts will sound
better when you wash up."

We all went back upstairs to the kitchen and dining room.
Harry went out somewhere. I sat and listened to my mother and
father and Linnie talk about it. Clifford went and sat down on the
floor in a corner. He had his legs crossed under him and just sat
and looked at the floor. My father went to the kitchen to wash
up and then he got the whisk broom and took off his coat and
went outside to brush his clothes. Linnie and my mother were
talking back and forth but my father did not say anything. He
came in and got his hat and then stood by the door as if he was
waiting until my mother and Linnie got through talking and he

could get a word in edgewise. My mother and Linnie saw him
there and they stopped talking and looked at him.

"Well," my mother said. "What is it?"

"It occurs to me" he said, "that Patchy has done us a favor.
She has helped us tell the boys some of the facts of life."

"Are you still on that?" asked my mother.

"People don't sit down with them and explain," he said. "Got
to keep the lid on, they think. Then along comes Patchy and a wildcat and kittens. Must be a big surprise to them. Especially Willie
and Clifford. No more storks."

We all looked at him, and Clifford stopped looking at the floor
and looked at him hardest. Then my father put on his hat and
went on off up to the store.

"Well, the lid's off now for sure," said Linnie.

My mother started clearing up the table and Linnie started
washing dishes. Then Clifford blurted out. "No Santa Claus.
No Easter Bunny. And now no storks. Now I'm gonta look into
this Jesus Christ business."

Linnie snickered but my mother shook her head at her.

Well, anyway, we took the milk down into the old cellar every
day. Nothing happened but the milk was gone every time when
we went back down again. Then the kittens started to come out
where we could see them. Three days after that they came right
out and drank the milk while we were there. We grabbed them
and carried them upstairs.

They were beautiful. We named them Brownie and Chub and
they grew about two times bigger than any other cats. They got
so they followed us around the Village and fields like dogs.

We never saw Patchy and the wildcat again. We wondered a
lot about them but my father said we might as well not waste our
time. "They must have gone off to the mountains," he said. "Some
cats may be like some people. They can't help being wild."

❧ Aunt Carrie's Trip to the Train

. . . and how the Methodist Palens are great worriers

It was Saturday and my father was awfully late for dinner again. When he came in my mother's patience was pretty strained.

"It is bad enough anytime," she said, "trying to keep the meals in shape and not having them overdone and all, just because you might come in at noon or you might come in at one or half-past. You know Carrie is visiting us and so I have some pride in our vittles just now. And there's Linnie's pride, too. She's about beside herself."

"I know, I know," my father said. "And I apologize to you and to Linnie and to Carrie. But this is Saturday, woman, and harvests are over and the farmers are swarming into the store. To make matters worse, there are two drummers at the store and I can't ask them to stay over till Monday. I'm sorry about the meals when there's company. When Carrie is visiting us, I mean. And that reminds me. There was a letter in the morning mail for Carrie. Here it is, Carrie. And I'll go and wash up."

"A letter for me?" said Aunt Carrie. "But nobody knows I'm here but the folks at home. Now what." She opened the letter and started to read it and then she said, "Oh, no. Oh, dear."

"What is it?" said my mother.

"El is down sick," said Aunt Carrie. "Oh, dear, I will have to go right home. And Abe says this is such a busy Saturday and how will I get to the train?"

"Oh, dear," said my mother. "Is he very sick? Who wrote the letter?"

"Vivian wrote it," said Aunt Carrie. "Viv is a good daughter but she is only fifteen and taking care of an invalid is beyond her. She says El is down in bed with a fever and coughing bad. They've had the doctor. But she says she don't know what to do."

"Well, I'm certainly sorry," said my mother. "And I can see you can't rest until you get there. Saturday or no Saturday, Abe will have to see to it that you get to the train."

And so what my father calls the Palen worrying began.

Aunt Carrie lives in Montgomery. That's on the Walkill Valley Railroad that runs into Kingston and that the U & D connects with. She is the wife of Uncle El Gardner who works on the Walkill Valley. She is my mother's sister and that makes her a Palen of course. The Palens are my mother; Aunt Carrie; Aunt Alice, who is the wife of L.L. Osterhoudt in Kingston; Aunt Tam, who is the wife of Tom Dixon in Newburgh; and Uncle Dell, who draws designs for carpets in the carpet mills in Rifton; and Uncle Abe, who runs trolley cars in Kingston. These are all Methodists, and that's what they believe and they believe it. Uncle Luther, who is the Secretary of the Rondout Savings Bank, is so strong in the Methodist Church that he is what they call a lay preacher. This means that he can preach when he wants to even though he is not a minister.

The Palens never sing anything but hymns and they are great worriers. My father says give them something to worry about and they are happy even if what they worry about never happens. If you tell them it's a nice day in summer they say it won't be long till snow is flying. They worry about there may be frost to kill fruit and flowers, and whether it will rain on a picnic day, and whether the roof will leak if there is a storm, and whether it is too hot or too cold, and anything you can think of. My father says he hopes Heaven will be perfect because if it isn't it is going to be a great disappointment to the Palens. But even if it is perfect, he says, he doesn't know. They won't run true to form unless they worry because there's nothing to worry about.

After Aunt Carrie read her letter my father came in from washing in the kitchen sink to ask the Blessing and start the dinner. Aunt Carrie and my mother stopped worrying about Uncle El and the busy Saturday till the Blessing was over and then they started right in again.

"What's the matter?" my father asked.

"Oh, Abe," said Aunt Carrie, "the letter Vivian wrote. She says that El is down sick. Fever and coughing. I have to go right home, but this is a busy Saturday and all. What time does the U & D train go to Kingston in the afternoon? There's a Walkill Valley train from there about seven o'clock, I know. But then I can't get to the train anyway, this being a busy Saturday."

"There's the livery," my mother said. "Could we get Stanley Longyear to take her to West Hurley?"

"I think you both worry too much about it," my father said. "Now let me see. You think El is pretty sick?"

"Viv says so," said Aunt Carrie.

"Well, you'll have to go then," said my father. "Now let me see." He chewed for a minute and thought and then he said. "The team has got to go to Mink Hollow. And that ties up Grove. But now there's old Dick. What about old Dick? He could make it to West Hurley and back if you take it slow."

"But who would drive him?" asked my mother.

"Well what about Harry? He's what? Nine years old now?"

"He's never been out with a rig alone," said my mother.

"I could do it as easy as pie," said Harry.

"Well, I don't know," said Aunt Carrie. "And Harry coming back all alone, do you mean?"

"He could be back before dark," said my father. "And Willie and Clifford could go along for company on the way back."

"Well, I don't know," said my mother.

"Now we will work it out and I would stop worrying if I were you," said my father. "There's just as much chance that El is not as sick as you think he is as that he is. And Harry and the boys will get you to West Hurley and the U & D if you will just stop worrying. Just settle down and things will come out all right."

"You don't think there will be any hitch?" asked Aunt Carrie. "It would be a shame to get all packed and ready and then not go."

"Yes, I suppose it would," said my father. "But you go ahead and get packed and ready and try it out. Harry knows how to drive. Of course somebody has been with him when he did. But Dick is so old and gentle and so fat that he couldn't run away if he wanted to. And he's not afraid of the steam cars or anything. All his life he has been going to West Hurley with the single rig to help the team unload cars. Not lately, of course. Just don't push him and you'll be all right."

"You see, he stumbles," said Harry.

"Oh, dear," said Aunt Carrie.

My father looked at Harry. "If you had any wisdom," he said, "you wouldn't just say that and let it go. You would tell your Aunt Carrie that Dick never fell down in his life."

"I didn't have time," said Harry.

"Oh, dear," said Aunt Carrie. "I don't know."

My father got up. "I've got to go back to the store," he said. "I'll tell Grove to hitch up Dick. The train goes at five so I would say you better start at about three. And now, Carrie, I am sorry about El and that you have to go. Tell El I have a new story to tell him. We have enjoyed your visit, Carrie, very much. You don't come often enough. Next time bring El with you. I'll bet El will be on his feet by the time you get there. Well, anyway, good-bye and good luck." Then he went.

"What did he mean by that?" Aunt Carrie asked my mother. "That good-bye and good luck? Does he think we will need luck to get to West Hurley?"

"I don't think so," said my mother. "Oh, no, I don't think so. Certainly not. Abe wouldn't send you out if he thought anything could happen."

"Gosh, no," said Harry. "Everybody says good-bye and good luck. It doesn't mean nothing except good-bye and good luck."

After dinner Aunt Carrie and my mother sat down for a last visit and to worry about whether Harry could drive old Dick, and it was too bad it was a busy Saturday, and how Uncle El might be, and how soon should she start to pack, and when would they see each other again, maybe never.

This wasn't interesting to me, so Clifford and I went out to the barn where Harry was and watched Grove getting old Dick hitched up.

We hung around and hung around and it seemed that Aunt Carrie and my mother were talking longer than they thought. It was really past three o'clock when my mother called to Harry to drive old Dick around in front of the house. Clifford and I climbed in and went with him.

My mother and Aunt Carrie were standing by the front gate when we got there. Harry had to turn Dick around to head through the Village and to West Hurley. He cramped Dick too short and one front wheel lifted the wagon box pretty bad on one side and Aunt Carrie saw it and she wrung her hands and called "Harry, Harry, careful," just as if Harry didn't know and hadn't already swung old Dick wider.

When that was over and we were headed right and stopped, my mother took a lot of time to tell Aunt Carrie to be careful of herself, and to hope over and over again that Uncle El wasn't very sick. And they both must have spent fifteen minutes wondering when they would see each other again. If Uncle El wasn't too sick, my mother said, maybe she could get back again next spring. And Aunt Carrie said maybe Uncle El was going this time, and then when would she ever see my mother? And she was afraid Uncle El was pretty sick or why would Viv have written to her about it? Uncle El had been sick before, she said, and Viv hadn't written. And my mother said that was because Aunt Carrie was home, so why would Viv write and where? Aunt Carrie said yes, that was so, but she was so worried, she guessed she couldn't think straight. Then they kissed each other and said good-bye four or five more times and Aunt Carrie climbed up on the front seat with Harry. Clifford and I got into the back seat.

Old Dick never worked himself very much at any time and now he was just jogging along. But everything was going fine. And it was only five miles to West Hurley.

We had just crossed the Sawkill bridge above Hugo Dish's grist mill when old Dick, who wasn't paying much attention to what he was doing, stumbled.

Aunt Carrie said "Oh, dear" and told Harry he had better slow up. But Harry said it didn't mean anything. "It's just that old Dick is lazy and does not pick up his feet," he said.

"Was your father telling the truth that he never fell down?" asked Aunt Carrie.

"Well, enough like the truth to be the truth," said Harry.

"But not the gospel truth."

"Now Aunt Carrie," said Harry, "he just fell down once and that was with Grove, our barn man."

And so Aunt Carrie began to worry and to talk about what would happen if old Dick did fall down with us, and us just little boys, and that maybe he would break a leg and maybe we couldn't get any help if he did break a leg. This scared Clifford and me and we got off the back seat and stood up behind the front seat where we could be right with Aunt Carrie and Harry. I watched old Dick jog along and it seemed to me that every once in awhile he wasn't sure what he was doing. Aunt Carrie always saw this too and she said "Oh dear" every time old Dick sort of put his foot down wrong.

When she couldn't stand it any longer Aunt Carrie said "Now see here," and she told Harry he must let Dick walk and not to have him trot at all. Harry said he was afraid we would miss the train if he did that because old Dick was a very slow walker as well as a very slow trotter. But Aunt Carrie looked at her watch and said we had almost an hour and a half and she believed old Dick could walk to West Hurley in time to catch the train. And so Harry had to do what Aunt Carrie said and besides I could see that he had started to worry, too, because he had a good hold on one of the leather lines in each hand and was watching old Dick like a hawk, ready to pull on the lines and hold him up if he stumbled.

We had not gone a mile yet, and when old Dick walked it was awfully slow work. Two or three times Harry tried having him trot a little ways. But every time old Dick would sort of stub his toe and then Aunt Carrie would grab hold of the lines and say "Whoa, whoa" and, of course, old Dick would stop dead still. Then Harry would say "Get up" and slap him with the lines and get him started on a walk again. The third time old Dick stopped when Aunt Carrie said "Whoa, whoa" and then Harry said "Get up" right away, old Dick turned his head around and looked at us with his ears up in wonderment, like he was saying "Make up your mind."

Clifford and I started keeping track of the time. We did not have any watches but Aunt Carrie had one. We asked her what time it was and how much more time we had left and then every couple of minutes we asked her again. After we had her look at her watch ten or eleven times she shouted, "Stop asking me that. Stop."

We had been with the team many times back and forth to West Hurley to unload feed and barrels of flour, and we had been to Kingston a few times with my father and mother to do the banking and take in the eggs and butter and eat at the Eagle Hotel, and so forth. So we knew all the landmarks and could tell how far we were from West Hurley all the time. We had a chance to make it but we couldn't be sure.

Of course Harry had stopped trying to have old Dick jog and trot along. Old Dick was just walking, taking his time. Aunt Carrie was worrying and fidgeting, and standing up in the wagon to look ahead. In the last mile she kept listening for the train whistle. Harry just sat in a heap on the end of the front seat, all tired out. Clifford and I kept wondering what we could do and asking questions.

About half a mile from West Hurley depot the road makes a turn and then runs straight to the depot through a lot of scrub oak and sumac. You stand up and see the railroad depot. We were just walking around this turn when we heard the train whistle up in the mountains. We could not see it yet but it was coming down and we knew it was almost there as trains go. Pretty soon we saw the smoke of it coming down out of the hills and it seemed to be going awfully fast.

Harry started old Dick on a trot again, but right away he sort of stumbled and Aunt Carrie grabbed hold of the lines and hollered "Whoa, whoa" and of course old Dick stopped. But Harry got him walking again. Aunt Carrie was talking a blue streak and turning and twisting and wondering what she could do. The train slowed down and stopped at the depot, but we were not there yet. Aunt Carrie stood up and waved and called "Wait, wait." The engine snorted and spit and acted important as if it wasn't going to wait for anything or anybody. Aunt Carrie tried to have me run on ahead to tell them we were coming but I would not do that because it would look so silly. What would they think with a boy running up to ask them to wait and then see a slow horse coming on a slow walk? And so old Dick kept walking along and we kept straining. And then the engine blew the whistle and rang the bell and started up, and the train got up speed fast and was gone right there before our eyes and Aunt Carrie plumped down on the seat like a toy balloon when somebody is mean and sticks a pin in yours. Harry had not stopped Dick because there wasn't any place there to turn around. Old Dick just kept walking along slow and Harry let him go on until we got to the space that was covered with black cinders at the depot. Then we stopped. Harry didn't know what to do and we just sat there while Aunt Carrie did all the thinking and talking. But in the end Aunt Carrie said to turn around and to be careful about it and she and Harry and Clifford and I and old Dick started walking back to Woodstock and just as slow.

It took an awfully long time. It grew dusk and then it got to be nighttime. I didn't think we would ever get home. None of us talked except Aunt Carrie, and about all she said over and over was that Uncle El was probably dead now, anyhow, so maybe it didn't make any difference, and then she started to worry about what she would do about the funeral. Harry just sat in the front seat all doubled up and holding the lines. Clifford got sleepy and Aunt Carrie took him in her lap. I stood up behind the front seat straining to help if I could.

When we were coming to the bridge over the Sawkill Falls by Aaron Riseley's we saw a light coming fast down the road. When it met up with us it was my father and Grove with the team, and the light was a lantern. My father had the lantern while Grove drove and he held it up high and looked at us as old Dick came walking along. The team stopped and old Dick stopped and Aunt Carrie talked fast to tell what happened and that Uncle El was probably dead anyhow, and my father tried to soothe her, and Grove didn't say anything but just sat there and smiled.

My father had Aunt Carrie get in with the team and he took over from Grove and told Grove to get in and drive old Dick. Then he turned the team around and followed us to the barns. Grove just slapped old Dick with the lines and old Dick broke into a fast trot and kept it up even up the grade past the sawmill and Pepper's blacksmith shop, and didn't stop until he was going down to the barns.

The next morning was Sunday but they took Aunt Carrie to West Hurley and the U & D just the same.

Well, we didn't hear anything about Uncle El dying so Aunt Carrie must have got home in time.

🙢 Graduation from Boys' Dresses

. . . and the power of pants and haircuts

My mother was rushing Clifford and me to get dressed in the living room on the upper level of the ground floor. When she came to Clifford's dresses she didn't pay any attention to them, but reached for a pair of short pants I hadn't noticed.

When Clifford saw that she was going to try them on him he got excited and jumped around like a pup that sees you are going somewhere and are going to take him along. My mother had a job getting his second leg in but she made it. She had a blouse, too, and a coat like my Sunday suit but a different color. And then a Windsor tie with stripes and colors like cinnamon ribbon candy. She took a lot of pains with the Windsor tie. It was fresh and hadn't been worn at all to make it stringy and limp and it tied into a very lovely big bowknot.

When she had finished she had him walk to the other side of the room and back to her while she watched him and I could see by the smile on her face and the light in her eyes that she was very proud of him. She had been so busy with Clifford that for the first time in my life I felt lonely with my mother right there. I wasn't in it at all and I had to stand and wait. Some of my buttons were hard to do and I wasn't yet buttoned up but I stood and waited while I held my own short pants up tight. I never had long curls, either.

Clifford was lighter and I was darker. He still had his long hair and curls and in his new suit and his Windsor tie and his light curls he looked like a picture out of a book. He looked at himself in the long looking glass we had in that room and walked away and came back and looked at himself in the looking glass again and straightened up and put his hand in his pants pocket like men do when they are trying to look free and easy and feel important. Then all of a sudden he took hold of his curls with both hands and yanked at them and squealed between his teeth. My mother said the curls were lovely and tears came in her eyes, but Clifford kept on with his tantrum and she sighed and said they would be cut off.

She turned to me and helped with the hard buttons. Then she had us stand up alongside each other. I was a little small for how old I was and Clifford was a little big. In his short dresses and never saying anything but just going around with us boys and watching, he always seemed pretty young. But when we stood alongside each other we matched. My mother said there was only seventeen months between us. She said she believed she would get me a new suit just exactly like Clifford's and then we would look like twins. I didn't see why it was better for us to look like twins and I did see that then Clifford would be equal with me, but I didn't say anything.

Clifford's short pants changed him so much I was surprised. I heard my mother tell Linnie that his tongue hung in the middle. After breakfast my mother didn't put him in a highchair to comb and brush his curls around her finger like always before. She took him across to Larry Elwyn's barber shop to have his curls cut off and I went along to see. Clifford talked about that and talked with Larry Elwyn, and Larry Elwyn joked and acted gay because he saw that my mother was very quiet. But Clifford talked with Mr. Elwyn and told him he was going to learn to skate on the quarry holes and was going to learn to swim in the Big Deep. And when we went outdoors to find the other boys he was talking right along and had ideas about what we should do. At first I was glad about that. It was like finding a brand-new boy.

But that night I could see that this wasn't the best thing, either. That night there was a bazaar at the M.E. Hall. I expected that my father and mother would take me and Clifford would stay home and go to bed while Linnie stayed in the house to be sure he was all right. There never had been any question about that.

But at supper Clifford said he thought it was his turn to go with my father and mother. He was still talking a great deal and I could see everybody was amazed at him. They looked at me when Clifford said he was big enough now to go along to the M.E. Hall, but I had not had time to think that out yet. I put up a little fight but it was very little because after all you have to be willing to be fair in this world.

"I think we could both go," I said.

"No," my father said. "One is enough to look after. And it is time now to divide, with Clifford a big boy. I know it is kinda sudden. It's a funny thing what a difference pants make. But in the end it will be good for both of you to learn that you have to divide in this world."

So they said Clifford could go this time.

After they had gone, Linnie and I played jacks until I beat her so bad that we decided to put the New York fire-engine puzzle together. Linnie was gay and said funny things and tried to get me to laugh and have a good time, but it was hard work.

When she put me to bed my head was full of thoughts and I didn't go to sleep. I just lay there and thought that now Clifford was as big as I was and how this was going to change things and how dresses and curls and pants make such a big difference. It was like Clifford had jumped two or three years in a day, and my whole life was changed.

I wasn't asleep yet even when I heard them coming back from the M.E. Hall, but I couldn't hear Clifford, only my father and my mother. My father came up the stairs and he was carrying Clifford because Clifford was asleep. Clifford did not wake up at all and they even had to take his short pants off him to put him to bed. When I was the one going to the M.E. Hall I was awake when we got home and I took off my own short pants. That eased my thoughts a lot and I made out that I was asleep and pretty soon I guess I was.

The Candy Wagon

... and the unsolved problem of Sunday afternoons

A one-horse wagon that was different and that I had never seen before came around Snyder's Corner and trotted up in front of our store and stopped. The horse was about like any other horse but the wagon was different. It did not have any seats across, only a four-legged chair in front behind the dashboard and another four-legged chair in the back ahead of the tailgate. The sides of the wagon box were about three feet high and it had rubber tires. A long name was painted on the sides that began with S. The man driving the horse sat on the chair in front. He was a slim man but he looked just like some of our farmers with a moustache and a beard. He was Holland Dutch, all right.

He tied the horse and went into the store and my father came out with him.

I grabbed my father's pants leg and said, "What kind of a wagon is this?"

"This is the candy wagon," he said. "This is Mr. Sudderlee from Saugerties. He wholesales candy. You know what wholesale is. Like Matthews and Harrison in Kingston, and Everett and

Treadwell, and Edward D. Depew in New York that Barney
Solon is drummer for."

"I know what wholesale is," I said. "It is different from retail,
like you do."

"That's a smart boy," said Mr. Sudderlee. "Yours, I guess?"

"Yes. This is Willie."

"If I had another chair he could help sample the candy," said
Mr. Sudderlee.

"I see you are a smart man, too," said my father. "I'm glad
there isn't another chair. Willie would like all the candy and
I'd have to buy you out lock, stock, and barrel. No, I guess I don't
need Willie's help."

"I could do it," I said.

"Yes, I know," said my father. "Too well."

Mr. Sudderlee turned the chair in the front of the wagon
around so that it faced the back and my father got up in the wagon
box and sat on it. Mr. Sudderlee got up and sat on the other chair
that was back in the wagon box. Then Mr. Sudderlee picked up
a box of candy from inside the wagon box between them and said
"Here's something new. Try these. A little higher by the box
but you sell them for two cents instead of a penny."

"No, I guess not," said my father. "No call for two-cent candy."

Mr. Sudderlee put that box away and picked up another one.
"Try these," he said.

My father had his derby on. He shoved it back on his head and
put a piece of the candy in his mouth. He chewed and his derby
moved up and down on his head.

"Three boxes," he said. I watched him chew and his derby
move and I thought this must be part of the store business that
was pretty nice.

This went on until my father had bought quite a lot of boxes
and then Mr. Sudderlee wrote on a pad and gave my father a slip
of paper and they went into the store. After a little Mr. Sudderlee

came out and turned the chair in front around again and sat on it to drive, and went on off toward Bearsville.

All this turned my thoughts to candy and I wondered if I would ever get out of my candy problem on Sunday afternoon.

This candy problem on Sunday really began one morning when we were having morning prayers in the living room. This is something that we do every morning. I have heard my father tell my mother that it is a question if it is not overdoing it to have family prayers on Sunday morning when there is plenty of church, and reading the Bible and preaching and singing hymns and praying on Sunday anyway, and both morning and night. But my mother says it is good for the boys, and when she says that there is not much more my father can say. Because one time Harry, who is getting quite old, said he didn't see what good there is in knowing everything in the Bible. "Like all the begats," he said.

"Oh, maybe not the begats," my mother said. "But Harry, suppose you were with some young people in a social group and everyone was expected to quote a verse from the Bible. You wouldn't want to be the only dumb one."

"I wouldn't be," said Harry. "I could quote one."

"What for instance?" said my mother.

"Jesus wept," said Harry.

"Oh, pshaw," said my mother.

That showed my father that we would have to keep on with the Bible.

And so, even every Sunday morning after breakfast, we go to the living room and sit down. Even Linnie and the baby, except that my father takes the baby on his lap. My father reads a chapter in the Bible first. We have been through it once since I can remember and are on the way through again. Then we all kneel down in front of where we are sitting and my father prays. We have to keep very quiet for all this and it all goes pretty smooth except one time. Alvarez, the baby, who is about three years old,

was awfully fussy one morning and wanted to get down and run
around and my father had trouble holding him. This kept up
right on into the prayer, with Alvarez pulling and hauling to get
away from my father and my father stopping the prayer every
little while to get a better hold on him. My father decided it
wasn't going very good for a prayer and he had better wind it
up. He said "We thank Thee for health and home, yes, and for
children, all in the name of Jesus, our Savior, Amen. And now,
young man, I'll take care of you." Then he got up and spanked
Alvarez.

The Sunday my candy problem started, the chapter in the Bible
that my father read was all about if a man asks you for your
coat give it to him, because it is not a good idea to be selfish in
this world and the thing to do is to divide what you have with
folks who do not have any. I didn't think much about it and I
didn't know that Harry and Clifford were paying any attention, but
I found out that same afternoon that they had it all down pretty
pat. Because that was the Sunday my father tried out the candy
idea.

You can't do much on Sunday because it is the day of rest.
My father says we have Sunday so that people will not wear themselves out chasing the almighty dollar. But I have found out that
you can wear yourself out pretty fast just by resting. Besides that,
you have to keep on your Sunday suit and my mother says you
mustn't rare and tear. You are supposed to just sit and be good
and my father says it is a day to meditate if you are up to it. Oh,
you can take a slow walk somewhere if you want to. There's
nothing in the Bible about not walking on Sunday. And you can
read, if it's what they call harmless reading. And you can go calling on some family so the women can talk about somebody else,
and the men can worry over when the dry spell will end and
whether things will go to pot if Bryan is elected. The farmers
have it a little better because they have things to do, like milking

cows and tending stock. But my father is a storekeeper and the store is closed down tight. And we don't have any cows to milk.

You keep fairly busy in the morning with Sunday School and church and with a big dinner that my mother and Linnie have to cook and wash up after, but then you are up against it. Even if Clifford and I don't get into a fight, and Alvarez feels good and keeps out of the way with his blocks, and Harry does not run off and get into mischief, Sunday afternoon is pretty tough. And, of course, fights and such things are worse. It is no wonder that about halfway through the afternoon we get to nagging pretty bad.

And so it was this Sunday afternoon when the Bible had been talking about selfishness in the morning prayers that my father's patience with us got to the breaking point. But this time he didn't scold and try to get some peace by laying down the law.

He called Harry and Clifford and me to him. "Is the word of you boys any good?" he asked.

"How do you mean?" Harry asked.

"I mean if you made a bargain with me can I depend on you to keep it?"

"You can with me," said Harry. "You can with me," I said, and Clifford said the same.

"All right. Now I have your word and I'll bargain with you. We'll see. We'll go up to the store and each of you can pick out ten cents' worth of penny candy. Each of you will have your own bag. And if you keep your word and we have an end to this nagging and fighting on Sunday afternoons, we will go to the store every Sunday afternoon for the candy. It is a bargain?"

We said it certainly was.

We went through the cellar door under the feed room with its smell of molasses and turpentine and vinegar and sawdust and up into the store that was cool and dark. My father lifted the mosquito netting off the candy counter and said, "There it is. Ten apiece."

Well, it was quite a long job deciding what we wanted, and it was a tough job to hold down to ten because we would have liked to have one of everything. But every time we said "Maybe eleven or twelve," my father said "Ten. Just ten. A bargain is a bargain."

So we came out and we had the candy and my father and mother and Linnie had some quiet and peace.

There was quite a while of the Sunday afternoon to go yet and the only thing we had to help us was the candy. I was wise enough to know that. And so I ate only a little, teeny bit at a time. But Harry and Clifford were not very wise. They started right in to chonk theirs right down. I warned them and said "You better take it easy. There's a long time yet," but they just laughed and enjoyed themselves. So theirs was soon gone but I had more than half of mine left.

They hung around a little and every time I took a bite they watched me. Then I noticed that they had gone off to the other end of the front veranda and they had their heads together. Then they came back to me.

"You must have picked out bigger penny pieces," Harry said. "You've got a lot left. So don't you think you had ought to divide up a little?"

"What are you talking about?" I said. "I just didn't chonk mine right down."

"Well, you see, we are weaker than you," said Clifford. "It was so good we couldn't wait. But you are strong and the strong had ought to help the weak, even with candy."

"I've got more sense," I said.

"But you are selfish," said Harry.

"Why am I selfish?" I said. "You had your candy. You chonked it all right down and now you don't have any."

"No, we don't have any," said Harry. "I guess prayers in the morning don't do you any good. Or you wouldn't be so selfish."

"Now look," I said. "I don't understand this. What do you mean?"

"Don't you remember prayers this morning?" asked Clifford. "It said if a man asks you for your coat to give it to him. That was the Bible, Willie. Don't forget that. That was the Bible."

"It's just the same with candy," said Harry. "If you didn't give the man your coat when he asked for it and he didn't have any coat that means you are selfish. If you have candy and you don't give some to anybody who doesn't have any, that is the same thing."

I thought that over for a minute and I had to admit that that was about the size of it. The Bible and prayers are to teach you what is the right thing to do and that was certainly what the Bible had said that morning. If there is one thing I don't want to be it is selfish. And so I opened up my bag and divided all I had left with Harry and Clifford.

The next Sunday we got our candy again and I ate only a teeny bit at a time and tried to make it last all afternoon. But Harry and Clifford chonked theirs right down again and then stood around and watched me every time I took a bite. Then they told me about the Bible and being selfish again and so I divided with them again.

But this time I found my father and told him about the problem I had. He asked me all about it and then he thought a while. "That is something that you boys will have to work out for yourselves," he said. "But I can give you a hint. If I was you I would chonk my candy right down, too. All of it. Then you would get all of it."

The next Sunday I did that. But I found that did not solve the problem either. In the first place, there was too much of Sunday afternoon left without any candy. And in the second place, I have what they call a weak stomach and it made me sick.

And so every Sunday it is the same old problem. I can't eat my candy fast without suffering of the body. And I can't eat it slow without suffering of the spirit.

They always say that you can't eat your candy and have it, too. But there must be something wrong with what they say because Harry and Clifford are doing it. Of course, it is not all loss to me. In the first place, it proves I am not selfish, and that makes me feel good. And in the second place, a little candy is better than none.

And I can see, too, that it makes Sunday afternoon a lot easier to get through for my father and mother and for Linnie.

🐝 Lesson in Economics

. . . and razors, chocolate men, pins and summer boarders

Just before school was over, Friday afternoon, Elijah T. Bovee said he wanted all the seniors to do a dictionary job over Saturday and Sunday and he would ask a few simple questions on it Monday.

"I want you to look up the word economics," he said. "Now there's a word."

Everybody looked puzzled.

"It's a new word for you," he said. "I admit that it is not included in the three R's in our school. But some of you will not be going on to high school and everybody has to know a little about what we call economics or you won't be smart enough to even vote when you are old enough."

I was just barely out of the little room and into the big room at district school when Elijah T. Bovee said this, but just the same I wanted to know about it. But the dictionary was too much for me then.

And so on Saturday morning, after breakfast and family prayers,

I told my father what Elijah T. Bovee said and asked him. He was shaving over the kitchen sink and his face was all full of soap.

"You better wait awhile on that," he said.

"Why? Isn't Economics a safe subject?"

"Sometimes I don't think it is," he said. "Anyway folks seem to get mired when they get into it. This 16 to 1 of Bryan's. You've heard about that. Silly and dangerous to money. But there are college professors who recommend it. Wages a dollar a day. The Klondike and more gold. New inventions. All that and a lot more is economics."

He took the razor down from his face and looked at it. "Even this dull razor and the way it got dull," he said.

"You don't usually shave yourself," I said. "You have Larry Elwyn do it."

"Larry had four ahead of me and I couldn't wait. This is Saturday. If Larry could have that many all day long, every day he'd get rich. That's economics, too."

"How do you mean? What's a dull razor got to do with it?"

"Why don't you run along? It would take me a week of Sundays to tell you about economics. Even if I knew anything about it. Or anybody for that matter."

"But what's your dull razor got to do with it?"

"Country-store business," he said. "And that's economics too. But do you think the experts on economics, or say they are, know anything about dull razors in the country-store business? No. Would they know that Wash Bonesteel has been buying a razor for two years? He takes one out. Says he wants to try it. About two months later he comes back, says it's not right for him and takes out another to try. I thought there were a few he hadn't tried but I see now he's been shaving for two years, maybe longer, and no sale yet. He just tries one after another till they are dull. I didn't know he had tried this one when I picked it up. Think what that does to economics. Now run along."

Well, I didn't learn much about economics from all that. But I could see my father's patience was pretty strained and I got out of there. And it was just as well. Because later in the morning I got to know something about economics. A glimmer, anyway.

Later in the morning I was in the side yard trying to catch that stubborn rabbit of mine and not getting very far. He is the long rangy one and not like the white ones with pink eyes that like to be picked up and petted. But I was just as determined as he was and so at first I didn't hear what little Johnny Pepper said. But he was there on the other side of the white picket fence with his nose and one eye peeking through and he was excited. He said his brother, Willie Pepper, had just found a penny in a chocolate man. "Up here," he pointed and took off and I took off after him.

Willie Pepper and the boys were under the apple tree by the side of the store. Egbert and Lancy Boice were there and Fred and Ira Elwyn and Clifford, and even Bill Lake, the summer boarder who is a New York City boy. Willie Pepper was eating candy and making a big time of smacking his lips and the rest watching.

Willie said that his father had given him a penny that morning and when he went into my father's store to buy a candy he had found something new. This was a little chocolate man and he had bought it because he never saw candy like that before. He expected to eat a little and save the rest and so he bit off only the head. But there was white cream inside and it tasted so good he took another bite. But his teeth struck something hard and when he took it out of his mouth he had found it was a new penny wrapped in wax paper. So, he said, he had his candy and still had his penny.

"Now this is a wonderful thing," Willie Pepper said. And, of course, it was. "This little chocolate man means just one thing," Willie said. "It means that none of us ever have to be without candy again because all you need to do is to get your first penny. Of course, it makes you stick to chocolate creams," Willie said, "but what is any better? So now I have not had enough chocolate cream and so I am going to buy and eat and buy and eat till I have had my fill. And when I have had my fill I will have a penny yet to start in again when I want to."

But Fred Elwyn said there must be something wrong somewhere. "If you spend a penny and you got a penny and the candy, where is the candy coming from?" he asked.

All of us argued that back and forth. Bill Lake said that in New York things like that sometimes happened but he didn't know how. "Maybe there is some rich man," he said, "who never had all the candy he wanted when he was a boy. And now maybe he is sick so he can't eat candy and is spending some of his money so that other little boys can have all the candy they want while they are boys and not sick and can eat it." He looked wise and said there are lots of men like that. Fred Elwyn didn't know anything about New York. So he shut up and didn't argue anymore.

Just then old Elijah T. Bovee, the schoolmaster, came down past the side of the store where we were to get his rig in the shed. He is the kind who believes in "Spare the rod and spoil the child" and we don't go for him very much. But outside of that he is very brainy.

We stopped talking and watched him come along.

"Good morning, boys," he said. "I trust all's well with you this fine morning?"

Woodstock boys know him and so we kept quiet. But anybody from New York City has more nerve and Bill Lake spoke up.

"We have a problem," he said. "Other than that we are all right."

"You wouldn't belong to the human race if you didn't have a problem," said old Elijah. "But I am glad to see you are wise enough to admit it. What is the problem?"

"Willie Pepper will tell you," said Bill Lake. And so Willie told old Elijah about the chocolate man and how the penny was inside and how that made it so you could have all the candy you wanted with just one penny. "Because you see," he said, "you've always got the penny."

"Yes," said old Elijah. "I understand."

"How can that be?" asked Fred Elwyn.

Old Elijah thought for a minute and then he said "It can't be. It is contrary to economics."

"There," said Fred to Willie Pepper. "I told you."

Bill Lake told how it might be a rich man, like he had told us.

"No, I guess not," said old Elijah.

"Well then," said Bill, "maybe it's the government doing it. Like in New York. Take parks. And the zoo. They don't cost anybody nothing."

"Oh, yes they do," said old Elijah. "The government collects ransom from all your fathers to give you what they call free parks and zoo."

"What's ransom?" asked Bill Lake.

"Ransom is taxes."

"Yes, I've heard of that," said Bill, acting wise.

"It is economics," said old Elijah. "Economics is a natural law that you can't get around. Lots of folks say you can, but that is only because they don't know the law of economics. You don't get anything in this world that you don't work for or pay for. Not even from the government. This candy man with the penny in it does not make sense and I believe I know why. I am in a hurry but you may learn more right here than if you had the same lesson in school. Now, let's see. Willie Pepper has his penny back, but he hasn't had enough candy. Now suppose he goes back in the store and buys another chocolate man. And I'll wait."

Well, Willie Pepper had found this thing and he began to act as if he was a big somebody. I wished it had been me and I guess all the boys did. You could see we felt like nobodies. So all we could do was stand there while Willie acted important and walked up and into the store to buy another chocolate man.

When he came out he showed the whole man to old Elijah and us. It was flat on one side but on the other were its face and stom-

ach and legs and feet. He pointed to the stomach. It was big. Then
he bit off the head and rolled it around in his mouth and smacked
his lips to show us it was awfully good and didn't we wish we
had some. We couldn't do anything but watch him and keep
quiet. It was his show. He wasn't saving his candy this time. He
didn't have to when all he had to do was take the penny out of the
chocolate man's belly and go and buy another one. So he took a big
bite into the stomach but he stopped chewing and he looked sick.
Then he chopped all through the man with his front teeth. He
acted sort of wild and his eyes went big and full of trouble. We
knew right away. His candy was all gone and there wasn't any
penny in this chocolate man.

Fred Elwyn said, "Ha, ha, ha."

"So there you are," said old Elijah T. Bovee. "It's like a lottery.
Almost like gambling for little boys. I am amazed that Abe Rose—
but never mind. It will make trouble. Mark my words." Then he
went on down to get his rig, shaking his head.

Willie Pepper sat down under the apple tree and moped. But we
couldn't bother about that and we went away.

That afternoon when we were swimming in the Big Deep,
Brook Romer showed up and brought the news. "There's a big
stink in the Village," he said. "Those candy chocolate men that
fooled Willie Pepper this morning. Somebody stuck a pin in the
bellies while the clerks were not looking. Some of the boarders
bought them and found the pinholes and they are mad."

Clifford and I were excited about the chocolate men at the supper table, and my father said he wished he had never bought them
for sale. "The candy is only fair," he said, "and not enough pennies in them to make all the fuss worth while. They say I'm
running a gambling joint and breaking the law and some say they
won't even buy a postage stamp in the store for fear of getting
hooked. And Will Longyear is mad again. Will is a reliable
partner, but I wish he wouldn't flare up at the drop of a hat. Be-

sides that, the young blades are making a joke of us. I mean the home-grown young blades. Jim Plass came in the store this afternoon with four or five of them. He had fixed up a tin star on his shirt and said this was the sheriff and his men and the joint was pinched. That made Will madder than ever. Sherm Elwyn bought a whole box of the chocolate men and said they would come in handy when they had the next party."

"Every girl that gets a penny in her belly gets kissed, I suppose," said Linnie.

"Oh, Linnie," said my mother. "Do be still."

"Mr. Rose will handle it," said Linnie. "You'll see. He always finds a way."

"I'd like to know how the pinholes got in the candy," said my father. "You wouldn't think a lot of cheap little candy could wreck a lifetime of honesty. If the summer boarders had only come to me instead of Will when they found the pinholes! Right away Will said the boarder had stuck the pin in himself and then had come back for another try. He told the summer boarder that New York people might be slickers but they were not that slick. And he wouldn't give the boarder another chocolate man. Then more boarders came in and bought, and then they showed us that a pinhole was in every one they bought. It's a mess."

The next day I was running past the front of the store when I noticed a cardboard sign hanging on a stick nailed to the side of the front door. It went on to say that free candy would be given to all children that evening when the mail stage came in. Seven o'clock, it said.

I was there when the time came. All the boys and girls anywhere around were there. And a lot of older folks, too, because it was mail time and, of course, all the summer boarders.

Just before the mail stage came in my father came out to the front door and made a speech. He was going out of the business of selling chocolate men with pennies in them, he said. He had three boxes left and after tonight he would not have any more. Then he asked the boys and girls to form in a big circle. They were to keep going round the circle and he would give every one a chocolate man and none of them had pinholes in them, he said.

There were too many of the chocolate men for the boys and girls it turned out. So after each of them had two or three my father handed the boxes to the older people and told them to pass them along and all have one. Everybody began to talk and laugh about it, and whenever anyone found a penny there was a squeal and a big shout.

Of course everybody knew now that my father and the clerks certainly did not put the pinholes in the chocolate men at all but that it must have been a trick by somebody else on the sly. They came up and patted my father on the back and shook his hand. Then one of the summer boarders said that there was something he needed and that while he was there at the store he guessed he would buy it. And then they all trooped in and the store did a rushing business while the mail came in and afterward.

I heard Will Longyear say to my father, "How is it you can always turn everything into a profit?"

"My backbone bends," said my father.

So all that's what economics is. It is a man who tries out razors for two years, and chocolate men without pinholes in them, and taxes and free parks, and making summer boarders happy, and getting nothing without working for it, and the government, and knowing how to teach and how to run a country store, and almost everything else you come up against. It is a natural law with everything mixed up into it.

✳ The Union Sunday School Excursion

. . . and God always raises up a man

At suppertime Harry said he had learned something at
school he didn't know before.

"Is that so?" said my father. "That's remarkable." He took a
sip of his tea and then he chuckled.

"You needn't laugh," said Harry. "Why did Abraham Lincoln
fight the Civil War?"

"I've often wondered why he bothered," said Linnie.

"He fought the Civil War to free the slaves," said my mother.

I was only listening, but I figured my mother must have it
about right. I have heard her tell the Ladies' Aid that she used to
teach school when she was seventeen, before she caught my father.

"There, see?" said Harry. "Well, he didn't."

"Harry," said my mother, "you must read *Uncle Tom's Cabin,*
by Harriet Beecher Stowe. And some of the sermons by Henry
Ward Beecher. And some of the writing of old Henry Cart-
wright."

"There you go again on Grandma Palen's old Henry Cart-
wright," said Harry. "Just because he didn't smoke or chew or
drink or swear; and just because, when some young people asked
him to dance the square dance when he was riding his horse
around preaching, he said he would but he would kneel in prayer
first."

"Harry, Harry," said my mother. "You mustn't talk that way."

"Well," said Harry, "Grandma Palen is so Methodist it makes
me sick. What good is school, then, if all you've got to do is read
Uncle Tom's Cabin? Just the same, Lincoln didn't fight the Civil
War to free the slaves."

"You excite my curiosity," said Linnie. "Let us in on the secret."

"He fought the Civil War to save the Union," said Harry. "Elijah T. Bovee says so and so does our history book."

"Well," said my father, "whatever was Lincoln's reason the war turned out to do both. One is sort of mixed up with the other. The thing that interests me is that Providence came forward and took charge the same as it always has in history. Moses. Christ. Peter. Paul. Luther. Washington. Grant. And so forth. God always raises up a man."

"God and women," said Linnie.

My father choked on a swallow of tea.

"I mean there's always a woman behind a man," said Linnie. She jumped up and said, "I'll get some more fried potatoes."

"Now that we've freed the slaves and saved the Union," said my father, "let's talk about the Sunday School Union excursion to Kingston Point Park."

"Are we going to have it?" I asked.

"It's all set," he said. "And I am glad to say that everybody will go. I mean the poor families and all the children along with the ones able to pay. I told the committee that this is not just an excursion to Kingston Point. It is a Union excursion and it seemed to me that if religion is for everybody the pleasures of religion had ought to be for everybody, too."

"That's all right," said my mother, "but what about the cost?"

"We decided that each Sunday School will get itself to the U & D at West Hurley. We have a special price for the special train. Some wanted to have tickets printed and the ones that bought them would go. But I said we want this to be a bang-up affair with everybody coming. When some hung out I said I would guarantee to collect enough on the train to pay for it."

"Oh, Abe," said my mother. "There you go again. Suppose you don't collect enough?"

"You have to have faith," my father said. "It's something all us church folks claim to have a lot of but it seems to me we are mighty saving of it sometimes. When they get into the spirit of this thing and see the kids having so much fun, we'll make it. You'll see. And if we don't, well, the churches will have to make up the rest or the men on the committee can. Look who's on the committee—Aaron Riseley, K'Neal Hogan, Chris Winnie, Eulie Boice, Elick Longyear, Levi Harder, Ed Snyder, Cal Short, Nelson Lasher, Hyp Bovee, Dr. Downer, and men like that. All these men know it is more blessed to give than to receive."

"Yes, up to a certain point," said my mother. "But big talk is likely to cost big money."

I didn't wait for any more talk, big or little. I ran out to tell the boys.

Fred Elwyn across the road was through with his supper and was on the horse block eating a piece of chocolate cake. I told him what I had just heard.

He was so excited he gave me the last of the chocolate cake, and sometime I'll tell you about the chocolate cake his mother makes. Four layers, with white boiled custard between all of them.

"Boy," he said. "Just think of it. Kingston Point Park and everybody going unless they're too sick. Not many will be sick, I will bet you. Even everybody in a big family like ours. This will be one time when my father can't say I'm too small, or we can't afford all of us, or what will you wear."

"Woodstock will be like the day Barnum's Circus was in Kingston," I said.

"Worse," said Fred. "Remember that day? Nobody left here at all except two or three of us kids they said was too small. You'd-a thought we were not out of diapers. Gosh, this town was dead that day."

"Let's go up in front of the store," I said, "and see what they're talking about tonight. Maybe they're talking about the excursion."

So we started off and we found quite a few there already. One bunch was arguing about the weather. We went on as soon as we heard that. A bunch of the young blades had their heads together over a secret picture and were snickering. But they stopped and looked at us when we stopped there and so we went on.

Ed Harder was talking to Dominie and Mrs. Park in front of Mower's Ice Cream Parlor. It was just something about religion, probably, but Fred and I drifted over there to hear, just in case. And it was something. They were planning a prize contest for the excursion. Or Ed was, anyway. Ed was all for offering a prize of ten dollars to the Sunday School that had the best turnout for getting over to West Hurley.

"It is a great idea," said Dominie Park, "but I don't know where the ten dollars would come from."

"What about asking Jake Wurts for it?" asked Ed.

Dominie Park smiled. "We are tugging at one side of the sinner and Mr. Wurts is tugging at the other side," he said. "Mr. Wurts conducts a barroom."

"You can't just exactly say that he don't want men to drink," said Ed. "But I'll bet a hat he's in favor of not too much. And I know for a fact that he likes kids."

Dominie Park acted like he was in doubt. He is a very fine gentleman. I have heard my father say that he is his idea of a real Christian. "I wouldn't want to offend him," said Dominie Park. "If you ask him, maybe he wouldn't want to say no and wouldn't want to say yes, but would say yes just because he was faced with the question. I don't approve of his business, and wouldn't it be heaping coals of fire on my head?"

Ed saw Fred and me listening. "What do you think, boys? Would he do it?" he asked.

"He certainly won't do it if you don't ask him," said Fred.

"It wouldn't be real coals of fire," I said. "I know that's in the Bible but it is just a saying."

"I guess it is," said Dominie Park.

"Well, let's try it," said Ed. He looked around and saw Jake Wurts talking with some city boarders while he waited for the mail stage to come in. Ed called to him and Mr. Wurts came over.

"I'd really like to do it," said Jake Wurts right away, when Ed told him of his idea for the prize. He took out his wallet. "Here's the ten dollars now, Dominie," he said. "And you and Ed go ahead and handle it."

Dominie Park thanked Mr. Wurts and said that the joy he was helping to give to little children was very great. Then Jake Wurts walked back to the city boarders. Dominie Park was looking at the ten dollars in his hand as if he was full of thought.

"You feel it's tainted money?" asked Ed.

"Oh, no, no," said Dominie Park. "There is the same amount of good in this ten dollars as in any other. The test is what it is used for. No, I was thinking how wrong we are in our small minds when we judge others."

Well, that was over, so Fred and I went looking for something else interesting.

"Jake Wurts is all right," said Fred.

"My father says that God always raises up a man," I said. "Like Lincoln in the Civil War. I guessed he just raised up Jake Wurts."

"What do you mean?" asked Fred.

"When there is something good to be done, somebody always does it."

"How about something bad?"

"Maybe the devil raises up a man then," I said. "Oh, I don't know. I just heard my father say so, that's all."

That night when I went to bed I added something to my prayers. It was that God would send us a nice day for the big excursion, and I added it to my prayer every night from then on.

I prayed about it because of something my father told me another time when I wanted a fair day. "About all you can do," he said, "is to put in an order for it."

"How do you do that?" I asked.

"In your prayers. When you pray you're talking to God. He's the only one who can do anything about the weather. You just tell Him you want to order a day without any rain. Then He will look over the other orders He has and He will get the fair day for you if He can. Of course, He may have some orders for rain the same day. In that case, He will have to use His own judgment about which is best. That's fair enough, isn't it?"

"Yes," I said. "So I guess I won't lose any time getting my order in."

"I will order a fair day, too," he said. "And that will help that much."

After supper, the night before the excursion, I asked my mother to come out in the yard and look at the sky.

"What do you think God is going to do about the weather tomorrow?" I asked.

"What a beautiful sunset," she said.

It *was* beautiful. The sun had just gone down behind the mountains over in the direction of Mink Hollow and you would think it had set fire to the whole valley over there. The clouds were all painted up and they looked like a giant sea of colored water. Over this way the side of the mountain was in shadow so that you really didn't notice it. The thing you saw first was the picture in the sky.

I think God is going to fill your order," my mother said. "You see, there's an old saying that people have learned through hundreds and hundreds of years. It is 'Red in the morning, sailors take warning; and red at night is sailors' delight.' It means that if the sky is red at night there won't be any storms at sea the next day."

She was right. We had a perfect day. The sky was all blue except for a few patches of white clouds that hung in the sky and did not move one single bit. When I had had breakfast and went out, other folks were all dressed up and excited and you could see that they expected a wonderful time.

Our Dutch Reformed folks had been told to go to the sheds down the little road past Ed Snyder's house and the parsonage, where Snyder's windmill is. They said a rig would be ready to take us to the excursion train on the U & D. We would start at eight o'clock, they said, and the train would leave West Hurley at half-past nine. The U & D would take us right through Kingston and Rondout and clear out to Kingston Point Park.

I didn't expect to see anything like our Dutch Reformed rig. But then I remembered what Fred and I had heard the Dominie and Jake Wurts and Ed Harder talking about, and I remembered that the Sunday Schools were in a contest.

Our rig was a hayrick but the sides had been built out and the whole thing covered with about a quarter load of hay. The driver's seat had been built up and above it was a big sign saying Woodstock Dutch Reformed. Aaron Riseley's big gray team was hitched to it and their tails and manes were braided with red ribbons. But the big touch was a painted red canvas which covered all the hay, and we sat on it.

Ed Harder was joking with everybody. I heard him say he had thought some of getting Wash Riseley's big white ox-team to haul the rig but he had gone up to Wash's and hitched them up and timed them for a quarter mile and found they were too slow. "We would have had to start about six o'clock," he said. "I tried running them but, hell, you can't run oxen without running alongside them yourself if you want to keep on top of them. Then I thought of trying to get the span of white mules that is hauling that Kalamazoo stove around for farm women to try; but they wanted the mint for hiring them. Anyway, these grays look pretty nifty."

We pulled up to the village green and found that the Methodists were already there. They had things fixed up fancy, too, but I thought our Dutch Reformed rig was better.

It was about time to start when there was a big racket in the upper part of the Village, shouting and horn blowing. Then there was a heavy rumble on the big bridge, and up the road past our house came the greatest thing in the shape of a rig I ever saw. It was Glenwood from just over the Ohio Mountain. They had come the long way round to West Hurley just to show off. Their rig was a big platform on a lumber wagon with a lot of seats at each end and a space in the middle. In the middle was Daniel and a make-believe lion, and every time Daniel and the lion hugged each other the people on the seats would get up and yell together and then blow little horns.

> *"Daniel in the lion's den*
> *Gave a lesson to all men.*
> *This is Glenwood you can bet*
> *Watch us win that ten bucks yet."*

Ed Harder laughed. "Well, there goes the ball game," he shouted. I thought then that people have a lot of funny ways. That was something the young blades and some older people always said when what they really meant was that hail in the summer had ruined the apple crop, or a storm on the Fourth of July swamped the celebration, or a load was so heavy that the team broke the traces, or any happening that wound things up for good. There might not be a ball game in a thousand miles. Just why they didn't say the hail had ruined the crop or the traces were broken, instead of always saying "There goes the ball game," I don't know.

What Ed meant was that Glenwood was bound to win the prize for the best rig. And that's how it was. When everybody had got to West Hurley the Sunday School teachers from everywhere went around and looked at all the rigs. There were ten of them. All of them were gay but the teachers decided that Glenwood was the only one with imagination and also pointed a moral.

The train was already there and it looked good. The engine

was snorting jets of steam as if it knew how important this excursion was and was impatient to get on with it. Mothers were
running around holding up their skirts out of the cinders and
calling to their children to get together so they wouldn't get lost.
The men were knocking out their pipes and throwing their cigars
away. Lewis Harder's grandfather, Peter Lewis Harder, was so
excited that he put his pipe in his pocket without knocking it out,
and caught fire and danced around on his toes in spite of his
rheumatism until they put the fire out. There was a lot of noise
over that to add to the crowd noise. Then, all of a sudden, there
was quiet. Then, after that, a big angry commotion. Us boys didn't
have to guess what it was, because we were first to rush to get on
the train. But the trainmen in their blue uniforms stood on the
ground by the steps of their cars and wouldn't let us on. "Orders,"
they said.

Some men came up and talked big to the trainmen but the
trainmen just stood there and shook their heads.

Pretty soon we knew why. Nobody was going to get on the
train until the price of the trip was paid down on the barrel
head. Some big mucky-muck in the U & D office in Rondout had
told the conductor that that was how it had to be. The conductor
wasn't around. People said he was in the station office with some
of the excursion committee. My father must have been there because I couldn't find him.

Aaron Riseley came out of the station office just then, and I
heard him talking to a bunch of the women. The railroad had supposed, he said, that the committee would have the money ready
before the train started. Maybe it was all that crazy idea of Abe
Rose, he said, who was a pretty good businessman most of the
time. "This is how sweet charity buckles back on you sometimes,"
he said. "Abe had the stationmaster wire to the official in Rondout
that he must have faith in human nature. But the official wired
back that he used to have, until the U & D got stuck on one of its

special trains and since then, he had insisted on cash in advance and it was wonderful what a strain it had taken off his faith.

"So, it's too bad," Mr. Riseley told the women, "but I guess all we can do is get in the rigs again and go home. Nobody here has enough on him to pay the cost of the train, and if we wait to collect it from everybody in small amounts before we start, we won't have any time at Kingston Point and we might as well not start at all."

A big man with a red face had come up and heard the last of what Aaron Riseley said to the women. "It's old Sam Coykendahl," he shouted. "He owns the railroad. He had ought to be kicked by a jackass and I'd like to be the one to do it."

"You would be," said Aaron Riseley. "Sam Coykendahl don't know anything about it. Men who own railroads don't run the trains. Some whippersnapper at Rondout has made this decision."

The crowd started surging this way and that. A woman with a baby in her arms was pushed off her feet and cried out, as she went down, but a man grabbed the baby in time. It looked dangerous to me. I didn't feel good and I was afraid.

"If God ever raises up a man, He had ought to do it right now," I said to Fred Elwyn.

Just then three men came running out of the station office. They were shouting and waving their arms and I saw that they were the station agent and the conductor and my father. They ran up the steps to the raised freight platform and my father waved a telegram above his head. He shouted for quiet.

"We got it fixed," he shouted. "We finally got hold of Sam Coykendahl. He said he remembers me and he took my personal guarantee that we will have the money when the train gets to Rondout. So everybody get aboard."

All of a sudden everybody was happy and there was a scramble for the train.

It was a thrill, all right. I don't think I ever felt so good.

I saw my father going through the train with the conductor and they were collecting whatever anybody wanted to give. Some couldn't give anything without the little kids losing their ice cream at Kingston Point Park. You could tell them by the clothes they wore and the hats of some of the mothers who had tried to dress up. When my father came to some mothers and fathers with big families he didn't even ask them. I saw one poor little mother with eight kids try to give him a few nickels but he wouldn't take them, and said to keep them so the children could have some ice cream and candy. When the train reached Roundout it stopped and my father and the conductor got off and went in the station. Pretty soon the conductor came out but my father didn't, and the train went on out over the trestle to Kingston Point Park.

After the dayboat from Albany came and went we waited quite a while for my father to come to our picnic lunch, but when he didn't show up my mother had us go ahead. We didn't see him again until the train was taking us back to West Hurley. It stopped at the Rondout station and he got on.

My mother wanted to know where he had been all day and he said that Sam Coykendahl had come to the station and had wanted to know all about the excursion and they had quite a talk. My father talked about Mr. Coykendahl as if he had known him for a thousand years. "Sam wanted to know how many children were on the train and how many had never been to Kingston Point Park, and all things like that," my father said. "He was very happy with it all, was Sam, and was glad it had worked out. Especially for the poorer children, he said. Then he asked me to drive with him to his place on West Chestnut Street and have what he called lunch with him. He said they eat dinner at night."

"Well!" said my mother.

When we got home my mother and Linnie hustled around and got some supper and after the Blessing my father was still talking about Sam Coykendahl. "He has a big mansion up on West

Chestnut Street," he said, "and big lawns and big flower gardens around. You look right out over the Hudson River. And enough people in the house to run a ship."

"Handsome is as handsome does," said Linnie.

"Well, Sam does all right," said my father. "And I guess you would call it handsome."

"Did you collect enough money for the train?" asked my mother.

"All but about fifty dollars. But I didn't say anything to Sam Coykendahl about that. I just filled out a blank check for what I didn't collect and gave it to the passenger agent of the railroad."

"That's too bad," said my mother. "I'm afraid you have too much faith in your fellow man. I thought you took an awful big chance this morning to get the excursion to go."

"I had given Sam Coykendahl my word. I wouldn't have gone back on it for ten times fifty." Then he smiled at her and got a hawkey look in his eye.

"Seems to me you're pretty light-hearted about it," she said.

"O ye of little faith," he said. "Cast your bread upon the waters."

"What do you mean by that?"

He wiped his mouth and folded up his napkin and put it in his napkin ring. Then he patted his stomach and said, "Ah, ladies, that was a nice supper. I needed it. Things with Sam this noon were so swell I was a little nervous and didn't eat much. A man needs his own home and table for his stomach's sake."

"Oh, Abe, don't be like that," said my mother.

"Anybody can see that something besides indigestion happened to you," said Linnie.

"Well, I'll tell you," said my father. "You know I've been worrying about whether I would be appointed postmaster again. I went against Jake Wurts in the local-option election. Jake was pretty mad until the Wets won and I'll say this for him. He came around and shook hands and said that he admired a man who stuck

by his principles. But my political standing is not too good, now.
Well, Sam Coykendahl and I got to talking about it. It was just the
right moment for it. The excursion, the people, jumping into the
breach and making friends for the U & D instead of a lot of
enemies, and all that. But the upshot is that he told me to consider
the post office settled. He will look after it, he said."

"I'm sorry you had to miss the excursion," my mother said.

"I never had such a remarkable excursion in my life," he said.
"But I hope I never have another like it."

And so we have not had another Sunday School excursion to
Kingston Point Park since then. I guess God does not figure on
raising up a man for an excursion every year.

✿ Widening the Horizons of Boys

...taking the boys to New York, and why mother stayed home

You could see that my father was feeling pretty good. He
wasn't hurrying through his supper and he didn't look at things
on the table and act as if he was thinking a hundred miles away.
He joked with Linnie and teased my mother.

Pretty soon my mother said, "What have you cooked up now?
It must be something."

"Who, me?" said my father.

"Pull the cork and let it out of the bottle," said Linnie.

"I must be made of glass."

"If you mean that folks can see right through you, you are," said
my mother.

"Well," he said, "I had an inspiration this afternoon. It's about time for me to make the buying trip to New York. Of course, I'll be busy and it will be work for me. But I thought I would make it a vacation trip this time for my wife and young sons. Clifford is six and Willie is a little more than seven and Harry is ten. It's time we broadened their outlook a little to let them know there are other places than this valley between the mountains. Travel is very educational. You can't learn everything from books at the district school."

My mother smiled at him. "It's a good inspiration," she said, "but there are two things wrong with it. First, it would be expensive. Second, if you want me to have a vacation take the boys with you and I'll stay home."

"Oh, the boys can't be so much trouble if you use your head," said my father.

"Take them with you and broaden your own education," said Linnie.

"Well, all right. But it isn't like the inspiration that came to me."

"I can see that," said my mother.

So my father found himself in a box. If he had told his inspiration to my mother in secret he could have dropped it. But we were on to it now and we were so excited that we couldn't let go. We clamored when he began to say, "Well, I don't know exactly." And my mother didn't aim to help him any. After supper I heard her tell Linnie that it would be a good lesson for him. "I have half a notion," she said, "that the real reason he says he has to spend all his time at the store is so he won't be at home with the children under his feet."

"Men are like that," said Linnie.

Almost every day for a week my father brought up some new reason why he couldn't take us boys unless my mother went. But she didn't give him an inch.

"Remember your inspiration," she said. "You always say that

you figure inspirations come from a higher intelligence and that you are not any hand to slap an inspiration in the face."

"That's right," he said. "It was an inspiration, all right. But you forget that you were a part of it."

"No," she said. "You supplied that part of it. You got an inspiration all right, but you went off half-cocked. The inspiration is that the boys go, but then you thought it wouldn't be any picnic. Then you thought of the vacation for me. The best vacation for me is a complete change right here at home. Just Linnie and me and the baby and no big meals and time to read and visit the neighbors."

So in the end my father had to give in. "I'm usually home in four days," he said, "but don't count on it this time. I'll have to look after the boys and do the work, too. So it may take five or six. I tell you I have to work pretty hard and fast in New York to get through."

He always claimed the New York trip was hard work, but things would come out later and my mother and Linnie took it with a grain of salt.

So Linnie said, "Give my regards to John Drew and see whether Lillian Russell is putting on weight. And I hope you'll have time to find out what Weber is saying to Fields."

The day we left opened up clear and hot and dusty. My mother and Linnie got us boys ready, but there was one hitch.

"I am big enough not to wear a blouse to New York," Harry said.

"What would you wear?" said my mother.

"A shirt and collar and necktie," said Harry.

"They will get dirty," said Linnie. "And no time for washing and ironing away from home."

But Harry fixed that. He went up to the store and got a celluloid collar that only had to be wiped off with a damp cloth. My mother dressed Clifford and me in our Sunday suits with Buster Brown collars and Windsor bows. My mother and Linnie packed two grips with extras and then they went with us up to in front of the store, where Johnny Saxe had the mule stage ready to go.

My father had last-minute things at the store and he looked a little pressed and nervous and ha-ha'd too much in a way that wasn't his style.

"Just relax, Mr. Rose," said Linnie. "Just meet every joyful hour as it comes along."

"Everything will be all right," my mother said over and over again, but it was plain to see that she felt guilty.

"You wish now that you had borne your rugged cross, don't you?" said Linnie.

My mother paid no attention to her. "The boys are all well," she told my father. "I don't see what could happen that would make any of them sick. Except maybe what they eat." She turned to us. "Be careful about that, boys, won't you."

"Oh, for Pete's sake," said Harry.

"You know what to do if Willie's stomach acts up."

"Sure. Give him boiled milk," said Harry. "We'll give him gallons of it. But he won't get sick. He wouldn't be such a little fool."

"It's not a case of being a fool," said my mother.

"Let's get going," my father said to Johnny Saxe.

All of us had been told our parts to do. My father was to look after the two grips. Harry carried the lunch for the dayboat. "You can get something to drink on the boat," my father said. Clifford and I each carried an umbrella. We promised about a thousand times that we wouldn't lose them.

We started, and Johnny Saxe seemed to know what was in my mind even if I didn't say anything. "I've only been to New York a couple of times," he said to my father. "I guess you would have to say it's quite a place. But look at the old Dutch Church there and the maples. Look at the mountains almost near enough to touch. And the fruit and grain ripening. Smell it in the air? But I don't suppose it holds a candle to New York."

He could talk like that because he would be back in Woodstock in about two hours.

"Wonderful place," my father said and I knew he meant Woodstock. He was looking back and so were all of us, and the last thing we saw when we turned the corner by the hotel was our own store with our white house and picket fence and yard, and locust trees alongside it, and my mother and Linnie standing there waving to us.

We had been to West Hurley lots of times and so it was a long and dull trip. We thought we would never get there. Harry kept sighing and said there must be some quicker way to get to the U & D. That made my father and Johnny Saxe laugh.

"It's pretty quick alongside of on foot," Johnny Saxe said, "and it's too far to run without resting. If there was any quicker way than a horse and wagon or mules I guess folks would have found it out by this time. A railroad, of course. But a railroad to Woodstock is too much to expect."

"Now boys, sit down," ordered my father. "You'll fall out. "No use to try to carry on a conversation, Johnny. Just drive."

Well, we got there. My father took the grips and saw to it that Harry had the lunch box and that Clifford and I had the umbrellas. He led us to the station next to the tracks and set down the grips, and said for us to stand by them and not go away while he went in and got the tickets.

The U & D came rushing down out of the mountain and stopped and huffed and puffed. My father is a great hand to stop and talk with everybody, and he didn't come. But just as the train was ready to start he came running out of the station. Harry had already climbed up on the platform of the car and stood there yelling, "Come on, come on." My father boosted Clifford and me up on the platform and then hoisted up the two grips and we got on all right just as the train started.

It wasn't long until we got to Kingston Point Park. The dayboat for New York was already there. The crowd was big and it was hot and we had to wait and inch along and wait and inch along. Clifford kept saying, "I'm hungry," and my father kept saying, "Yes, yes, I know. Do be patient."

After a long time we got on the boat and got the grips checked and then we hunted on all the decks to find a place to settle down, but the crowd seemed to have every place. But my father saw one empty chair and carried it along, and then another and carried it along, and then we came to two more out in the blazing sun, but my father said we had better stop there.

My father wiped his face with his handkerchief and I could see he was awfully uncomfortable. But he untied the shoe box and started handing us sandwiches and hard-boiled eggs and cold chicken and cake and things like that. Harry and Clifford and my father started to eat like everything and I took about two bites. But then I started to think.

I could look across the big river about a mile and see a train going up the river on the other side about as big as the toy train at home. And then all I could see was my mother standing back in front of our store, waving good-bye to us.

I stopped eating. I didn't want another bite. I felt awfully sad, and then all of a sudden tears started to run down my cheeks.

My father saw me and looked worried.

"What's the matter?" he asked.

"I don't feel good," I said.

"Don't feel good? Do you hurt anywhere? Feel sick? Is it your stomach?"

"No," I said. "I feel all right. My stomach's all right. I just feel sad."

"Oh, you'll be all right," he said. "Just think, boy. You are sailing down the Hudson River."

"That's just the trouble," I said. "I am thinking."

"You're on a trip to New York City, boy. You are going to see lots of wonderful things. The thing to do is to enjoy it. Every minute of it."

"It isn't even raining," said Harry.

But none of it did any good. I just couldn't stop my crying.

My father looked discouraged and he threw up his hands.

Harry patted me on the back. I cried all the harder.

"And I thought you would be goggle-eyed," said my father.

"I am goggle-eyed," I said. "It isn't that."

"Well, Willie," pleaded Clifford, "what is it?"

"Mamma ain't here," I sobbed.

"Well, for heaven's sake," said my father. "Your mother didn't want to come along. I tried to have her come along. I tried for days. You know that."

"I mean," I said, "here we are with all this wonderful experience and having this wonderful trip and Mamma is home alone."

"She isn't alone," said Harry. "Linnie is with her."

"Your mother is all right," said my father. "She is where she wants to be." He took out his handkerchief and dried my face. "Your mother has had lots of trips you haven't had," he said, "and she will have lots more. I'll tell you what. We will finish our lunch and now you eat some more. Then we will find the refreshment counter and have some soda or ice cream or whatever you want. And we will take a walk around the boat. You must see the big engines run. You can see them right through a big glass. There's lots to see."

After that it wasn't long until I got over it.

In spite of all the things to see along the river, it was a long afternoon on the boat and we got awfully tired of it. There wasn't a cool place on the boat. Clifford went to sleep with his head in my father's lap. If we hadn't been coming to New York at last with its tall buildings and big ocean steamships and ferries and tugboats and whistles I don't know what we would have done.

We landed but my father said we couldn't get off because it was too soon. "We are going to Smith and McNeil's," he said, "and that won't be till we land at Desbrosses Street."

When we got there he said, "Now listen. We must all keep together, even touching each other, because there will be a big crowd and they will be hurrying this way and that. If we get separated we might not find each other again."

The dayboat was slowed down and we were coming to the dock. Clifford and I had been left on deck and told to stay right there while Harry and my father went to the checkroom to pick up the grips. When they came back Harry said that he would take both umbrellas now because he didn't have the lunch box any longer. I had not eaten much of my share but there was no use saving it, my father said, because the hotel would have lots of everything in the food line.

Harry said it would be best for my father to go ahead with the two grips and lead the way. Then would come Clifford and me, and Harry would keep right behind us. My father thought that was a good idea.

But the crowds and pushing were terrible. It took just about all your strength to keep close together and not be pushed this way and that. And this was while we were on the dayboat yet. We had not even got off yet.

When we did get off, we rushed with the crowd toward the street through a long shed that smelled of water and wet wood and horse manure and then we came out to a wide street of cobbles that ran along the river and that my father said we had to cross to get to a streetcar we could see standing on the other side. But I did not see how we could make it. The street was as wide as from our store in Woodstock to the Woodstock Hotel. It was swarming with big, heavy wagons with big, heavy horses. Sometimes one horse, sometimes two. Some of the wagon boxes were way up high and some were very long or no boxes at all and just long platforms. They came along five and six in a row. It seemed as if all of them had horses on a trot and you wouldn't have thought they cared whether people got run down or not.

Part of the crowd would rush out into the street and then a policeman would blow a whistle and the heavy rigs would slow down to a walk or even stop if there were people right in front of them. But before you could get across the wide street the policeman would blow his whistle again and down would come the rigs on you unless you stepped lively. We dodged and we dodged with my father and the grips in front, and Clifford and me next, and Harry bringing up the rear with the umbrellas, and we made it. But I'll tell you one thing—and that is if New York don't do something about that street somebody is going to get killed.

We got to the streetcar and got in the line pressing to get on the back end so we could move inside. My father was doing his best with the two grips and he figured that his boys ought to be able to follow close behind. We made it, but the conductor seemed to be terribly mad and excited and just then he reached up and yanked on the cord that rang the bell over the head of the motor-man, and the car started up with a jerk.

All the seats were taken and the aisle was full, but my father pushed our way in and set down his grips and straightened up and got hold of something so he wouldn't fall down with the jerking of the car. I was behind him, and Clifford was behind me but Clifford pushed past me and started tugging on my father's coat-tails. He tugged and tugged but my father had not come to himself yet and besides he was used to having Clifford tugging at his coattails. But he did look down and almost shouted, "What on earth is it now?"

"Harry," said Clifford. "Harry ain't with us any more." I looked then and he wasn't.

"Oh, for heaven's sakes, what next?" my father said. "Well, get off, get off."

He reached up and rang the bell and picked up the grips and

the car stopped at the next corner and we got off and started back. We found Harry where we had left him, hanging onto the umbrellas.

My father's patience was very strained but Harry held up his hand just as if he was a policeman or something.

"Now we will plan this thing right here before we go any farther," he said. "If any one of us gets left behind we will stay right where we are left. Then we will know exactly where to find him and won't get all bothered about it."

"That's a first-rate idea," my father said and Clifford and I nodded our heads.

We waited until the next car came along and it wasn't crowded at all. All four of us got on easy.

All of a sudden my father started to laugh. It eased things up a lot. We asked him what was so funny and he pointed at Harry. "You certainly are all right," he said. "And all we had to do was wait a little, anyway, until the crowd went on and got out of the way. But nobody seems to know that in New York."

"All the brains are not in New York," said Harry. "It's only that people think so. I guess that Woodstock can tell them a thing or two if they only knew it."

Harry and my father settled down in one seat and Clifford and I sat on the edge of one behind them. But my father was pointing out of the window at things for Harry to see as we went along and so Clifford and I stood up behind their seat and tried to see, too.

Somebody said, "You will have to get the suitcases out of the aisle." We looked up and it was the conductor, but he went right on to the front of the car. My father got up and put the grips on the seat back of Clifford and me because we were standing up and did not need the seat.

Once in a while somebody would get up and would yank on the bell cord and the car would stop, to let him off. All of a sudden my father jumped to his feet and yelled, "Hey, wait a minute." Then he walked toward the back and took one of our grips from a man who had just rung to get off the car. "Guess you got the wrong grip," my father said.

"Oh, I'm sorry," the man said. "For a moment I thought it was mine."

"For a moment I guess it was," my father said.

I guess all of us were glad to get off the streetcar and the streets and into Smith and McNeil's hotel. My father got us a big room with two beds in it, and then we went back down into the dining room and had lamb chops. They called it dinner instead of supper.

After dinner there wasn't much place to sit down and so we went back to the room. My father lit a cigar and read a newspaper. We jumped around on and off the beds, but there wasn't much to do. My father said he was played out and we went to bed.

The next morning he and Harry were dressed when they woke Clifford and me. My father and Harry helped us dress and then took us down the hall to what they called a bathroom. It was a place to wash. There was a big tin tub there, too, and my father said that was a bathtub. There was another thing. He said it was for privy work, but you sat on it and then you pulled a chain and everything washed away. Clifford wanted to know where it went and my father tried to tell him something or other. Clifford kept pulling the chain to see the water gush until my father was out of patience and told him he would have to stop.

My father took us out of the hotel and said we would go to have breakfast. We followed him along the street quite a ways and came to a big place all white inside and outside that my father said was Childs Restaurant. "It is only *a* Childs Restaurant," he said, "and what I mean is that there are a lot of them scattered around New York." He had trouble getting Clifford and me to go inside because we wanted to watch two men, in white coats and big white hats, behind the window baking pancakes and tossing them in the air and catching them on plates. But my father said we could have some for breakfast, and so he got us inside.

After breakfast Harry said, "Now what do we do?"

My father said he had thought that all out. "I will have to go buying," he said, "but you boys would find that tiring, and you might get in the way and take my mind off my work. What I am going to do is to give you a ride on the elevated railroad down to the Battery and leave you there until I come for you."

"What do we do at the Battery?" Harry asked.

"Lots of things," my father said. "It's a park. You watch the boats in the harbor. There is the Aquarium, where they have all kinds of fish and all sizes. You can watch through the sides of glass tanks. You will be so interested and have such a good time that I'll be back before you know it. Then we will get something to eat, and we'll see what's next for this afternoon."

So that was what we did. It was half-past eight when we got to the Battery. My father pointed out the Aquarium and said we could walk right in because it was free. He pointed out the harbor and the boats, and the paths we could walk on and the benches to sit down, and then he said, "Have a good time," and left us and went back on the elevated. He said he would be back about noon.

We went through the Aquarium. It had a lot of fish, but they all act about the same, just floating around as if they are bored. We got bored, too, just looking at them. We went through in about five minutes.

We came out and watched the boats for a few minutes, and then we walked along the paths for awhile. Then we sat down where we could see the shiny brass engines pulling in the elevated trains.

After awhile we got up and went through the Aquarium again, and the rest of it all over.

Clifford and I played tag a little while.

We went through the Aquarium again.

When we were sitting down again and watching the shiny brass engines Clifford got up and said, "Do you know something?"

"What?" said Harry.

"This New York—I'm tired of it."

"There's nothing you can do about it," I said. "We're stuck here. How much longer is it till noontime?"

"It's two hours," said Harry.

So we went through the Aquarium again.

Then we just sat.

But it came to an end at last. My father came walking along fast and said he was sorry he had been held up. He looked at his watch. "My goodness," he said. "I've been gone four hours."

"Seems like ten to me," said Harry.

"Well," my father said, "just to make up I'll take you to a restaurant where we can get some fresh ocean fish to eat."

That sounded good. In Woodstock we never had any fresh ocean fish, only salt mackerel and smoked halibut. We did have fresh shad and roe when the fish wagon came through from Rondout but that was only once a year in May.

"After we eat," said my father, "we will get on a Fifth Avenue bus. You can go up on the top of them out in the open and see everything. We will ride up to Central Park and you can see what a wonderful place that is. We will take a boat ride on the lake. Then we will see Grant's Tomb and then it will be suppertime. The restaurant is about seven blocks away. Shall we take a street car?"

"No," said Harry. "Let's not take any more chances of getting left than we have to."

So we walked and we walked, and Clifford said he was tired out and my father carried him the last block. Each of us got a whole fish on a plate with the head and eyes and tail on it and it was full of bones. My father did not get to eat much because he spent so much time fixing some of it without bones for Clifford and me.

And then we said we were feist of the head and eyes and didn't even eat what he had fixed. That strained my father's patience and so we did eat a little bread and butter and ice cream and coffee.

Then we walked and walked some more and came to a curve with four streetcar tracks and lots of streetcars running both ways. My father said it was called Dead Man's Curve and that we had to get across it, and to be careful because so many had been killed there.

Clifford and I were trying to keep up when my father and Harry crossed fast, but a streetcar came at me with the bell clanging to get out of the way and I ran back. And the same thing happened to Clifford. But when we ran back we only ran right in front of another streetcar coming the other way with the bell clanging. And so we dodged streetcars back and forth. My father and Harry stood on the sidewalk on the other side and they shouted to us to look out and back up and come this way but we didn't know what to do by that time. Harry began to holler, "Oh, dear, oh, dear," and my father started right out into the street to get us but then he dodged back when he found himself in front of a clanging streetcar.

I guess maybe Clifford and I would have changed the name to Dead Boy's Curve if it hadn't been for a policeman. He blew a loud whistle and kept blowing it and walked right out in the middle of the street and held up his hands against the streetcars both ways. They all stopped. Then he got Clifford and me and took us to my father and Harry. And then he blew his whistle again and waved to the streetcars to go on.

"There they are, safe and sound," he said, and laughed. Then he said to my father, "From the country?"

"Yes," said my father, "I'm indebted to you, officer."

"Not at all," said the policeman. "You have your hands full.

Next time bring the battle-axe along. Women know enough to take the kids to the park or the zoo."

"Their mother said she preferred a vacation," said my father.

"Divorced, eh? Well, cheer up, there ain't no hell hereafter anyway."

"No, no," said my father. "Not divorced. It's a long story."

"I'll bet it is. Too long," said the policeman. And he went back into the street.

Clifford was crying. Harry was mad and disgusted and said he was ashamed. My father said, "Well, what next?" and took out his handkerchief and mopped his face. There was a park right there with benches and so we sat down for a spell until Clifford stopped crying. Then my father said we could get on a Fifth Avenue bus on the other side of the park, and so we went there.

We got to Central Park and rode in an open carriage and the boat ride was nice. We went on somewhere else and saw a zoo with a lot of animals in it. Then we went to Grant's Tomb that we had heard about all our lives, but we didn't see why folks made such a fuss about it. It started to rain and this brought on dark sooner. We had left our umbrellas at Smith and McNeil's. We waited at the Tomb hoping that the rain would stop, but it didn't. And so we went on anyway and got all wet and got on a bus and New York had a nasty and dirty look. We got off the bus and ate in another Childs Restaurant all wet and then we got to Smith and McNeil's.

After we had hung out our wet clothes on chairs my father said how did we like New York and were we having a good time, and we didn't say anything.

"That's what I thought," he said. "Woodstock is pretty nice. Well, travel may stretch the horizons but there's something to be said for home. But we're in luck. I had a good buying morning and got all of it pretty well done, maybe. So we can go home tomorrow and not stay a couple of more days. Shall we go back on the dayboat? It's a nice sail up the river. Or shall we take the train?

If we take the train we can be home on the mule stage tomorrow afternoon."

"The train," we said all together.

We were ready long before time the next morning. It was raining yet. My father did not trust to streetcars and piled us into a funny rig with a driver with a plug hat way up above the horses' tails outside and we went way down below with a roof over us inside. We went to the ferry and then to Weehawken and then got on the West Shore RR. When we reached Kingston, we got on the dayboat train going up into the mountains.

I never saw anything that looked so good as Johnny Saxe and his mule team when we got to West Hurley on the U & D.

Linnie was in the front yard when the stage drove up to our store in Woodstock. She saw us on the stage and called back to my mother in the house, and came running over.

"Must have been a quick buying trip this time," she said. Then she saw our clothes all wrinkled up. "Oh, I see," she said. "You fell in the river and never got there."

My mother came running up and hugged us. "My days," she said. "What happened?"

"Do you know something?" said my father. "One or two trials were left out of the Book of Job."

I didn't know what he meant and I didn't care. I was back in Woodstock again. I ran for the house to get out of my Sunday clothes and you can bet I didn't take long to get into all the interesting things in Woodstock.

The next day at dinnertime my father had not come in from the store but my mother had us sit right down and not wait for him or send anybody after him and she asked the Blessing.

When she finished the Blessing I said, "Why don't we wait for Papa?"

"He's gone back to New York," my mother said.

"Alone," said Linnie.

❧ The Medicine Show

. . . and the victory of the most popular lady

This man walked up to Clifford and me in front of the store. He looked very different from our men in Woodstock or anywhere around and so I knew he was a stranger.

He called me Bub and wanted to know how long we had lived in Woodstock and I told him all our lives.

"At your age that is a long time," he said. "It is longer than it will ever be again. It is so long that I suppose you know everybody in every house and who runs the farms and business places."

"We would be pretty dumb if we didn't," I said. "And some outside the Village, too."

He looked at Clifford and asked if we were twins.

"No," I said. "It's just that my mother has us wear duds alike. There is seventeen months between us but Clifford is big for his age and I am small for mine."

"Well, well," he said and looked solemn. His eyes were brown, and Linnie says that brown eyes in a man are best.

"I guess you two are just what I need," he said.

He had on a pair of long corduroy pants stuffed into black boots with red bands and a star in their tops. His shirt was blue silk without the collar buttoned, and a big red handkerchief went under the collar and was tied down on his chest. His chest bulged like the middle of a barrel. His hat was white and big with a wide brim. In the opening of his collar you could see that his chest was covered with hair. The skin on his face made me think of copper. He had a big diamond ring on each one of his hands. His belt was wide and studded with gold stars. He was one of the biggest and nicest men I ever saw and I asked him who he was.

"I am a showman," he said.

"Like Dan Sully," I said.

"No," he said. "I have heard of Daniel Sully. But he has what they call a play. Mine is a medicine show. I am going to have my show at the M.E. Hall, and I want you boys to peddle bills for me —not just throw them around on stoops and store floors but hand them in and talk to people about them."

He took a folded paper out of his pocket and showed us what a bill is. It was a long piece of yellow paper with big printing telling about the show, and pictures of a horse and of a man and woman doing physical stunts like we did when we played Follow the Leader and lifted heavy stones and stood on our heads.

"If you will peddle these bills," he said, "I will give both of you free tickets to the show Friday and Saturday nights."

It was Thursday and that made it only a day to wait. We said we would do it, of course, and he said to come with him.

We went down alongside the store to the shed next to the barns. Mrs. Lown was going into the store and she stopped and watched the man and us. Bill Lake, the summer boy from New York City who runs with us, was having a dish of ice cream in Mower's, and when the man was talking to us he came out on the stoop with his dish of ice cream in his hands and watched us. I felt important with this big showman in his wonderful clothes.

It turned out that we were going down to the shed because he had his horse there out of the sun. She was the loveliest horse I ever saw, rich cream color all over, except for her long tail and her mane and forelock and fetlocks that were dark brown. She kept her neck arched and her ears pointed up watching and looking around. When she heard the medicine man's step she turned her head and whinnied and he called to her in a sweet and loving voice.

She had the most wonderful, big, carved saddle I ever saw. That and her bridle were all decked out in silver. The lines of her bridle just hung down to the ground and she wasn't tied. The man said a word I didn't understand and she wheeled and came trotting to us. She scared Clifford and me first because she put her nose down against both of us and nuzzled us.

"She wonders if one of you might be little Jim," said the medicine man. "He was my little boy. He died and she has been looking for him ever since."

"What's her name?" I said.

"It's Queen," he said. "This is Queen. She is the brainiest and most beautiful horse ever born."

"What's your name?" asked Clifford, who had found his tongue at last.

"It's Big Jim," he said. "Captain James Grant Brown. You call me Captain Jim. What's your name?"

"My name's Willie Rose," I said. "And this is Clifford, my brother."

"You told me that," he said. "What does your father call you? Bill, I suppose."

"He calls me Willie."

"He had ought to be shot," said Captain Jim. "I'll call you Bill. Now stand back a little."

He swung into the saddle. He reached down a hand toward me. "Swing up here," he said.

"Are we going to ride with you?" I asked.

"Yes," he said. "We will go up to the hall and get the bills."

"Are both of us? Three of us going to ride?"

"Yes," he said. "One of you in front of me. One of you behind."

"Jimminy!" I said.

He was strong and he put Clifford in front of him and told him to hold onto the saddle. He put me behind him and told me to hang onto his shirt. Then Queen started off loping up to the M.E. Hall. But she was just like a rocking chair. And everybody who saw us stopped and stared.

Captain Jim had a big wagon with a team. The wagon had a top

and sides on it and it was like a room inside with two cots and
other things to live with inside it. The team was a good team and
they stood under the shed of the M.E. Church back in the lane
between the church and the hall.

We went into the hall and Captain Jim told a very pretty
woman about us. He called her Nell and said she was his wife. He
hugged her and she liked it. She looked younger than he was.
She had a short skirt made of some sort of soft leather and it
showed her ankles and a little more. They were different kind of
limbs than I had ever seen because they were pretty and not like
men's and boys' limbs. She was very pretty and maybe too pretty
somehow, and she took so much interest in us and paid so much
attention to us that it didn't seem she could mean it at all. But
maybe she did. She said something to Captain Jim about little Jim
and that he would have been like us and they both looked at each
other and Captain Jim patted her shoulder.

Captain Jim gave each of us a big pack of bills and he gave each
of us two tickets to the show. We could use one ticket for Friday
night and another one for Saturday night, he said, or we could use
both tickets for Saturday night and bring somebody with us.

We went off with the bills and began putting one of them in
every house and store and everywhere in town and telling people
about them. Some of the boys joined us because by now the news
about us and how we knew Captain Jim and had ridden on Queen
had been noised around. Fred Elwyn joined us and Lancy Boice
and when we got down to the center of the village Bill Lake had
finished his ice cream and he came along with some of the other
boys.

Two men standing in front of our store took one of the bills
and read it out loud. It told about Cream Queen and said she could
add and subtract and tell colors. It told about Captain Jim and said
he was the world's greatest outdoor rider and had combed the Wild
West with Buffalo Bill. It told about a woman that the men said

was Millie Dupree with a French name and was the world's greatest acrobat and sharpshooter. I thought that must be Nell because she was the only woman I saw with Captain Jim. But the picture didn't look like her except maybe for the same ankles and limbs, and the picture had a skirt that was higher than Nell's had been. And then the bill said that Captain Jim would give a free outdoor exhibition of riding at half-past seven, both Friday and Saturday nights in the road in front of the hall.

At dinner time we told my father and mother about Captain Jim and the show and that we had free tickets and they said, well, they didn't know. My mother said we would be the only little boys there but we told her that Bill Lake had said that his father was going to give him two dimes to go. So we wouldn't be the only little boys there; and besides we had earned our tickets. My father said he guessed there probably wasn't any harm in it.

There was a big crowd in front of the M.E. Hall, Friday night, to see the free riding. Right on time Captain Jim came riding out from behind the hall on Cream Queen. People watched him come and everybody said what a beautiful horse Cream Queen was. The crowd was men and none of the older wives seemed to be there like my mother and Mehalie Elwyn and Mrs. Boice and so on. Ophelia and Libby Riseley were not there either, and I didn't see Ceily Lasher. But there were lots of grown-up young women there and some of the young blades had brought their girls, or some girl anyway. Of course, I did not know them all. But one thing I did notice. The girls glanced at Cream Queen, but they had their eye on Captain Jim. He certainly was a wonderful-looking man.

But none of them knew Captain Jim like I did and he just looked at them all in a crowd without knowing any of them. But when he went past me I said, "Hello, Captain Jim," and he looked down and smiled and said, "Why, hello there, Bill," and I felt pretty proud that I was the only one who knew him, beside Clif-

ford, of course, and that he knew me right away. And he called
me Bill.

Captain Jim certainly could ride. He picked up his silk handkerchief from the ground first with his hand and then with his teeth
while Cream Queen was galloping fast. He rode standing up in
the saddle. He jumped Cream Queen over some sawhorses and he
also rode her with one foot in the stirrup and one knee in the
saddle. He did something that scared people almost to death. He
walked away from Cream Queen about a hunderd feet and said
she would gallop toward him when he called her and jump right
over his head. And she did, but he did bend down a little because
what could you expect? Captain Jim was away over six feet. Then
he said he had one more free stunt, but before he did that he
wanted to tell them that if they came to the show they would see
some amazing things.

They would see sharpshooting, knife throwing, magic, acrobats,
and best of all they would see Cream Queen do figuring, pick
colors, and help him on with a lot of coats. And, besides, he said,
everybody who bought a ticket could vote for the most popular
lady in Woodstock or anywhere around.

Then he had Queen gallop as fast as she could and while she
was running he got out of the saddle and went clear around under
her belly and back up into the saddle again. Then Nell, who was
in front of the hall on the stoop, began to talk fast about the show
and sell tickets. Just about everybody bought and went in and the
hall was filled.

Clifford and I and Bill Lake got seats right down in the front
row. It was a wonderful show. They did lots of things. Queen
really could add and subtract and she would give the answer by
the number of times she pawed with her front foot. Captain Jim
put Nell in a big box and closed it up. He counted six and when
he opened it up Nell was gone. Nell stood at one end of the stage
and shot at a big white wooden square on the other end, and the

bullet holes drew an outline of a dog. Nell walked on her hands and did cartwheels and the people liked that very much.

Then Captain Jim told how he was lost in a snowstorm way out West one time. He struggled for days. The cold made rheumatism all over his body, he said. He had a bad cough and pains in his chest. He had pains in his stomach. He sprained one ankle. His head ached. His throat was like sandpaper. He smashed one of his fingers and he held up one hand to show a finger gone. He would have died, he said, if he had not been found by an old Indian he had saved from a mountain lion once. This Indian chief took him to his village and called in the tribe's medicine man.

The medicine man shook his head, Captain Jim said, but the chief gave an order just the same and then the medicine man began to mix up a black-looking mess over a fire and it had such awful things in it that you wouldn't swallow it unless you were dying, and maybe not then. He made Captain Jim swallow this and he also rubbed it all over his body. In a month he was as sound as a dollar, Captain Jim said, and he could wrestle and throw the strongest Indian in the village.

He asked the Indians for some of this medicine and how to make it but they wouldn't give it to him. But he sneaked some one night, and when he got to the city he got a chemist to find out what was in it.

Now, said Captain Jim, you all know about chemistry. All the awful things in the Indians' medicine are just so many chemicals, like some kinds of salt and acids that are not hard to take and taste good. After all, all that's in a snake's head or the tail of a buffalo or anything else, Captain Jim said, you can get out of bottles of chemicals if you know what ones. That's how he had the Indian medicine made for sale. He had a few bottles with him, he said, but he made it a point never to sell this medicine at his shows. But he and Millie Dupree would be on hand all next day, and on Sunday, after Saturday night, and anybody could come and get a bottle or a couple of bottles in the daytime and nobody would know the difference. It was only two dollars a bottle, he said, and what was two dollars or even four dollars if you could get over the pain and trouble that had bothered you all these years? Look at me, he said, and look at Millie Dupree, and think how you would like to feel like kicking the footboard off the bed every morning again.

"I do not have to sell this medicine," Captain Jim said, "because I have a big ranch out West and that makes my living. But I know the world is full of pain and I am so happy about being saved myself that I can't rest without telling others about this medicine, part of the year. And if you wonder, then, why I have the medicine show, well, that's only to attract folks together in a crowd so I can tell that many more about the medicine."

A man I had never seen before got up in the middle of the hall and called out to Captain Jim. "I live over the mountain," he said, "and I won't be here tomorrow. Can't you sell me just one bottle now?"

"I'm sorry friend," said Captain Jim, "but I can't. If I did it for you I would have to do it for everybody. But my advice to you is to stay overnight somewhere and get the bottle tomorrow." The man sat down and grumbled but that's how it was. So the man called out, "I'll stay over. I ache with rheumatism all the time and this is my chance to get over it."

There was a big whispering in the crowd and I saw a lot of people nodding their heads.

Captain Jim said it was time now to vote for the most popular lady. This would run two nights, he said, and everybody in the hall, either night or both, would have one vote. The lady who won would get a prize of a hand-woven Indian blanket that he had made special for him and that could not be had anywhere else for any kind of money.

Nell began to bring out beautiful Indian blankets and spread them over chairs and tables on the stage. The most popular lady could make her own choice, Captain Jim said. Any one of them was worth at least fifty dollars. At the end of the Saturday night show, he said, the winner would be called to the stage and could look over all the blankets.

Nell brought out a big blackboard and Captain Jim said that names in the contest would start now. Nell would write down the names and the number of votes as they were called out. They could start with the back rows and when anybody voted they must stand up and stay up so that nobody could vote more than once.

This was a big honor to win this contest, it seemed to me. It also seemed to me that my mother ought to win the contest, because she was pretty and everybody knew her and she was friendly to everybody.

The first vote was by a bashful young farmer who named the girl he had brought to the show, who was beside him. She giggled and blushed so hard that she kept twisting and turning. Her name was Nettie Duberry, the young farmer said, and then, because he was bashful, he struck a pose like pictures of Napoleon and made a funny face with his eyes crossed.

"Hi, Nettie," some man called out and everybody laughed, but I could tell that I never saw her before and so she couldn't have much chance of winning if nobody knew her.

"I name Evelyn," the next man called.

"Evelyn who?" asked Captain Jim.

"Evelyn Black," he said.

"Yeah, Evelyn," that same man called out again the same as he had for Nettie. This time I could see who he was. He was young and laughing and his eyes were partly closed and he acted as if he was about three sheets in the wind. Men near him were laughing and poking him in the ribs.

The next name was Linnie Jewel, and the next was Minnie Whispel, and then I had to stop and think. I liked Linnie so much. And Minnie Whispel was awful pretty. But I could not vote for both of them and so I decided to stick to my mother.

Addie Winnie was named, and Salo Shultis, and Addie Johnson, and lots of others. These made another strain for me. Addie Winnie was Chris Winnie's daughter in the Dutch Reformed Church, and Salo Shultis and Addie Johnson were big girls in district school and big for their age. All of them were pretty. But you had to vote for one and I couldn't decide which one, and so I stuck to my mother.

And besides, all of these named so far were more like girls than like ladies and this was to decide the most popular lady. It seemed to me like you had to be a little old to be a lady. There was something else that bothered me, too. As the names went on, some that I have overheard the young blades talk about went onto the blackboard, and when they did I could see men nudging each other and laughing.

I was beginning to be afraid to name my mother and all the time it was coming closer and closer to my turn. But then I thought about being loyal to my mother in the face of any kind of danger, and so I doubled up my fists and got ready. When it came my turn I jumped up and shouted, "My mother."

Up to this time there had been a lot of joking, and when someone of two or three who were getting most of the votes got another, there was some cheering. But when I named my mother everything quieted down and you could have heard a pin drop. I saw people craning their necks to see who I was, and I guess they saw that Clifford and I and Bill Lake were the only boys in the hall.

Nell wrote down on the blackboard "My mother." Clifford was next and he said "My mother," and Bill Lake was next and he got up and pointed and said, "That last one. Put another vote on that 'My mother.'"

There were three more votes for Evelyn Black after that, and the man who was three sheets in the wind cheered all by himself on each vote and then looked around surprised when he heard his own voice, as if he was trying to decide if he was left alone in the hall. At the end of that show Evelyn Black was ahead and Nettie Duberry was second.

Saturday night the same thing happened all over again. Captain Jim's riding outside was not changed. The crowd was bigger. In the hall the show was the same except that Captain Jim and Nell did different things but the same kind of things. The voting was just the same. Everybody who wasn't voting for Evelyn Black was voting for Nettie Duberry. While the voting was going on the shouting and laughing was louder.

The voting got to Clifford and me down in the front row again. I wanted my mother to win but I knew she wouldn't, of course. I was sorry for my mother with only three votes on the blackboard. I was scared to vote, but no matter how much I suffered I was going to stick to my mother. And so when it came my turn I got up and said, "My mother." Clifford said, "My mother," too, and that gave her five votes. Bill Lake wasn't there Saturday night.

Nobody paid any attention this time except that Nell wrote down two more votes for "My mother." The crowd went on laughing and voting. Then something happened. A man got up to vote and he said, "Put down another vote for 'My mother.' " He was in the other side of the front row and I leaned out to look at him. He was a summer boarder from Aaron Riseley's. He was a youngish man with a pair of glasses that I had heard people call Doctor Glenford, but folks said he was not a real doctor like Doctor Downer. He was a writer, they said.

The crowd was surprised by that for a second but then went right on voting and laughing. It was about over and Evelyn Black and Nettie Duberry were almost tied. There was a lot of commotion and noise in the hall now, and then Evelyn Black won and it was all over.

Captain Jim called Evelyn Black to the stage and I saw her good for the first time. She wasn't a girl but she wasn't a lady, either. She was like a picture of an actress from packages of Sweet Caporal cigarettes with a big hat, and with a big top and bottom but with no middle, like the middle of a wasp or an ant. She had paint on her face. She joked with Captain Jim when he was asking her to pick her blanket, and she put her hand on his shoulder and called him "Handsome," and I could see that he did not like it.

When she had left the stage with her blanket Captain Jim held up his hand for quiet and then he made a little speech. He said that something had happened in his shows at Woodstock that had never happened before. He pointed to that Doctor Glenford down in the first row and said, "You called my attention to it and you know what it is." He said that the most popular lady not only in Woodstock but in the whole world had not won the vote at all. He said that he guessed that if every man in the hall had voted really for the most popular lady the voting for "My mother" would have swamped everyone else. Then my heart jumped. He asked them if they didn't think that "My mother" had ought to win a blanket.

A big shout went up in the hall and Captain Jim called Clifford and me up on the stage. He told us to pick out a blanket and to take it to our mother. And we did. And then the show was over.

When Clifford and I got home my father was already home from the store and he and my mother were waiting up for us. We gave my mother the blanket and told her what had happened.

When we said that Evelyn Black was first and that my mother was last and that Clifford and I were the only ones that had voted for her except Bill Lake and that Doctor Glenford from Aaron Riseley's my father said, "Oh, my."

But we told my mother not to be sad because Captain Jim showed them they really all voted for her. And she had really won, we said, because there was the blanket to prove it.

But she wasn't sad. She smiled as if she was happy. She called us to her and put her arms around us.

"It was wonderful to be last if Evelyn Black was first," she said. "And besides, look what a pretty blanket and wonderful boys I have." So I guess that Clifford and I did right in voting for her after all, and that she liked the blanket pretty well.

✻ The Church Donation

. . . and why you should find out how you were baptized

In the afternoon, Fred Elwyn and I noticed that some of the women were doing things at the Dutch Reformed Church, so we went over there to find out.

Nobody was ever around the church in the daytime unless there was going to be a funeral or the women had to clean and dust. There wasn't anything interesting about that, but the church was open and we had never been inside to see what it was like when there wasn't any crowd there and no singing hymns and looking and acting religious.

The women were all down in the basement where you went down stone steps outside and went in from outside, but one of them would come out every little to dump a dishpan or something in the long grass down there. So we watched our chance when nobody was looking and scooted into what they call the vestibule of the church.

There wasn't anything in the vestibule except a table with some papers on it and the long rope to ring the bell up in the steeple. Fred grabbed hold of the rope and made out he was going to ring the bell, but he was too little, of course. I had seen men ring the bell. First it took a lot of strength to pull the rope down quite a ways. Then the man would let go of the rope and it would run back fast up into the ceiling till the bell rang. Then he would jump up and grab hold of the rope again and hang on to pull it down. That took a man, and a pretty big man, at that. Most always it was one of the fat men.

We didn't expect it to be so cold in the vestibule. Outside the sun was bright and the leaves on the trees had turned red and copper and it was warm. But the vestibule was sort of damp and seemed to smell a little of pipe tobacco.

We pushed one door and peeked through to see inside the church and we heard men talking in there. We saw that the men were in a corner by the door that went in on the other side of the vestibule. They were standing around the big stove but there wasn't any fire in it. We had seen them around but didn't know them except for Jim Plass. He always seems to be everywhere he can do something wrong, and then we knew why the vestibule smelled like pipe smoke. Jim was smoking a pipe right there in the church.

One of them said they wouldn't need any fire there because all the doings would be in the basement anyway, and another man said, well then they had ought to get going because it was too damn cold in there. Besides, he said, he had heard Jim's story and he didn't have anything to match it and so they might as well be getting out in the sun or downstairs. And one of the men said he didn't think Jim had ought to be smoking a pipe in there, either.

But Jim laughed. He said that religion today is too namby-pamby. The trouble is that the women took over, he said, and they set the pace. The Bible does not say anything about not smoking a pipe, he said. But not many of the tough old timers are left, like old Bill Henry. Now there's a man, Jim said. He likes to smoke a pipe and even if he wakes up in the middle of the night and feels like a smoke he just loads up his pipe and smokes away right there in bed.

"Must be tough on old Aunt Hannah Henry," said one of the men.

"Old Bill says she's just a wife," said Jim. "He says the trouble with religion is that the women have made it too white-livered and not at all like old times my grandpappy has told me about."

"Why, what times were those," the others asked him, "and what did they do then?"

The men ran things in the church in those times, Jim said. When his grandpappy was a boy the men all wore long whiskers to keep their lungs warm. Not just handlebar moustaches. They weren't Willies. On zero mornings when they opened up the church, they built a fire in the big stove and all stood around it till the church got warm. And they always had a snort.

The other men said they guessed that was stretching it.

His grandpappy might have stretched it, Jim said, but he had his doubts. They had to be strong men coming off the Overlook and the Ohio Mountains in winter, and no real roads, and drifts ten feet deep. Horseback, of course. They certainly weren't Willies.

Jim said the men there acted to him as if they didn't know any history. "Why, look," he said, "two or three more years and this what they call the congregation will be one hundred years old. Let me see now. Yes, that will be in 1905. Why, this damn building has stood here since 1842. I don't go great guns for history either, but my grandpappy told me that. And he told me about what they called the Down Rent Wars. In the old days a few men owned all the land and they figured to keep it. The old Dutch had to rent and they got damned tired of it. They wanted to buy and own their own farms. So they dressed up like Indians and made it so hot for the rent collectors that they got their way. It was just like the KKK in the South after the Civil War. You know about that, don't you? Stretching it? I guess not."

Then they started talking about something different. It wasn't interesting to us and so we let the door close and we tiptoed out of the vestibule to the porch.

Out there I asked Fred Elwyn what a snort was.

He said it was the way real men talked.

"Yes," I said, "but just what is a snort?"

Fred said it was snuff. Yes, he said, that's what it was.

"Maybe," I said.

Fred didn't say anything and I could see that he didn't know. But he always acted as if he knew. "Well, shut up about it," he said. "What difference does it make to you? You're Willie, you know. They said these men were not Willies so you don't have to worry about a snort."

I didn't say anything more but I did worry about it. My name was Willie. I wondered if it made me different. I wondered if I could ever be a real man if my name was Willie. I wanted to know what a snort was and I decided right then that I would have a long beard when I was a man.

But just then Libby Riseley came to the top of the stone stairs from the basement. She called to me.

"Oh, Willie," she called. "You and your little friend are just the ones I am looking for. How would you like some ice cream?"

We didn't stop to answer. We just ran to her and I forgot all about my Willie worries for then.

"If you will turn our freezers for us," Libby said, "you can have the paddles and a spoon. A freezer apiece."

"Why are you making so much ice cream?" I said.

"Why you silly boy," she said. "Don't you remember? We're having the donation tonight. It's after the harvest. Bringing in the sheaves." And while she was talking she was laughing too and her laugh was running up and down. "We fill the Dominie's cellar," she said, "and raise money for the church."

"Like last year?" I asked.

"A big crowd," she said. "Supper. Big circle games. Fancy work and other things for sale. Everybody has just the most wonderful time. And tonight we are going to have a talking machine."

"What's a talking machine?" I asked.

"A machine that speaks," she said. "You'll see. One of the boarders has stayed on into the fall at Aaron Riseley's. He paints. He has it."

The big main part of the the basement was warm because the
stove was lighted. The men were moving chairs and putting long
boards on wooden horses for a long table. We followed Libby
Riseley on into the kitchen. This was warm too, and smelled fine
because the women were cooking ice cream on the stove. Then we
turned into a little outer room where wood and kindling are kept.
There was a big tub of cracked ice and some wet burlap bags
around. There was a burlap bag of coarse salt. Two big freezers
were filled with ice and salt and ready to turn. It was colder here,
almost too cold.

"But turning the freezers will warm you up," Libby laughed.
"And when you have your paddles to eat you can put them into
dishpans and go up into the sun."

Before long it turned out to be hard work and I thought the
ice cream would never freeze. Before we were through Fred said
this was the hardest way he knew to get a little ice cream. But
when we were eating the ice cream off the paddles he said he
could turn four more freezers for four more paddles for him to
spoon and lick. I said, "Yessir."

We said we didn't suppose there ever has been anything that hits
you all over like licking an ice cream paddle.

"Maybe that's how dogs feel when they get a bone," Fred said.

"Maybe it's like men feel when they drink or smoke," I said.

"Maybe it's the way young couples feel when they spoon," said
Fred. "If it is, it must be wonderful to be a dog or a man or a
young couple."

We turned two more freezers apiece and then we were full of
ice cream. Before we ran along Fred took hold of my arm and
said, "You'll be going to the donation because it's in your church.
Now see here, Willie. You find out what that talking machine is
and you be ready to tell me tomorrow or I will punch your nose."

When we were getting ready for the donation at our house I
asked my father what a snort was. He looked at my mother and

made out he didn't hear me. I asked him again. So he said it is something that a horse does when he is frightened.

"Like old Dick," my little brother, Clifford, said, "you know, like this." He snorted like a horse, twice.

I said maybe that was so but what did it mean when a man took a snort.

Well, my father said, he didn't exactly know. But if he was me he wouldn't worry about it.

But I said I had to worry about it because my name was Willie. I told him about the men we saw in the church and about what Jim said his old grandfather told him. "Those old men took snorts in the church," I said, "and Jim said it was because they wasn't Willies. They were real men."

"Who do you mean by this Jim?" my mother asked.

"He means Jim Plass," my brother Harry said.

"Oh, him," my mother said.

"Well," my father said, "religion is for everybody. Him, too. Come unto me all ye that are heavy laden."

"Well, he isn't heavy laden," my mother said. "Not yet."

"Willie," my father said, "how would you like to help me get a store ready for the donation tonight?" When he said that name Willie it went through me like a knife.

But he began to ask me what kind of candy I thought would sell best at the donation and I forgot all about being Willie and snorts for then.

"Do you mean you run a candy counter over in the church?" I said.

"In the basement. For the donation. Yes," he said.

"Not for himself," my mother said. "Abe, you mustn't let them get the wrong impression. The church gets the profit."

"What's the profit?" Clifford asked.

"You kids make me sick," Harry said.

"You see," said my mother, "papa buys wholesale and sells retail. Wholesale is less. Retail is more. The difference is profit. It is what papa gets for risking his money and for his work and having the goods the people want when they want them, and in small amounts. The profit is his pay. It is what we live on. It is the return for the service."

My father was smiling as he looked at my mother and listened to her and I wondered why.

"But," I said, "if Papa can buy for less why can't other people buy for less, too?"

"They do," my father said.

"Oh, Abe," said my mother, "why do you fool about it? Now you have them all mixed up."

"Well," my father said, "you take a day or two off some time and gather them all around you and make it perfectly clear. My boy," he said, and he laid his hand on my arm, "don't you start worrying about all this sort of thing at your tender age. You just get the fun out of it. Tonight you and I will sell them candy and cigars. And some knickknacks and so forth. And we'll charge them plenty and give all the profit and some more to the church because we like the church and it is the Lord's work. Of course," he said, and he winked at Linnie, "it's not bad advertising, but can I help that?"

"I think you're very foolish to joke about it," my mother said. "You should not joke about something sacred. It gives people and the boys the wrong impression of you. You know you're not doing it because it's good advertising, just as well as I do."

My father got serious. "The Lord doesn't question my talents, such as they are, if I offer them in His work," he said.

"What are talents?" asked Clifford.

"We will go into that later sometime," my father said getting up. "Well, I've got to get back to the store. Willie, you come along. You and I will put the Lord into business tonight. It will be a strange place for Him and He needs our help."

"Oh, Abe," said my mother, "why do you be so?"

At the store my father was busy but he told me I could be looking around and if I saw something that I thought little boys and girls would tease their fathers and mothers to buy for them, to tell him and he would put it in our stock. Soon he came along and we began to pile up the stock for our little church store on one of the counters.

He brought a box of two-for-five cigars and said he would sell them for a nickel. He brought a box of five-cent cigars and said he would sell them for a dime. We took three boxes of different penny candy to sell at two cents apiece. And we had fancy boxes of candy in different sizes that he said young blades would buy for their girls at double the price. Then he picked up another box of penny candy and looked at it for a spell and then turned to me.

"Willie," he said, "don't the youngsters like this candy? It's been here a week and only three pieces sold. Try a piece," he said.

It tasted like medicine and I spit it into a spittoon by the big white-bellied stove.

"It's supposed to be raspberry," he said.

"It ain't raspberry," I said.

"This would be a good time to turn it into money," he said. "But no, I guess not." He put it back. "It wouldn't be right."

"The Lord won't get to taste it," I said, "and He won't know the difference."

"Oh, yes He would," said my father.

"You always sit up on Mr. Sudderlee's candy wagon and sample the candy before you buy it," I said. "What made you buy it?"

"It cost less," he said, "and sold for the same. I was greedy. But if people had liked it they would have come back for more at the price and they would have got their money's worth. That would have made it all right. It's a tough business, the store business is."

I wanted to help him. "Take it over to the church," I said, "because over there people will be buying it for the Lord and that makes a difference. They won't mind its being bad candy if they buy it and eat it for the Lord."

"Now let me see," said my father. "How would that work out?" He shook his head. "No," he said. "Because I would be money ahead. I made a mistake and I'll have to pay for it."

"Well, then," I said, "take it over and if anybody buys any give all we take in on it to the Lord. That way you lose, too. But the Lord will be farther ahead than if you don't take it over."

"Well, my heavens," said my father. "I guess that's right."

We put some packages of dates and some oranges and chestnuts with the stock. And some small toys and puzzles and some whistles and some sets of dishes for dolls and girls. And then he carried two handle-baskets full and he had me carry the box of raspberry candy and we started to walk past Mower's to the Dutch Reformed Church.

People were already coming. Rigs were tied all around the green. There was a lot of talk and calling back and forth in the dark and you could hear the feet of people rustling through the dry leaves on the ground.

The oil lamps on the porch of the church, like the square ones on carriages, were lighted, and people were going into the real church to lay their wraps in the pews. We did, too. Inside the church only one wall lamp was lighted. The pulpit was in the shadows and looked solemn, and when the oil lamps flickered when somebody opened the door to come in, the shadows moved around. There wasn't any heat in the real church. It felt like a tomb.

Roy Harder came in with his father and mother. He had on leather boots and the tops had wrinkled down almost to his ankles. Roy was a lively boy who was always carrying on. He took a run up the aisle into the shadows toward the pulpit and made out as if he would slide on the carpet the way you slide on black

ice. But he found himself looking up at the pulpit in the moving
shadows. He pulled his coat around him tighter and ducked his
head and came running back. He was very quiet after that until
we went outside and down the stone steps to the basement. Down
there it was warm and a crowd of people was giggling and squealing. All the lights were on and it was bright.

My father and I set up our stock on a table.We marked all the
candy two cents, except the raspberry. We marked that one cent.
Most all of the kids bought the raspberry because it was so much
for a penny and it was soon all gone. My father winked at me
but I didn't say anything or even smile. It was our secret. Ours
and the Lord's.

The young people old enough to form couples and some of the
older ones who could still cut capers formed a circle game in the
center of the big room and were having a great time. Some of
the women were already bustling around in the kitchen and they
were setting up the first table and already had the cold dishes and
platters laid out on it.

Just then there was a rush toward the door and I saw that the
boarder at Riseley's was coming in carrying a box in his arms. Neil
Riseley was helping him, and Aaron Riseley with his white beard
and his cane was in front of them spreading people out of the way
with his cane and bossing the whole thing. The room got quiet
and a whisper ran over it. It was the talking machine.

When they had set it up it looked something like a sewing
machine with black iron wheels and a couple of little belts. Two
rubber tubes came out of it and people put the ends of these into
their ears. Then the boarder at Riseley's wound it up and pushed
a little lever and you could see from the expression on the face of
whoever had the tubes in his ears whether he was hearing sad
stuff or funny stuff or serious stuff or puzzling stuff. When the
boarder pushed the lever and the machine stopped people took
the tubes out of their ears and said such things as, "Well, I never!"

Some said it in a mystified manner as if they didn't believe yet that they had heard a machine talk. Some shouted and laughed and paid to hear it right over again. Some of the grandmothers acted scared. One started to hear and then yanked the tubes out of her ears and walked off while the machine was running. They tried to get her back but she said no. " 'Tain't natural," she said. "I don't want anything to do with it."

Bruce Herrick, who was a serious young man and studied a lot and wrote poetry, moved around among the people and told them that they were hearing the human voice of somebody alive. Of course the machine didn't talk, he said. What you heard was just sound waves on wax, he said.

The Riseley boarder was charging five cents to listen to the machine talk and giving the money to the donation fund. He did a rushing business until most of the grownups had listened. Then the little girls and boys got their turns if they could get nickels. My father gave me a nickel and I went to hear it.

It was a wonderful thing, of course. I mean the idea of listening to somebody speak and sing and recite who wasn't there and who had done this speaking and singing months before and maybe hundreds of miles away. It was a miracle. But what you heard wasn't much. It squeaked, and some of it I didn't hear at all. But I knew now why the grandmothers had looked a little afraid of it. With that contraption people could leave their voices behind them after they were dead. They really could speak from the grave. I heard Mrs. Lown whisper as much to my mother. "It's the Devil's work," she said. "It don't belong in the church."

They were calling the last table to eat. Our store was about all sold out, so my father got my mother, who had been helping in the kitchen, and Harry and me, and we went to eat. Clifford was too small to be out at night, so he was home with Linnie.

There were plates of ham and tongue and roast pork, dishes of scalloped potatoes, pickles, preserves, mashed turnips, citron, pickled green tomatoes, smoked sausage, slices of headcheese, chicken and biscuits, mashed potatoes, gravy and all kinds of pies and cakes, coffee, baked beans, homemade cooked ice cream and a lot of other things. The land around Woodstock was bountiful, my father said. I did not eat much because I had a weak stomach. I liked the citron, baked beans, ice cream, cake, and pie best.

I was the only boy at the third table. That was because I had been helping my father with our church store and had not been able to eat yet. The rest at the table were mostly the women who had been working in the kitchen and helping with the table. The women praised me and they made little squeals with their fast talking and sometimes all talking at once. My father said I had the makings of a merchant and he told them how he would have thrown the raspberry candy out, but now it had been turned into money for the Lord and that it had been Willie who had found the way.

The women squealed and talked excited again and paid a lot of attention to me. I liked it and yet it wasn't a nice feeling. I scrooched down against the back of my chair and leaned the side of my head against it. My mother put her hand on my head and rubbed it a couple of times.

Addie Winnie, who was a beautiful big girl in the big room at school, said that some of them there had not heard Willie recite Demosthenes and Cicero like he had at the school entertainment that had been put on in the M.E. Hall and that they should have Willie recite it now. I hoped they wouldn't have me do this, but they moved their chairs back from the table and put one of them out in front of them and lifted me up on it on my feet.

Now this is the sort of thing that is awfully hard on boys and girls. Maybe in school it is all right because it is part of the schooling. But old people do not seem to know that it is awfully hard to do it anywhere else, like a church donation and maybe even in children's exercises in Sunday School. I know that one time Roy Harder and Lewis Harder and Harry and I had to sing together on the stage for children's exercises. But the three of them didn't sing at all but just stood there and I had to sing the thing alone, and I got the thing started way up high and couldn't get down from there all through the song. And then when the three of them heard how I was doing it they giggled all through it.

So now at the donation I would have scrambled down and run away but Addie Winnie is awfully pretty and I liked her more than I would say if anybody asked me and I wanted her to like me and would do anything she wanted me to. Or I would try, anyway.

"Go ahead, Willie," Addie said. She was sitting in the first chair to my right and when she spoke she put her hand on the shoulder of my coat and made as if to make me not afraid. Then she got up a little and hugged me and she smiled. Her perfumery was like arbutus we hunt in the spring.

So I rushed into the story of the Greeks and then it happened again just like at the school entertainment. Something took hold of me and lifted me out of there. It was like somebody singing far away, but the song came out of me. Words that I didn't know at all came out of my throat. It just seemed I had to lift my arm and my hand made a sweep around. I was tingling so that my voice moved up and down.

Then it was over, and I was just a little boy again back there in the donation. There was a lot of clapping and the women oohed and ahed and Ceily Lasher, who doesn't have any little boys or girls, and Clara Shultis got up and hugged me and I saw my mother wipe her eyes. My father was looking at me as if he was seeing right through me with his eyes narrowed, and his face looked serious.

But it was Willie this and Willie that and Willie something else and I thought I never wanted to hear that name Willie again. I jumped down and ran off and tried to lose myself in the crowd. Pretty soon nobody paid any more attention to me and I was free.

Well, that was all of the donation. But the next Sunday morning Dominie Park stopped the services for a spell. He came down to the floor in front of the pulpit and my father got up and went to the front of the church. He got a bowl of water and came over to where Dominie Park was and stood beside him. The Dominie said there was to be what he called a baptism and would the parents bring the child forward.

Young John Vanderwort and Lizzie Coons, who are married, walked up the aisle and John was carrying their baby. Dominie Park spoke some words to them and then he dipped his fingers in the bowl my father held for him and laid his hand on the baby's head and said, "William Henry, I baptize thee in the name of the Father and the Son and the Holy Ghost." Then they all went back to where they came from, but the baby had started to cry. The Vanderworts sat near our pew and I turned around to look at them. Lizzie Coons held the baby close to her and I heard her say, "Hush, Willie. Darling, hush." I don't know whether the baby hushed or not because it started me to thinking and I wasn't there at all after that.

That afternoon I watched my chance, and when my father was alone out on the veranda reading *The Ram's Horn* and my mother and Linnie were in the kitchen yet, and Harry and Clifford were off somewhere, I went to my father. He kept right on reading when I spoke to him but he said, "What is it?"

"When I was baptized," I asked him, "was I baptized Willie or William?"

His eyes had been running back and forth over the lines in *The Ram's Horn.* He didn't look up but his eyes stopped moving back and forth and seemed to look right at one small spot in the page.

"Which would you prefer it was?" he asked.

"William," I said and I said it strong because I meant it.

"Well," he said, "that's what it was. William."

I was leaning against his knee and looking up at him.

"William—?" I asked again.

He looked at me then and smiled. "William," he said.

I backed off trying to whistle the way Harry was teaching me and then I ran out into the yard and flopped on the ground and rolled over a couple of times.

My father never called me Willie again. When he spoke to me he always called me William. My mother said Will. Harry and Linnie started calling me Bill. Clifford kept up Willie for awhile but now even he calls me Bill.

It has lifted a big load off my shoulders and I appreciate it very much. So that is my advice to all Willies. Find out how you were baptized.

❧ Square Dance in Riseley's Grove

. . . and the logic of two small philosophers

When Johnny Saxe pulled up his mules in front of the store, Ben Johnson was waiting and he stepped up to Johnny and said, "Did they come?"

"Must have," said Johnny. "Anyway there's an express package for you from the *Kingston Leader*. But I say again, I don't think we need them."

"I've been talking to some," said Ben. "But we need the bills to tack up around to be sure of a big crowd. Boarding houses, stores, mills and even bars. Here, Bearsville, Van Dale, Shady, Milk Hollow, everywhere."

"I don't know about bars," said Johnny. "We can't have any drunks at the dance."

"Not drunks, no. But lots will see the bills in bars."

"Stop worrying," said Johnny. "Say, wouldn't it be wonderful if Mrs. Dan Sully came down with a few of the young actresses? The ones that spend the summer with Dan and the Missus? Their show is in from the road for the summer, you know."

"But there's another thing," said Ben. "The boarders don't know the square dance. A girl down at Aaron Riseley's was telling me all they know is what they call a waltz and two-step. Just couples. Modern stuff. With their arms around each other."

"Not modern," said Johnny. "European stuff. Didn't you ever hear of the Strauss waltzes? Old as the hills. Dreamy stuff. I've got a book about it with pictures. One-two-three time, but you don't jig and clog and carry on. And you don't whoop."

Ben got the package and started to tear it open.

"Here, wait," said Johnny. "First sign for it. It's in your name. Maybe it'll take a couple of dances for the boarders to catch on. The waltz and two-step may be all right, but give me the square dance. Livelier. More fun. And it's more decent. This hugging on the dance floor—I don't go for that. We've got to keep this thing decent or there will be a lot of talk."

Just then Ben was getting the package open and one of the bills slipped off the top and floated to the ground. I grabbed it and was off like a flash down around the side of the store.

"Hey," yelled Ben, like he was mad. But they did not run after me and then I heard them laugh. So I knew it was all right. Then I stopped to look at the bill. I had never seen such fancy letters and it was hard to make it out. So I laid down on my stomach under the willow trees in our back yard and studied it.

It was something about a dance all right, and I made out Riseley's Pine Grove. It was nothing for a boy and if I was wise I would have chucked the paper but I didn't know then, of course, that this dance was going to make a fool out of me and give me one of the worst heartaches in the world.

I folded the paper and put it in my pants pocket and went over

to Elwyns' to find Fred. I peeked in Larry Elwyn's barber shop
but all I could see was the seat of Larry Elwyn's pants, because
he was shaving somebody. I went out to the road and kicked my
feet in the dust for a minute and then I looked down by the creek
and there was Fred by the tannery dam trying to snare pollywogs.
I ran down to him.

"You don't know what I've got," I said.

"I know you've got a nerve," he said, "rushing up like that.
Now the pollywogs have scampered into deep water."

"Pollywogs is nothing alongside of what I got," I said.

"Don't you think I know pollywogs is no good?" he asked.
"Don't be such a dummy. Don't think you have to tell me anything about pollywogs. It's just fun to snare them. You know
that. What did you think?"

But it was all just his way of trying not to let on that he wanted
to know what I had. It didn't work. I waited.

"What have you got?" he asked, "seeing as you want me to
ask."

"I've got this," I said, and I showed him the paper.

He looked at it and then he said, "What is it?"

"It's a dance," I said. "I heard Johnny Saxe and Ben Johnson
talking about it. They had these and I grabbed one and ran. It's a
dance. At night. In Riseley's Grove, on August 21. When is that?"

"Say, that's something," he said.

"I wonder if we can get to go," I said.

"Say, that's something," he said again. Then he turned impatient with me. "Why didn't you ask Johnny Saxe and Ben
Johnson all about it?"

"I'm not big enough to count," I said.

"The trouble with you is you're too 'fraidy-cat," he said. "What
you do is just step up and make them tell you all about it. Wish I
had been there. Now we've got to guess about it."

"We can go up and if they're still there you can step up to them," I said.

"Oh, they're gone by now," he said, and he shrugged his shoulders.

"We could ask somebody to read this," I said. "And we could get a calendar and find out when August 21 is."

"We can't ask anybody. That would give us away. That would prove we are too small to go. But we could get a calendar. Nobody has to know we got ourselves a calendar. Where is there a calendar?"

I knew I had seen a calendar somewhere but I couldn't think where. I though hard for a minute. "I know," I said. "In the privy."

"Your privy or our privy?" asked Fred.

"Our privy."

Fred pulled his line out of the water. He took the copper snare wire off the line and stuffed it into his pocket. Because he could get a line anywhere but a snare wire is worth four agates and twenty marbles. Then he dropped the pole and line on the bank and we started off.

We went across the road into our yard and on past the pump and the doors to the house and into the back yard where the weeping willows are and where we would be close to the privy. Then we kinda hung around until the coast was clear and then we beat it into the privy and closed the door.

There was a big calendar on the back of the door just like I said, with the picture of the stallion at the county fair on it. The cover over the calendar pad had never been torn off and all the months were still there.

We looked up August and the 21, and the 21 was on Sunday.

"Something's wrong here," said Fred. "They wouldn't have a dance on Sunday night. Here, let me see that handbill again."

I handed it to him. "It's 21 all right," he said.

I looked at him and he looked at me and we wondered. But if anybody could figure it out I knew Fred could. He studied the calendar and then he studied the handbill. Pretty soon he said, "What year is this?"

"It's eighteen hundred and ninety-seven," I said just as if I was answering in school, because I had answered that question in school before vacation started.

"Sometimes my birthday is on Saturday and sometimes it is on Sunday and sometimes it is on Monday," Fred said. "Do you suppose that sometimes August 21 is Sunday and sometimes it is some other day? I'll betcha that's the way it is. What we need is to find a calendar for eighteen hundred and ninety-seven. This one here with the stallion is eighteen hundred and ninety-three. How long ago is that?"

"It's three from seven," I said. "That's four. This stallion calendar is four years old. So maybe that's it. But I know where there is a eighteen hundred and ninety-seven calendar. I just remembered. It is back of Will Elwyn's bookkeeping desk up in the store. But why do we have to go to all the trouble to figure this thing out? Let's ask somebody."

"No," Fred said. "If nobody knows what we're going to do nobody will start thinking up reasons why we can't. If we want to get to this dance we better be pretty careful about it."

So we went up to the store and Fred sent me in to look at Will Elwyn's calendar. The figures eighteen hundred and ninety-seven were on it plain as day. The little slip on the pad was **August**. And 21 was on Friday, all right. But I didn't know whether it was this week or next week or maybe the week after that.

Then I had a thought. I asked Will Elwyn for a sheet of paper and a pencil and told him I wanted to write a letter. He smiled at me and his dimples showed but he gave me the stuff. I sat down to write and then I asked him what date it was today.

He said it was the 17th. So then I knew all I needed to know.

Because there are seven days in the week and 17 is only 4 from 21 and so it would have to be Friday night of this week that 21 was. Then I told Will I guessed I would go home to write my letter and I ran out.

But as it turned out we wouldn't have had to do all this figuring and we wouldn't even have had to ask anybody. Everywhere we went around the village the young blades were talking about the dance and slapping each other on the back and laughing. Fred said we would just go to the grove, we would get home late, that was all, and we would be honest about where we had been. We would get a licking, he said, but he had had lots of lickings and he would rather be at the dance and get one than not to be at the dance. I didn't think I would get licked. Only scolded maybe. But Larry Elwyn believed if you spared the rod you spoiled the child. Only he used his razor strop.

But I told Fred we couldn't sneak it. Because, I said, we would have to be dressed up or we would have to keep out of sight in the pine trees and wouldn't see much. That stumped him, so we had to figure out some other way.

"We'll tease," I said. "Look here. We'll ask our mothers. Not our fathers. You tell your mother that my mother is going to let me go. And I'll tell my mother that your mother is going to let you go. And we will say that Lancy Boice's mother is going to let him go and so is Willie Pepper's mother. And we will use just as many mothers as we can till all of them say Yes."

Fred wasn't quite sure about it. "I'll catch hell for lying if they find it out," he said. "But if we can spring one of the mothers it won't be lying, will it?"

"No, it won't be lying," I said. "Not really. It is like this. First off, we didn't make the rules for this kind of thing, did we? No. They made them. Our mothers. What kind of rules are they if one mother can say No and another mother can say Yes?"

Fred squinted one eye and looked off at the Ohio Mountain.

"It's like this," he said. "It can't be much of a rule if one mother can say Yes just because another mother says Yes. Or if one mother can say No just because another mother says No. Can it?"

"Anyway, it wouldn't be lying," I said. "Because lookit. Let's say my mother says No even if your mother has said Yes. But after awhile, when she hears that all mothers have said Yes, she says Yes. So then when you boys tell your mothers that my mother has said Yes you would be telling the truth. Because in the end she has. And when I tell my mother that your mothers have said Yes I would be telling the truth because they would have said Yes, too. So you see?"

"It is clear as the water in the Sawkill," said Fred. "That's something my father always says. As clear as the water in the Sawkill. And that's pretty clear, you know."

My mother turned out to be easy. All she said was Yes, if I would take Clifford along and would promise to come home early. I ran out and found Fred and told him.

"We would not have had to plan so hard," said Fred, "if we had only had brains enough to think about Clifford. Seems as if it is all right to go anywhere in this world or do anything if you will just take Clifford along."

Riseley's Grove is a wonderful place. It is all straight pine trees that are awfully high. The lower branches are cut off. All the scrub is kept cleaned out. The upper branches come together to make a green top over the whole grove and in the daytime there are deep shadows inside, but very nice shadows. It is big. It runs all the way from the open field across the road from Eulie Boice's new sawmill where we found the nest of baby bunnies one day to the Big Deep. And on one side is the Sawkill and on the other Tannery Creek. Years and years of pine needles are on the ground, softer than a carpet.

We do not stop there when we go to the Big Deep to swim but we always stop on our way back. Sometimes we play Indians.

Or we climb one of the trees to get some of the gum that runs out of a broken limb. Then we take flat stones and make a stove with a slant top. The pitch melts and runs down the slant and we have black chewing gum.

There is a covered dance floor in the center of the grove. And near it are some counters for selling watermelon and ice cream and candy and ginger ale. The frame of where they dance is made of skinned pine logs. So many feet and pine needles have scrubbed over the dance floor that it is slippery as black rubber ice. There is a raised platform for the fiddle players. The sides have long boards to sit on. And there are three or four small shelves built in the side about four feet off the slippery floor. I don't know what they are for but they can hold five or six boys, if they crowd back and draw their feet in.

Johnny Saxe and Ben Johnson had changed the dance floor and the counters where they sell things and part of the grove into a fairyland. Gasoline torches blazed above the stands where things were sold. These torches and the grove and all made it seem like a different time in history, like pictures of Ye Olde England. But you could forget the torches if you tried and see only the Japanese lanterns with candles in them. They hung over the dance floor and about thirty feet out into the pine trees all around.

Fathers and mothers were not there. Just younger folks like Johnny Saxe and Ben Johnson and Ed Harder and Jim Plass and Sherm Elwyn and Harry Short and Addie Johnson, Salo Shultis, Linnie Jewel, Minnie Whispel, Clara Shultis, Addie Winnie, Blossom Teller, and a lot of others. And all the boarders, young and old. The girls from the city wore nice dresses and fancy things and acted just a little too flip because they were away from home. The home girls had been brought by some young man, but you could come along and team up afterwards, and some of the New York girls did. Mrs. Dan Sully and three actresses did come and seemed to have a time, learning how to do the square dance.

The dancing was free but the sale counters did a rushing business. The fiddles played lively tunes and the men sawing them called out what the dancers should do, the lights flickered, the men jigged and clogged through the dances, and there was lots of screaming and laughing.

It was all wonderful. I never saw anything like it. How I wished that night I was grown-up, too, and knew how to square dance. I don't know how long it lasted because we couldn't stay to the end. We waited till the next square dance finished and the dancers sat down to rest or walked out to the sale counters, and the dance floor was clear. I was nearest the edge of our perch with my legs hanging off and I went off first. I wanted to do it free and easylike, because some started to look at us when we started to go. I gave a little jump to the floor by pushing down with my hands against the shelf and swinging my backside and feet ahead. I expected my feet to strike the floor and stay there. They struck the floor, all right, but it was so slippery that my feet flew right up in front of my face and I lit on the seat of my pants and skidded along into the feet of a city girl and she came down on top of me. Everybody saw it and started to laugh at me. The boarder with the city girl lifted her up and she was mad and he bawled me out. I scrambled up and tried to get out of their sight fast but I slipped and skidded all around and nearly went down again. My idea had been to do this little jump from our shelf graceful and easy, like I was pretty smooth and these dances were old stuff with me. But that's what happened and I wanted to die.

As we went out of the grove the boys laughed about me, but when I didn't come back at them to make it any fun for them they started to talk about the dance. After a little while my heart stopped pounding and then the heartache would drift away and come back again. I felt better when it drifted away but then I would see myself making such a fool of myself and the heartache would drift back. I would have cried if I had not been so mad and the boys had not been there. But after a while I did get over wanting to die on the spot.

The heartache kept going and coming quite a ways into the night, but not so much the next morning, and when I saw Fred he had help for my ache.

"Let's go down to the grove," he said.

"What for?" I asked. I wasn't very strong for the grove that morning.

"I got a hunch," he said. "If it is good I'll tell you and you'll be in on it. Maybe then you can forget last night."

We went down the dusty road past Fred's father's barber shop and the Whispels' and Herrick's tintype shop. Going to the grove brought my heartache back again.

"If a boy could dance," I said, "that would have been the thing to do last night when I skidded. I don't mean square dance. I mean dance alone like on the stage. If I could have got up and gone into a nifty tap dance, that would have made it so I wouldn't be ashamed of myself."

"Yeah," said Fred. "That would have been the ticket, all right." I could see that he didn't care one way or the other except to help me forget it and that made me feel better.

When we got to the grove Fred made right for the counters where they sold things. He started walking around slow, looking at every inch of the ground. And every little while he dug easy at the pine needles with his toe.

Pretty soon he shouted, "Boy, boy, I knew it. Lookit." He pointed to the ground.

There was a dime gleaming there.

"Quite a lot of coin handled here last night," Fred said, "and some of it could have slipped and been lost in the dark. Besides, the young blades wouldn't have looked for it very hard so as not to look cheap to their girls. A real sport wouldn't act like a nickel or a dime amounted to anything in his life, you see."

When he kept on looking and I hadn't moved yet he said, "Look dummy. We found this gold mine together and half of it is yours. Start looking."

We looked and looked till noon. Then we had 4 dimes and 2 nickels to divide. And Fred said he guessed that was just about it.

I had two dimes and a nickel and that changed the world for me. I told Fred so.

"I guess now you won't care if you had slid around that dance floor and knocked the Queen of England on her ass," he said.

I wouldn't, either. Not with two dimes and a nickel in my pocket.

✻ The Wife-Beater

. . . and the elm tree that grew out of a grave

Fred Elwyn is President and Brook Romer is Honorary Backslider. They are the two biggest officers in the Woodstock Temperance Club, and so they were already there. This is a secret club and so nobody must know when we meet or where. We picked out a pretty good place. It is in the gravel pit up on the rise on the back side of the cemetery. It is too far away from the road in front of the cemetery for anybody to see us. In the bottom of this pit the big boulders make places for us to sit. The two biggest officers have a right to the biggest boulders and that's where they sit when we have a meeting.

In front of the President's boulder is a flat tombstone that is not marble like others are but is a kind of stone, and maybe Ulster County bluestone. It is all beat up with weather and it has rough green spots on it. Some writing has been on it sometime but you can't make much out of it. Before we turned it over to put in front of the President's boulder for him to strike on for order, Brook Romer stood in front of it and made out "In memory of" but the name on the next line was smoothed out by wear and tear, and about all else that showed was "Died 1801." Brook thought a minute and said, "Whoever you were, nobody cares now. Who is anybody?"

We do not come to the meeting together. Each one sneaks to it by himself. I went up to Cal Short's farm and then cut across and back. Willie Pepper showed up next, and he climbed over the back fence of their home and came up that way through a tall cornfield. Bill Lake, from New York City, who is a grandson of Ed Snyder and lives at Snyders' in summer, is what Brook calls an Associate Member. He went down past the windmill and cut around that way. Delancy Boice crawled through a field of rye and popped up. Secret ways like that brought Ira Elwyn, Roy Harder, and my brother, Clifford.

At first we did not know where to meet because it was hard to find a place that measured up. This was because Brook Romer told us that all secret clubs like the Masons, Odd Fellows, Red Men, Knights of Pythias and such, had to have things about them that are mysterious and spooky and that only the members know about, and that's what makes men want to join them. Then one day we were sliding down the bank of this gravel pit and a lot of gravel let loose and slid down and there, all of a sudden, halfway up in the side of the bank where the gravel let loose, was a skull and some bones. We got Brook Romer and took him to see, and he said there wasn't any grave or slab of marble right there on top of the bank and no sign of a rotted coffin, so he would guess that this was the skull and some of the bones of an old Indian. That could be, he said, because Woodstock went back to 1770, before the Revolutionary War, when there were lots of Indians and, of course, they must have buried them somewhere. He said just to be on the safe side we must go down to the village, maybe to the men in Abe Rose's store, and tell them about the skull and bones. Maybe they would want to do something about them. It is not a good idea to fool around with human bones that somebody may want, he said. Or if they're historic.

We did that and Brook waited. But all the men said was, "Well, well. You don't say so." And so when we came back and told Brook that, he said, "Then that makes it perfect. We will use the skull and bones in our club and this gravel pit will be our secret meeting place."

He said that the Honorary Backslider, which was him, had the right to make the rules of the club. So, he said, we will hide the skull and bones and we will have them out for every meeting. Whoever had this skull and bones in the first place we would call our patron saint and he would be our visitor from the Great Unknown and his name would be Sakaham. We asked him why it would be Sakaham and he said he would tell us if he knew, but it was a good name wasn't it? And everybody would have to kneel to Sakaham and we had better be pretty careful that everything we did was right or the voice of Sakaham would be heard.

"That's stretching it," said Fred Elwyn. "A skull can't speak."

"Then a lot of people must be crazy," said Brook. "Because they swear it has happened. Or about the same thing anyway."

So that was how it happened that the gravel pit was the secret meeting place of the secret Woodstock Temperance Club.

All of us had sneaked in by now and so Fred and Brook sat on the biggest boulders and we sat on the others. Fred had a spindle that Lancy Boice got from his father's mill, where they turned spirals and chair legs and such, that we kept hidden and that Brook said was the club gavel. Fred rapped it on the tombstone and said to stop talking and get down to business.

We decided that Willie Pepper would fix the loose board in

the top of the raft at the Big Deep and that Delancy Boice would build another crook in the entrance to the den in the corner of the school lot. You had to get down on your hands and knees and crawl in around two corners in the den entrance, but we voted that three would be better.

That was all the business, the President said, except for the Temperance lecture by the Honorary Backslider.

"Mister President," said Willie Pepper. That was how Brook Romer, our Honorary Backslider, had told us we must say when we "addressed the chair." "Mister President," said Willie, "why is it that we all get to do work and you never do any? Like fixing the raft and luggin' stone for the den."

"Well, you dumb cluck," said Fred Elwyn. "I am President, that's why. Ain't that right, Brook?"

"Address me as Honorary Backslider," said Brook Romer. "Yes, that's right. It's that way in all clubs. The President must be dignified, and work interferes with his dignity."

So Willie Pepper shut up.

"We will now hear a temperance lecture from our Honorary Backslider," said the President.

Brook Romer started out by saying that people think that there isn't any temperance except with whiskey. But that's all wrong, he said. Take the case of John Van De Bogert, who never drank a drop and yet was one of the finest examples of intemperance ever produced by the human animal, which is the meanest animal on earth when he is mean. This John's intemperance was anger and jealousy. You can be intemperate with anything, not just whiskey, and it's no trick at all, the Honorary Backslider said.

Well, this was pretty dry stuff but we paid attention because you could always trust Brook Romer to come up with an astonisher and we were waiting for that. And here it was.

"You may be sitting right now alongside the rotten coffin and the skeleton of John Van De Bogert," Brook said. "That is, except for maybe a foot or two of dirt and gravel you can't see through. For he died a long time ago and he may have been buried right in that bank."

I kinda shifted and looked around at the gravel bank where we uncovered the skull and bones we called Sakaham; and then I looked at Sakaham on a boulder right in the middle of us. I noticed the others did, too.

"But nobody gives a sniff where old John is buried," said Brook, "if what they tell is true and they say it is. Because he was so intemperate that everybody hated him."

"He was an older man and big and strong. But the trouble was that he married a girl who was maybe seventeen going on eighteen. Now that is a bad thing for an older man to do but I won't go into it now because that is another lecture on temperance for later. Quite a lot later for you boys, I would think.

"And so tragedy happened, and a murder, and sorrow and hate, and that always happens from not being temperate, except that there isn't always a murder.

"This older John Van De Bogert probably had a sneaking hunch that a seventeen-year-old wife would a lot rather be in love with a young man her own age. He would have been pretty dumb if he didn't. And so it was only a step for him to believe that she was. He let his jealousy run away with him. And this made him angry and he let that run away with him, too.

"One night he came home from work and his wife was gone. His house was dark. There wasn't any supper ready. Old John was sure she was off somewhere spooning and had forgotten the time, as is likely to happen in spooning, they tell me. So instead of believing the best, his jealousy and his anger made him believe the worst and his intemperance stepped in to take over. He went out and cut himself a stick. Then he waited until his wife came home and he beat her almost dead. He did this in spite of the fact that she was almost ready to have a baby.

"Well, of course, the neighbors came running. They carried the young wife into the house and laid her on a bed. She said she had been called out to help a sick neighbor, but she would not blame old John. But that night the baby was born and it and the young wife both died. All she asked before she died was that her baby and the stick that had killed her be placed in her coffin and buried with her.

"So that was done and then a great mystery arose. That stick must have been slippery elm and it slipped right up out of that coffin and a big elm tree grew right on that grave to remind folks forever about old John's intemperance with jealousy and anger. So you see it isn't only whiskey you have to be temperate about. It's almost everything."

Our Honorary Backslider bowed to President Fred and to Sakaham and sat down on his boulder.

We all were turning the story over in our minds and looking at Brook for a time with nobody saying anything, and then Lancy Boice spoke up.

"Mr. President," he said, "that was a hell of a tall story."

"Mr. President," said our Honorary Backslider, "does our respected member refer to the height of the elm tree? Or does he doubt the veracity of my temperance lecture?"

"I don't doubt the veracity," said Lancy, "whatever that means. I just don't believe that tree business."

"Mr. President," said Brook. "I move we adjourn and that the club follow me."

"We are adjourned," said Fred hitting the tombstone with the spindle. He probably didn't believe it, either. I know I didn't.

Brook started to scramble up the gravel bank and we followed him and Fred did, too, as soon as he had hid Sakaham and the spindle. We weaved down through the gravestones to the old part of the cemetery where some of the graves go back to maybe a hundred years, and there it was. A big elm tree grew right up out of what must have been a grave because it was so big that it had spread the big tombstone and the footstone apart.

We went around to the front of the tombstone and Brook read it: "In memory of Catherine, wife of John Van De Bogert (also her infant child) who died August 2nd, 1821, aged 18 years, 2 months and 13 days."

"Well, that's a tree, all right," said Lancy. "But how do we know you didn't make up all that stuff? That tree could have been planted."

"Come with me," said Brook.

We followed him down to the Woodstock Hotel and he started right into the barroom. We hung back right there but he said, "Come on. I'll get past the bar this time without a drink." So we followed in and took off our caps before we noticed that the men in there had their hats on. I didn't like the smell; it was like you get when you find a whiskey bottle in the grass and sniff it. The men all looked at us in surprise but Brook said, "Where is Jake Wurts?" The bartender back of the bar in a white apron nodded toward the hotel office and parlors, and we went on through.

Jake Wurts was behind the hotel desk and Brook asked him if he could take us into the parlor to show us something in a magazine. "It will be just a minute," Brook said, and Jake Wurts said, "Help yourself."

The magazine Brook went for was one of a set called *Picturesque Ulster,* which is the name of our county. The one Brook picked up was about the Town of Woodstock, Woodstock Village, Bearsville, Shady, Lake Hill, Yankeetown, Little Shandaken, Wittenberg, Zena. It was full of pictures of the green, our store, the Dutch Reformed church, Aaron Riseley's, the Tannery dam, grist mill and a lot of others.

And there it was all printed out just about like Brook had told it. And it said "The story above is vouched for by an elderly lady

now living in the village who had it from her grandmother."
And there was a picture of the grave and tree we had just seen.

It was a spooky thing all right. The temperance lectures at our
meetings by our Honorary Backslider go into a lot of stories you
have to take with a grain of salt, like the one that he ran with
Jesse James once and he knew for a fact that the only times Jesse
robbed trains was when he didn't know what he was doing because he was drunk. But this one about the elm tree he wasn't
stretching.

✻ The First Bicycle

. . . and how the bicycle circus developed

Will Elwyn had a folder and he was showing it to my
father.

"It's funny nobody ever thought of it before," he said. "The
world has been waiting a long time for this safety bicycle. Funny
it has taken so long. We've had the axle ever since Old Testament
days."

"Come to think of it," said my father, "the chap who invented
the axle must have been quite a man. Never thought about it
before."

"I never thought about that axle business, either," said Will.
"But with this new bicycle I see something else, too. Today you
can walk five miles but you won't be able to do much else all
day. You can drive or ride horseback but very few have the price
of a horse, let alone a rig. Of course, you can get that contraption
where you ride up on the big wheel in front with the little wheel
behind but it's a toy as far as travel goes."

"Oh, they're no good," said my father. "I tried to ride one once. You can't ride it on a road; you need a smooth floor. Away up in the air, too, and a long ways to fall."

"The chain and the sprocket wheel make all the difference," said Will. "Both wheels can be the same size, and low enough to put your feet on the ground. The wheels go round about four times while your pedals go round once. That's speed. Faster than a horse. No harnessing. No feed. Always ready. From one to ten miles anytime, quick. And cheap—you couldn't buy a cheap harness for the same price. And you can keep it on the porch or in the woodshed. Even in the house."

"You sound like a salesman for them," said my father.

"Well," said Will. He smiled a little and blushed a little and the dimple came out in his cheeks. "I can get the agency for the Columbia. I guess I better take it, don't you?"

"You're leading up to something," said my father. "What have you got on your mind?"

"Well," said Will. He smiled again with his white teeth and his dimples, and then he said, "You furnish the capital and we will go into the bicycle business as a side line. Not repair or anything like that. Just selling new ones and maybe trading a little. I miss my guess if folks don't go crazy about this safety bicycle. About two hundred dollars and we could stock three of them for men. No ladies' model now, but that will come later. Girls, anyway, as soon as it's the fashion. I'll bet Mrs. Dan Sully would buy one now. No crossbar, you see, so their skirts will stay down, and there's a guard over the chain so their skirts don't catch. They get on different, too. A man gets on a bicycle just like he gets on a horse. But a lady stands inside the bicycle and puts her foot on a pedal and lifts herself up on the seat. It's all worked out, you see, to keep their skirts down—to their shoe tops, anyway."

"Could work out to be interesting, but perfectly modest and ladylike, if the fashion catches on," said my father.

"Well, if we stock them, and what they call accessories, and they didn't sell, we could each buy one and use them ourselves. We would learn to ride and demonstrations would help."

My father didn't say anything to that for a minute while Will watched him. Then he said, "Do you think I could learn to ride one? A man almost forty?"

"Age don't have anything to do with it," said Will. "As long as a man can move his limbs he can learn. You just relax and let nature take its course. It's like swimming. You won't sink if you lay out straight and don't sink yourself. Just keep going and don't fight the front wheel."

Then they looked at the catalogue together, and discussed this and that—pants guards, bicycle caps, and special colored coats for bicycling. The pants guards were circular bands of light, springy steel. You folded the bottom of your pants legs around your ankles, and then snapped these guards around them, and they wouldn't tangle with the bicycle chain. The bicycle cap was colored—most any color or combination of colors. It fitted snug over your head, and it stuck out in front to keep the sun out of your eyes. The coat was lightweight and striped.

My father said that these things might grow into profitable store stocks, and Will said, "Certainly."

"Not only the bicycles but the accessories," said my father, "such as the caps and coats, and maybe complete outfits. And the repair parts, and sure as preaching there will be inventions to improve on this or that. But if you're going to sell it you ought to be able to demonstrate it."

"Abe," said Will, "you really catch on quick. You're a born merchant."

"Think so?" said my father. He had a faraway look in his eyes, and I knew right then he was planning something.

I waited until I was sure my father and Will were going to order these bicycles, and then I ran down to the house and found my mother and Linnie. They had their heads tied up and an upstairs room all cleaned out.

"Papa is going to demonstrate bicycles," I announced.

"He's going to what?" exclaimed my mother dropping her broom. She thought a minute. "Oh, pshaw," she said. "You must have misunderstood. Abe ride a bicycle? How would he learn? He'd break his neck. A man of his age, nearly forty? You must be just imagining things again, Will."

"I wouldn't be too sure," said Linnie.

"Now you run along," said my mother, "we're house cleaning."

I know I don't understand what I hear sometimes, so I figured my mother must be right. My father didn't say anything about it at dinnertime, and I wasn't fool enough to ask what he and Will Elwyn were up to. By nighttime I had forgotten all about it.

But one evening when Johnny Saxe drove the mule stage around Snyder's corner and pulled up in front of the store, it had three crates strapped on behind, and anybody could see in a minute that bicycles were inside them.

Johnny carried the mail sacks in and then my father and Will Elwyn came running out. They got the crates off the mule stage right away, and Will got a nail puller and started taking them apart.

"That red one with the upturned handle bars is mine," my father told the men who had gathered around.

"How long do you think it will take you to learn to ride?" asked Larry Elwyn.

"Will Elwyn is going to demonstrate first," my father told Larry.

Will's bicycle was black. He took it out in front of the store and headed it to go past Mower's ice cream parlor, alongside the store toward the Dutch Reformed Church and the village green.

"I know how this thing is done," he said, "but it may take some practice." He waved the crowd out of the way. "Can't mount the right way," he said, "but I'll just run alongside and jump on.

He landed on the seat all right, and got his feet on the pedals after feeling around for them quite a spell, and with the bicycle weaving this way and that. He was beginning to pedal, but he was covering the whole road from side to side.

"That's the greatest demonstration of man over natural forces I've ever seen," said my father. He didn't laugh when he said it, either. "Will was never on a bicycle before," he said.

But just then Will's front wheel hit the curb that runs all around the village green, and he went right over the handle bars, kerplunk, and landed on his back on the grass.

When they saw he wasn't hurt, everybody laughed.

By this time the word had gone around the Village and a bigger crowd had gathered. My mother and Linnie had come running up from the house, and so had Mrs. Lown from her house across the street, and Mehalie Elwyn, Fred's mother, and a lot of others.

Will came pushing the bicycle back, and then he said, "Now, Abe, you try it."

"Well, I don't know," said my father. "I'm not as young as you are, and I don't know whether I could take a fall like that or not." He saw my mother out of the corner of his eye, and he said: "I wouldn't want to break a limb or maybe my neck, you know."

Maybe he thought my mother would say something. But she just looked worried and didn't say a word.

"No time like the present, Abe," laughed Jake Wurts.

Others joined in, urging him to go ahead, and I could see that they kinda hoped he would take a tumble. It's funny how people are that way.

I could also see that this was all that my father was waiting for. He wanted to be pushed into it.

"Well," he said at last, "we're in the bicycle business now, and we always rise or fall with our merchandise. But if I am going to do it, I'll do it right. Wait a minute."

He went into the store, and when he came out again, he had the clips on his pants. He had also put on a bicycle cap of blue and orange and a bicycle coat with stripes of blue and white in it.

The crowd shouted when they saw him, and laughed. "If he kills himself, he's going to die right," Larry Elwyn shouted.

My father took the red wheel with the upturned handle bars and walked out in front of the store with it. He didn't head it past Mower's alongside the village green, but acted as if he was going to ride right out the main street toward Snyder's store.

He stood alongside the bicycle, took hold of the upturned handle bars, lifted the rear wheel and put the left pedal so that it was up on an angle toward the front wheel, and placed his left foot on this pedal.

He turned to the crowd. "Well, boys," he said, "here goes."

He stepped on the pedal and lifted his other leg over the bicycle, and rode off in a beeline as easy as pie.

The crowd went quiet as if a big blanket had dropped over it from the sky.

"Well, I'll be damned," said Ed Harder.

I wondered for a minute if they were mad about it. Crowds are funny that way. By this time my father had circled the village green, but he kept right on going and when he passed the crowd he took one hand off the handle bars, put it in his coat pocket, and started to whistle.

The crowd laughed.

When he came around again, he got up a little speed, and when he passed the crowd he put both feet up on the little brackets on the long prongs that held the front wheel, and coasted around the turn.

Mrs. Lown clapped her hands and the crowd laughed some more.

The third time around, he headed right for the crowd and some of them started running out of the way. But he slowed the bicycle down before he struck anybody, and he seemed to bring it to a dead stop and swing his right leg back over and get both feet on the ground at the same time.

Quite a little cheer went up.

When they quieted down, my father said, "Well, folks, see how easy and pleasant it is? If I can do it, anybody can do it. Any age, too. And girls and women. Just as easy as taking candy from a baby. Got to sort the mail now. It will be ready in about ten minutes." And he went in the store.

"Just a matter of confidence and poise," said Dominie Park. "Another example of how a man is a different kind of a critter. I guess man can find a way to do anything he thinks he can. That's why he isn't just another animal. I never thought I would preach about a bicycle but I guess that's my next sermon."

The next morning at breakfast my father asked my mother and Linnie what they thought of his bicycle demonstration.

"I was afraid you would break your neck," said my mother. "But I might have known you had something up your sleeve."

"I often wonder what you do all day long in Kingston every week," said Linnie. "Now I know what. The last few times, anyway."

My father laughed. "You can be sure I always tend to business," he said. "You're right, Linnie. I learned to ride. Folks won't buy bicycles if they think they have to cripple themselves. It has to look easy and pleasant and so I figured that I would prove it."

Well, this was how the bicycle came to Woodstock. This was along in May after the spring rains stopped and the roads dried up. My father and Will Elwyn liked their bicycles so much they wouldn't sell them but they did let folks learn on them and it wasn't long before they were ordering ones for Ed Harder and Sherm Elwyn and Jake Wurts and a half dozen of the young blades. Dickey Short asked my father if his job as youngest clerk was safe for a time, and my father said he guessed it was, short of an act of God; and Dickey had him get him a bicycle and take a couple of dollars out of his pay every week.

There was just one thing wrong. The road was level and dust not very deep around the village green and for a ways out toward the cemetery and Bearsville, and bicycles went fine there; but they weren't so good out on the country roads till later in the summer, after the men who worked out their taxes on the roads had a chance to get them in shape. Besides, the young blades wanted to go in for speed.

So one night in front of the store, Sherm Elwyn got the young blades together and said he had an idea. It was just about a mile to Bearsville, he said, and he had been looking over the lay of the land. It was level all the way to Bearsville and plenty of room beyond the ditch to build a track just for bikes. They had got to calling them bikes because bicycles was too long.

So that's what they did, and by the middle of June all the young blades with bikes were trying to see who could make it to Bearsville and back the quickest.

And then, lo and behold, when the boarders started coming in July some of them brought bicycles along. It seemed that Woodstock wasn't the only place with the bicycle craze. It wasn't long until all that had bikes were riding around the village green after supper and doing stunts or just acting social. They called it the bicycle circus.

"Ed Harder is best for stunts," said Fred Elwyn one night. "Look at him."

Ed was showing how he could stand still on his bike. He had been around the green three times without ever getting off or touching his feet to the ground even though he stopped dead still whenever he wanted to.

"That was nothing to what *I* saw him do," I said. "I saw him come down the hill from Rock City yesterday. He had his feet up on the handle bars and his arms folded. He was smoking a cigar and just letting the bike run lickety-split. Look. He's riding without hands."

A couple of riders were young women from New York City. One had a skirt that came down only to awfully high laced shoes. The other one wore a kind of pants but awfully baggy. These pants were fastened in below her knees. She had heavy black stockings and tennis shoes. These two city girls wore white shirtwaists with bones in high collars and big hats that all the city women seem to wear when they are outdoors in the sun. They look mighty pretty.

More men watched the bicycle circus when these two city girls started in to ride. I heard old Sylvester Bower say the one with the baggy pants was a bloomer girl. Old Sylvester is about eighty or one hundred and is always crabby. "Probably sensible," he said, "but not very ladylike. If girls are smart they'll keep their limbs covered up."

"What's he mean?" Fred whispered to me.

"Shut up and listen," I said.

Just then Ed Harder was coming around in front of the store and old Sylvester called to him to stop. Old Sylvester waved his hand at the two girls. "Bicycles are all right," he said to Ed. "But do you think many girls are going to wear stuff like that?"

"If it gets to be the fashion they will," said Ed. "Any girl who has nice ankles will help along the fashion. How old *are* you Sylvester?"

"I'm eighty-five, God damn it."

"I thought so," said Ed and started off again.

"See?" I said to Fred. "If you want to know what people mean, keep your mouth shut and listen."

"I don't know anything more than I did before," said Fred. "And neither do you."

The riders rode around, two or three together, and joked and laughed, just as if they were walking along and not having to manage bikes while talking.

Ed Harder had been riding with two city girls but the next time around he saw Fred and me standing in front of the store, and got off. He made it look so easy and simple. He just let his bicycle slow down and then when the left pedal was almost down, he just used it as a step and swung off.

"Did you kids see the small bike Will Elwyn got in today?" he asked. "Why don't you ask Will to let you try it out? It would be good advertising. I heard him say the other day that the big sale is going to be to boys and girls. But it won't be unless he gets them started. Go on. Ask him. And I'll teach you to ride."

When Will Elwyn came around the green again we stopped him and told him what Ed had said. "It's a good idea," he said. "Sure."

The little bike was for a girl and Fred didn't know if that was good for awhile. "We don't want to be sissies," he said. But he was so anxious to learn that he gave in. "You go first," he said to me. I knew that it wasn't that he was afraid to try but that he was afraid the people in the crowd would laugh at him if he wasn't perfect right off.

Let them laugh, I thought, and went on first.

Ed was a perfect teacher. He explained that you turned the front wheel the way the bike is falling, and at first he had one hand on the handle bar and one hand on the seat with me on the bike and going slow while he ran alongside. When the bike was going to tip I always wanted to turn the front wheel the other way. But he was stronger than I was and kept me going. Pretty soon I stopped trying to work against him and pretty soon after that I could ride with Ed just running alongside.

Fred had been running along with us and watching and he caught on quick. When his turn came he seemed to know to do the right thing with the front wheel. Fred is always best.

It wasn't ten minutes before he was riding around the green alone. "Hey," he hollered to Ed when he came around about the fifth time, "when I come around again I am going to get off. Get ready, will you?"

Ed knew what he meant. This getting off business is the hardest thing to learn. Everybody needs help to learn it. So Ed got ready when Fred came around.

Fred was coming pretty fast, I thought. "Don't try it," I hollered. But there's no use trying to tell Fred what to do.

I saw a kind of serious look come over Ed's face. "Slow down," he hollered but Fred's face was set and he came right on. He made the mistake of swinging his right leg up over the bike while his left foot on the pedal was coming up and he was too far away from Ed, too. He rose right up in the air with his rump highest, just as if somebody had lifted him a good one in the seat of his pants. And he made the mistake of letting go of the handle bars at the same time. He came flying through the air against Ed's chest and both of them went down in the dust in a scramble. The bike went free. But it made a half circle clear across the road and it was still standing up when somebody caught it over there.

Ed and Fred got up and Ed started dusting himself off. "By God, boy," he said, "this ain't any trapeze, you know."

"By God," said Fred full of anger, "let me try that damn thing again."

And he did. Four times he tried it before he managed to get off and keep hold of the bike. Of course, nothing more happened to Ed because he was ready for him each time. But Fred's nose was scratched and the knees of both his stockings were out and dust and sweat had smeared him from head to foot.

"That's worse than riding a calf," Fred said. "But I'll make that damn bike talk before I'm through with it."

And he did. In a week he could do anything with it. Will Elwyn was smart enough to let Fred use it to teach me and the Boice boys and Willie Pepper and it wasn't long before our fathers gave in and we all had bikes.

✤ The "Fresh Air Boys"

. . . and the great social experiment

I saw this elegant lady get off the mule stage in front of the store one Friday afternoon in March. She went inside the store, and after she went in I saw Johnny Saxe nod his head after her and pull a long wink at Ed Harder who was standing in the doorway because there were no customers just then. Ed stepped aside and bowed big when she passed him, and after Johnny Saxe pulled that long wink I saw Ed make his eyes big and pull his jaw down at Johnny.

I thought that something was up and I didn't wonder, because this woman was so different. She was old, about thirty-five or forty, and in some ways she looked it and in some other ways she didn't. She was as tall as any man and slim, except in two places. She had on a brown suit, like Nestlé's sweet chocolate, that sort of sparkled where the sun hit it, that was longer in the tail than the front and looked like it was a little too small for her. Her chest was on one side of her waist and her rump on the other. She had a fur wrapped around her neck and she had a coat made of fur over her arm, and she had a little fur hat instead of a big floppy one with flowers.

My father came out of the store with her and picked up her two grips and they walked over to the Woodstock Hotel. I watched and pretty soon they came out of the hotel and walked down to Dominie Park's parsonage. I guessed she was some friend of the Parks' and my father was showing her where they lived, and didn't think about it any more. So as far as right then, my curiosity went down.

184

But the next afternoon my curiosity came up again. After dinner my mother appeared all dressed up with a hat and all, even better than Sunday. She was certainly going somewhere and I asked her where.

"To the church," she said, "for a meeting of the church ladies."

"What for?" I asked. "The Ladies' Aid?"

"If you must know," she said, "a lady from New York is going to tell us about a social experiment and we may decide to join in."

"A lady from New York," I said and I thought a little. "Is that the woman who got off the mule stage yesterday afternoon?"

Linnie Jewel joined in. "It is," she said. "The story is around that she is a fashion plate, and I guess that's mostly the reason all the women in town are turning out. To see her fashions."

My mother seemed a little put out, and so I guess that maybe Linnie had it about right, but my mother did not want to admit it. "No," she said. "This is a good work, what they call social uplift. She may be a society woman. She may be rich and she may be fashionable, but the Dominie says she has gone out of her way to do good work."

"Out of her way is right," said Linnie. "Until she gets tired of it and finds something else. I have read about her kind in books."

"You're not very charitable," said my mother.

"All right," said Linnie. "You win. But be careful what you get into."

"Can I go along to the meeting?" I asked. "I have never seen social uplift. This is Saturday. No school, remember?"

"Well," my mother said. "I hadn't thought of it. Will you be quiet?"

"I always am," I said.

"You can't go like that."

"I'll put on my Sunday suit."

"All right," she said. "But hurry."

"I'll help you button your shoes," said Linnie.

There must have been twenty-five women in the Dutch Reformed Church, and rigs were tied all around the green. Dominie
Park and the woman from New York sat in front of the pulpit.
They looked at the women coming in. The woman from New York
said something to the Dominie kinda perky every second or so,
and Dominie Park smiled or raised his eyebrows at her and nodded
when she spoke to him.

She had on a different outfit altogether from when she got off
the mule stage. It was a green velvet dress and a big hat. The inside of the church is always too hot or too cold in winter and sort
of a musty smell from being closed up. This time it was a little
cold. So I saw her pick up a lot of fur from a chair. It was gray
and soft and turned out to be a big wrap when she put it around
her shoulders, and it came halfway down to her hips.

I looked around and could see all the women watching her with
nothing else on their minds.

In the face you couldn't say that she was pretty. Kind of too thin
and long and what Ed Harder called horsy.

When it looked like nobody else was coming in, Dominie Park
took out his watch and opened it and snapped it shut with a
flourish and then put it back in his vest pocket and got up.

"If I may have your attention now," he said. This was because
he wanted them to stop looking at the woman, I think. "I had the
honor and pleasure of meeting our distinguished guest several
times when I was in New Jersey," he said, "and, of course, I knew
her by reputation anyway." He stopped a minute like he was
thinking and then he hustled up to say that what he meant by that
was that she was wealthy and had many interests and that she could
have spent the rest of her life amusing herself if she had wanted
to. "But for the past two years she has devoted her life to the less
fortunate," he said, "and that is what she wants to tell you about.
May I introduce to you Miss Arabella Morgan Depew." He

turned to her and bowed and waited until she had got up and said "Thank you," and then he sat down. It was all very elegant.

She certainly could speak and was so comical with it all that pretty soon everybody was laughing, but after you boiled it all down what it was was this. She was the head of what she called a great social experiment with the underprivileged in New York City. These underprivileged turned out to be boys from the dirty streets who never saw farms or mountains or even blue sky and didn't know the difference between a cow and a bull, and she was making them into little gentlemen. If she and other good people did not try to do something they would grow up in sin and crime. One of her ways was to hold out a prize to the ones that tried to be little gentlemen. She had forty that had tried. They were eight and ten years old. The prize she had promised them was a week in the country. She was at her wit's end to know where. And then she had remembered Dominie Park. And now would each of the women take one or two of them into their homes for a week? She had a pencil and pad ready and would take down the names. She would pay their fare on the dayboat and U & D to Woodstock and back, and outfit them in their little shoes and clothing like little gentlemen, and Dominie Park would have a little spending money for each of them and he would meet them and take them to the homes when they came in. And now did anybody have any questions?

Not many of the women spoke up but Ceil Lasher and Libby Riseley had the nerve, and they tossed the idea back and forth with her. They were not getting anywhere and then Libby Riseley said something that was probably in the back of all their minds. "Wouldn't it get rid of a lot of fuss and feathers if you sent somebody along with them and they all lived together in a camp? They could see the farms and the mountains and the blue sky and the cows and bulls, just as well," she said, laughing while talking the way Libby does.

"But it is the influence of Christian homes I want them to have," said the lady.

When she said this I heard my mother say to Roy Harder's mother in a low tone. "It would be an awful nuisance," she said, "but the trouble is I feel guilty."

But you could see easy that the thing was going against Miss Arabelle Morgan Depew and the women were growing restless. Mrs. Cole who took boarders and was in the back of the church had already slipped out.

Right then Miss Depew said, "Oh how stupid of me. I have overlooked a very important part of this plan. My trouble is that I pity these little children so much that it runs away with me. What I mean is this. If you women will cooperate with me, I will give two hundred dollars to the Dutch Reformed Church right here in Woodstock. Then you can get a basement furnace or new kitchen, or maybe even pipe in water. I am sorry I did not mention that before."

Well, that put a different light on it. There wasn't much the women wouldn't do for the Dutch Reformed Church. One time I heard Ceil Lasher say that she guessed from all the time and work they put in they would give their souls for it. But she was fooling, of course.

My mother got up and said, "I will take two of them." Ceil Lasher followed suit and so did Libby Riseley and that got it started and it went right through to the end.

One afternoon in July after everybody had pretty much lost track of the whole thing, Dominie Park came to the door. Linnie Jewel answered the door and then came back to the kitchen and said to my mother, "Get ready for a surprise. Your urchins are here."

My mother was puzzled. "My urchins?" she asked.

"Your fresh air kids," said Linnie. "The little gentlemen, remember?"

"Where?"

"Up by the front door. Dominie Park has them."

We rushed up to the front of the house. Out in the road, Grove, our barn man, and Dominie Park had our team and lumber wagon and it was filled with boys, some shoving others, some sitting down in the wagon box and a few jumping over into the road. One was trying to crawl out on the back of Jim, and Carrie, the other horse, was acting up so that Grove had his hands full and Dominie Park had hold of the coattail of the boy trying to haul him back. They all had on coats and short pants and stockings and shoes, but the sight was that all of them had on sailor straw hats with the tail of the hat band hanging down the back of their necks. Boys don't wear hats like that in Woodstock. Anyway, we wear caps.

When Dominie Park had got the boy back from Jim and Grove had slapped him down, Dominie Park slid around to the wagon box and spoke to two boys and handed them a grip and motioned for them to go to us. Then they drove away to parcel out the others. If the two we got were eight and ten, I am forty-two years old. They looked fourteen anyway, and big for that.

My mother asked them their names and they said Mugsey and Skinny. She said No, she meant their real names, and they said Michael O'Leary and Samuel Jaffey. She said she hoped they would like it with us and then she asked Linnie to put them in the spare bedroom. Linnie took them up and they came right back down and stood around and Harry and I and Clifford stood off and watched them.

"Little gentlemen have big lice," said Linnie.

Linnie set up a washtub in the back yard and filled the kettle on the stove. When it was hot, she got two towels and soap and dumped the kettle in the tub and then tempered it from the pump. She took Mugsey first and stripped him down to his waist and scrubbed his hair with soap and water and dried it. He shoved and pulled away at first but Linnie shoved and pulled harder and when

it was done she told him to put his shirt back on and he said two
things.

"Feels good," he said, and "You're quite a chick."

"Shut up," she said, "and get Skinny."

But Skinny wasn't there. They looked around and saw him
peeking from behind the corner of the barn and Mugsey took after
him. But Skinny took off with Mugsey after him and they disap-
peared over toward the Dutch Reformed sheds by Ed Snyder's
windmill.

We didn't see them again till my father brought them in for
supper. He said he had found them behind the candy counter
sampling all the candy.

Two places extra were at the table and my mother said to them,
"Come and sit down."

They did and reached right away for the platter of cold meat
and fried potatoes and helped themselves. Everybody was kind of
astonished and my father spoke up strong. "NO, none of that,
boys," he said, "you wait until after the Blessing, and then the
vittles will be passed to you." Then he asked the Blessing, with
something about the strangers in our midst, but Mugsey and
Skinny kept right on eating and looking at him as if they thought
he was crazy.

They were offered some other things, like green tomato pickles
and bread and sliced cucumbers in vinegar and stewed dried apri-
cots, but they shook their heads. As soon as they had finished their
meat and potatoes they got up and left.

We talked about them, of course. My mother was worried.
Linnie was mad. We boys laughed and made out like them in
snatches and Harry asked Linnie how she liked being a chick. But
my father said we must remember that they are strangers in a
strange land and must be patient and charitable. "Suffer little children to come unto me," he said.

"If these little children come unto you very much you will

suffer," said Linnie. "And if they come unto me more than is necessary they will suffer."

During the evening I saw them down by the edge of Tannery Creek trying to stab pollywogs with a stick. When it was dark they came to the house and started for the spare bedroom but Linnie collared them. "Take that broom and go in the backyard and scrub the mud off your shoes," she said. They just stood and looked at her for a minute and first I thought they were going to act mean. But then Mugsey shrugged and got the broom and said, "Come on, Skinny."

"Got another broom?" said Skinny. Linnie went and got him one and they went out.

I went back to my Oliver Optic but pretty soon there was a lot of yelling and laughing and swearing out in the back yard and we looked out. Each had a broom and they were trying to knock the other on the head or poke him in the stomach with the broom ends.

"Stop!" Linnie shouted. "Stop!" But just then Skinny shouted, "Scram!" and lunged with his broom at her but missed and the broom went right through a windowpane.

"You dirty skunks," shouted Linnie. "Get upstairs. Git!" And they ran in and up the stairs.

Next morning they were not on hand for breakfast and Linnie went upstairs to get them up. When she came down Linnie was madder than ever but she didn't have time to say anything because my father's patience seemed to be under a strain, too, and he told us to sit down and went right into his Blessing.

Then Mugsey and Skinny came down, and just like the night before they grabbed right in and ate like pigs. This time we had a head start and so we finished by the time they did, and my father said like he meant it and no fooling that we would all go up to the living room for family prayers. When we got there he said, "Sit down," but they stood up and watched.

They watched while he read the Bible and then when we got

down on our knees with our backs to them and my father started to pray I heard them snicker and I peeked and saw them sneak out.

My father's patience was really strained when he got up.

Then Linnie said, "Now may I have a word?"

"What is it?" said my father.

She turned to my mother and said, "We have other guests in the spare bedroom."

"What do you mean?" asked my mother.

"Bedbugs," said Linnie.

"Oh my days," said my mother and she sank into a chair.

"And that is not all," said Linnie. "We have the worst pair of sheets you ever saw. Do you know what they did last night? They went to bed with their clothes on, even their muddy shoes."

"What will we do?" asked my mother and she shook her head from side to side like she had given up.

"This can't be possible," said my father.

"I know what I will do," said Linnie. "The sheets and everything else on that bed goes through the suds right now. And I can suggest what you had ought to do. And that's to get out of the social uplift business today. If not, they can sleep in the barn tonight. And let me tell you something else. These fresh air kids are really fresh. This Mugsey called me a chick again up in the bedroom and this Skinny asked me if I wanted to wrestle. He almost got ahold of me before I got out the door."

"Well, that settles it," said my mother.

"Yes. There is a limit to everything," said my father. "Even social experiments. I wonder how the others are making out?"

He didn't have long to wait to find out. When he went up to the store he found Chris Winnie, Will Longyear, K'Neal Hogan, Charley Riseley, Ellie Harder, Levi Harder, Jim Lasher, and Dominie Park in a group with their heads together. They were waiting for him and said they were a committee. Their wives had all had about the same experience.

One thing was certain. The great social experiment had come to an end. One suggested that they call the sheriff and have the whole kit and caboodle locked up for the rest of the week. Another said Abe Rose could hustle down to Kingston and rent a big tent and they could put them all out in a field somewhere with Brook Romer to cook for them. But Dominie Park said either one might get them all into trouble.

"You can't put them in jail without signing a complaint," he said, "and who wants to sign it? A camp has to have equipment which we do not have, and suppose one of them gets killed or hurt or drowned or runs away?" He went on to say that the safest thing to do is to do nothing. He said it's like a man who is drowning. If you just watch him drown and don't try to save him you are in the clear as far as the law is concerned. But if you jump in and try to save him and you happen to hurt him and his relatives blame you you are in trouble with the law.

"Yes," said Will Longyear. "That's the law for you."

"Well, what in hell can we do?" asked Ellie Harder.

"I guess we are in hell all right," said the Dominie. "So being in hell we are justified by Scripture in trying to get out. First, does anybody want to continue the great social experiment?"

"Nobody is clamoring to," said Charley Riseley.

"I will go over to Byd Snyder's," said the Dominie, "and telegraph Miss Depew that the boys are coming back to New York today and to have somebody meet the dayboat. My idea is that she doesn't know much about these boys anyway and couldn't stand one of them in her own home for a minute. Then if Abe will lend us his team and lumber wagon, and send Grove along to drive, we will gather them up and take them to the train at West Hurley. We will wire the sheriff at Kingston to see that they get on the dayboat."

So that's what they did.

The funny part about it was that there was no trouble with the boys at all. They seemed tickled to death to get going back to New York.

My mother said she guessed that only Miss Arabella Depew was interested in uplifting the underprivileged. Not the boys.

"And then only if somebody else does the lifting," said Linnie.

✻ The Romance of Hannah Van Etten

. . . or, the spinster with two great loves

I perked up my ears because the men around the stove started to talk about Sudsley Wooster and Hannah Van Etten and what could come of it.

I had seen Sudsley Wooster lots of time around the Village that summer. He kind of stood out among the summer boarders because he was staying at the Woodstock Hotel at a higher cost and not at Aaron Riseley's boarding house for five dollars a week for room and board, and they said he wasn't going to be there for just a week or two but was going to stay in Woodstock right along. He had joined the Dutch Reformed Church and everything. At first folks called him Mister Wooster when they spoke to him, but then he got into things so much that my father and Ed Harder and some others called him Sudsley, and one or two who didn't have any respect for anybody, like Jim Plass, called him Suds when they spoke of him.

We boys had noticed that there were some funny things about him. He was a tall man with a thin face and a big nose, and he always wore a cutaway coat and striped pants and carried a cane that looked like it had a gold head. We had seen him out in the country walking sometimes, but not walking either, but just going around in a big circle in a field, and sometimes speeding up a little in the circle, and always striking out at something with his cane. One time we sneaked up behind a stone wall covered with frost-grapevines and chokecherry bushes, and laid behind it and watched him. When he came close to us, we heard him talking to himself, and what he was doing with his cane was striking out at butterflies.

We watched him for a while but nothing else happened, and Fred Elwyn said, "I guess all it is is that he don't like butterflies."

And we got tired of watching him and left.

That's about all I knew about him except that after he joined the Dutch Reformed Church and got into things there, he took a shine to Hannah Van Etten, and that's what the men around the white-bellied stove in the store were talking about. I have overheard them talk lots of times about folks courting, and would it make a match, but they wouldn't talk very long about it because that happens all the time and there's nothing very interesting about it. But this Sudsley Wooster and Hannah Van Etten thing was different. It was like Stanley Longyear was saying, "Now there's a subject for discussion that stirs the imagination."

"The thing that stumps me," said Neil Riseley, "is that Hannah has turned kittenish. Sudsley has melted her. She's turned woman. By God, she wears a dress, even on the farm! First time in her life. We all know that one or two have tried it, if for nothing more than that fine farm of old Cornelius Van Etten. But they didn't any more than try it once. Hannah just wouldn't play. I can't figure it unless it's the poetry Sudsley writes and reads to her. Do you suppose poetry will do what nothing else will?"

This made me think about Hannah Van Etten. She is the old-maid daughter of Cornelius Van Etten, and has kept house for him ever since Old Hannah, his wife, passed on, a long time ago. Hannah is well along. She must be all of thirty and maybe thirty-five. She is tall and thin but full of muscle, and she works all the time except when the Ladies' Aid meets. She even works in the hayfield, and we have seen her ride the team in from the hayfield, bareback, with a bonnet tied under her chin. Until Sudsley showed up, she wore Sweet Orr overalls just like a man, and she looks about like a tall man except for her bonnet. Folks said she had just two loves—her father's farm and the church. If poetry made Hannah Van Etten kittenish, I thought, it must be pretty strong stuff.

There was the day when the Ladies' Aid was at our house and I was listening to the women talk. Before the tablecloths for the church were mended, here was Sudsley Wooster at the door asking for Hannah, and she was flustered, but she did leave with him.

The women started working harder, and nobody said anything for a while but just glanced around at each other, and then Ceil Lasher spoke up. She's Jim Lasher's wife and the one that is always doing things to shock the members of the Ladies' Aid, like one time when they were going to stay for supper Ceil said she had to go home a few minutes to feed her chickens. It was dark already and when she came back she rushed in all excited and exclaimed that she found a man in her chicken coop. The Ladies' Aid all fluttered up, of course, with "Dear me" and "My heavens" and "What did you do?" and so forth. She dropped in a chair and grabbed up a magazine and fanned herself while my mother ran for the smelling salts and the women stood around her, and then she sat up and said, "It was Jim." And so, when Sudsley called for Hannah and after she went with him and with the women glancing around and not saying anything, Ceil Lasher spoke up.

"Well, I don't blame her," she said, "Sudsley's got what other men could do with a little of it, and that's romance and what they call chivalry, like in France, and he's a fashion plate into the bargain. All Jim ever says is when am I going to pick the plums and what they're paying for pork. I don't wonder that Hannah sets up and takes notice, because with it all, she is not the most handsome woman in the world. It's a case where she is so good and fine and wonderful that everybody loves her, but nobody ever has personally. You can get awful tired of being loved by everybody instead of personally."

"Why, Ceil," said my mother. "How you talk. I guess you're just talking to hear yourself talk."

"Not at all," said Ceil Lasher. "If Jim Lasher hadn't already hooked me, I wouldn't mind listening to some of Sudsley's poetry myself."

"Oh, tut," said my mother.

"Tut nothing," said Ceil. "I just hope Hannah catches fire, for her own sake."

"You mean,—do you hope she marries Sudsley?" asked my mother.

"Well," said Ceil.

"Marry or not," said Linnie Jewel. "I go along with Ceil. I hope Hannah catches fire, this once, anyway."

My mother glanced around and noticed me. "Willie," she said, "you forgot to feed your rabbits."

I wanted to hear what the women would say and didn't want to go and so I said, "I could tell you something about Sudsley."

"Never mind," my mother said. "You go feed your rabbits." So I didn't get to hear what the Ladies' Aid decided.

And now here were the men talking about the same thing around the stove in my father's store.

Ed Harder chimed in and said, "Well, Hannah is the salt of the earth, but I haven't figured out what Sudsley is yet. If there is a match, I don't give a damn about Sudsley, but I hope it'll be all right for Hannah."

Just then Jim Plass came in with one of his cock-and-bull stories about how one of the tow mules from the Hudson and Delaware Canal that Peter Lewis Harder had wintered had been fed too

much grain and when he got back on the towline he had tried to
make love to the other mules. That started a lot of talk about
whether mules make love even if they don't do anything else, and
the men forgot all about Hannah and Sudsley Wooster.

But it turned out that Woodstock wasn't going to be able to
forget these two. The next Sunday morning in church I was all
ready to watch Vern Lown's Adam's apple go up and down when
he sang his bass solo, but he didn't get up. He just sat there and
looked gloomy. Flossie Bovee, Hyp's daughter, who plays the
organ, started in on the song, and when she didn't hear Vern, she
stopped and looked around, and then she started playing it again.
But Vern didn't join in, and so she just stopped playing, and
there was a dead silence except that folks in the congregation were
whispering to each other and wondering what was up. It sounded
like twenty hives of bees.

Dominie Park got up to say something in the pulpit. He said
that everybody thinks the world of Vern's singing, and he hoped
he would go on and sing. But Vern just sat there. Then Dominie
Park said the whole trouble was that Mister Wooster had asked
to sing one of his own songs for the solo that morning, but some
of the elders and deacons had said Yes and some had said No, but
there were more nos than yeses, and he was sorry that the few
yeses had offended Vern.

Just then Sudsley Wooster got up and walked up front and
handed Flossie some music and said he would fill in. Flossie
didn't know what else to do, so she started playing, and Sudsley
sang. Sudsley had not stopped to ask Dominie Park anything about
it and so the Dominie just sort of shrugged and sat down. Well, it
was a pretty good solo at that, and the way he did it, swallow-tailed
coat, gold cane and all, it was what they call dramatic. But they
fixed things up with Vern and next Sunday he sang the solo as
usual.

I suppose that could have been all and things could have run along toward whatever was going to happen between Sudsley Wooster and Hannah Van Etten, but two Sundays later something else came up. I didn't know anything about it, except that when church ended I noticed my father didn't drift home with us. He had hurried right up the aisle and met Dominie Park coming down out of the pulpit, and they whispered together, and then they called out to all the elders and deacons to wait and come forward for a meeting.

But I learned about it at dinner. My father was late, of course, and Linnie Jewel was stewing about the dinner, and so when my father came in she hustled it right on the table and we sat right down and my father was asking the Blessing before anybody had a chance to talk about anything else.

But as soon as he said "Amen," my mother looked up and said, "Well, what happened?"

"The Consistory put an end to it," said my father while he was passing around the chicken and biscuits.

"Well, I should think so," said my mother.

When the chicken and biscuits came around to my father he helped himself and started to eat, and then when he had swallowed he went on.

"There will be no more solos by Sudsley," he said, "and, of course, letting him preach a sermon is out of the question. What an idea! It's just out of the question. The Consistory was firm on that."

"Even Cornelius Van Etten?"

"Even Cornelius. He said he is an elder and his first duty is to the church and not to any love match. Besides, he said, people would know more about the facts if they would stop guessing and mewing around and ask Hannah. She is nobody's fool, he said, and he guessed she knew as much about Sudsley Wooster as the next one. Nobody had ever led her to the altar yet, he said, and he doubted if Sudsley could. So there you are. The Consistory is glad to have Sudsley working in the church as long as he stays in the congregation where he belongs, but he must not expect to take over the whole shebang."

"Well, I'm glad the Consistory stood up to it," said my mother.

"Sudsley's the kind that if you give him an inch he takes a mile," said my father. "Who does he think he is, going to Dominie Park and saying that there are a few things the folks were not getting from the Dominie's preaching, and he would be glad to preach the sermon and point them out."

It turned out that Cornelius Van Etten knew Hannah better than anybody else, even Sudsley. The harvest was coming on with lots to do on the farm and either that or because she put the church first and Sudsley second, she had less and less time for his poetry and the stuff that Ceil Lasher had talked about.

One night, when you could smell black buckwheat and ripe apples in the air, the harvest moon came up big and red. It must have been about two o'clock that night when I woke up and heard a hard rapping on our front door, and I got out of bed and went to the little window above the porch roof over the front door to find out what was up.

I heard my father come to the front door and open it and say, "Why Sudsley, is something the matter? It's the middle of the night."

"I have to talk to you," said Sudsley.

"What about?" asked my father.

" 'It's time to talk of many things,' the walrus said," said Sudsley.

"Well, I'm not a walrus," said my father. "We can't talk now. It's the middle of the night. I can't ask you in. The family's asleep and it'll wake up the whole house."

"Come outside," said Sudsley. "We can talk just as well outside."

"But I'm in my nightshirt," said my father.

"Nobody's abroad," said Sudsley. "Nobody will see you."

I could tell my father was considering, and I suppose he thought the quickest way to get rid of him was to listen to what he had to say and get it over with. I heard the front door close and then they seemed to stand on the front porch and talk.

Sudsley wanted my father to help him with Hannah. He said Hannah had changed and he couldn't understand it, and I thought right away that Ceil Lasher and Linnie Jewel would be interested in that because it must be that Hannah hadn't caught fire.

I heard my father trying to get away without hurting Sudsley's feelings, but Sudsley kept on and on. Sudsley complained about the Dutch Reformed Church, and told of preaching he had done, and poetry he had written, and talked about what he called his philosophy of romance, and how he had always attracted women, most of them handsomer than Hannah, and that he was sure that if the church would only let him sing solos and preach, Hannah would be impressed. He recited some of his poetry that Hannah had liked, but he said he had just written the best one of all and Hannah wouldn't listen to it.

"Yes, yes," my father said, "but . . ."

But Sudsley went right on. He said he wanted to read this last poem to my father, and then he wanted him to explain why Hannah would not listen.

"I don't know anything about poetry," my father said. But Sudsley went right on and read it. It was kinda long and pretty mushy.

The window curtains waved a little where I was. I heard my father say he was getting chilly standing there in his nightshirt and that whatever Hannah wanted to do was her own business and he would just simply have to go back in the house.

"All right," said Sudsley, "I'll accompany you. For the hour of the day or night matters little to me."

"Well, it does to me," said my father. "My patience is strained and I am cold and now I am going to inform you of one solid fact. I am going back into the house, and you are not coming in with me."

"Very well, then," said Sudsley. "But I beg one more slight favor. Will you step out into the open yard with me a moment?"

"What for?" my father said.

"I want to show you something and ask your opinion."

I saw them come out in the yard under the open sky. Sudsley pointed up. "Why are there two moons up there?" he asked.

My father looked up and then he said, "Either you are crazy or I am. We will get the doctor and the sheriff tomorrow and let them decide which one, but I think it will be you." Then he hurried back to the door and went in and bolted it and left Sudsley standing there looking up into the sky.

I leaned way out the window and looked up. There was only one moon. Sudsley stood there alone looking up into the sky for quite a time and then he left and walked kinda slow toward the Woodstock Hotel and every once in a while he shook his head hard.

The next morning I was standing in front of the store when Johnny Saxe and the mule stage were leaving for West Hurley. Sudsley Wooster came over from the Woodstock Hotel with his gold-headed cane. With him was Corn Van Gaasbeck, the fat, jolly colored porter that Will Longyear asked once, when Corn was sick, how he felt and Corn said he felt like an infidel. Corn was carrying two big grips. Sudsley told Corn to put the grips in the stage and then climbed in himself.

I ran into the store and told my father, and he and all the men in there came out front. Johnny Saxe came out with the mail bag and chucked it in the stage and looked up and saw Sudsley.

"Going on a trip?" he asked.

"I am going none know where," said Sudsley. "I am cutting all ties."

I saw Ed Harder wink at Johnny. "What about Hannah?" he asked.

"I have mailed a farewell poem to her," said Sudsley.

Johnny Saxe started up the mules and all the men shouted good-bye.

When the mule stage came back in the afternoon, Johnny said that on the way to West Hurley Sudsley was full of a lot of stuff that he guessed was philosophy, but then he took the U & D and that's all he knew.

That's all anybody knows because Sudsley Wooster has not come back to this day. Hannah Van Etten doesn't seem to mind. She comes striding into the store just like she used to in her bonnet and Sweet Orr overalls and folks say she has gone right on with her first two loves, which are working her father's farm and devoting her life to the work of the Lord.

So the men around the white-bellied stove in my father's store have dropped it, but the Ladies' Aid goes right on talking about it and will, I guess, for a long time.

🐾 The Lawsuit

. . . and the appearance of the Lord's messenger

After breakfast my father put a toothpick in his mouth and went over to the window of the dining room and stood looking out at the fall freshet. "It seems to me the sun is taking a long time to cross the line," he said.

When my father finished eating and didn't rush right off to the store, it was a sign of some worry on his mind.

I went to the window and both of us stood looking out at the Tannery Creek over its banks below our back yard. It looked like a lake of boiling cocoa. It was deep down below the wall and the privy, and under the warehouse that stood on heavy wooden posts to make the floor level with upper ground. I looked across the water to the field back of Hyp Bovee's building and I thought that his coffins would soon be lifted off the saw horses and floating around if the rain didn't let up.

"I hoped the rain would stop today," said my father, "but just look at it."

"Don't you feel good this morning?" I asked.

"As far as my body is concerned I feel fine," he said. "It's my spirit that's sick."

"What's the matter?"

"It's that lawsuit," he said. "All over one single dollar. A round piece of silver with the words *In God We Trust,* and I wish folks would."

I knew what he meant. Every man in Woodstock was slapping their legs and laughing about it.

Will Longyear had caught Brook Romer sober one morning and asked him to go up in the feed room and clean it up. Maybe it was a dusty job, but not hard. It meant getting the bags of different feed set up nice and straight again and sweeping the dust and siftings off the floor.

Brook did a good job but he was busy only about an hour. When he came down to the store again Will went up into the feed room to see if the job suited him. Then he asked Brook how much he owed him and Brook said, "One dollar."

"You must be fooling," Will said.

"No," said Brook. "One dollar."

Will looked at him pretty sharp. He could see that Brook wasn't smiling or trying to wink at anybody. Brook was looking him straight in the eye. He meant it.

The blood came up in Will's face with a rush and his tongue broke loose. He was a very strict church man without a single bad habit, unless it was smoking one cigar a day. He almost never swore. But he rounded Brook Romer off that morning to a T.

Brook just looked at him and listened, and when Will finished he said it again. "One dollar."

"I won't pay it," said Will.

"I'll sue you," said Brook.

"Go ahead and sue," shouted Will. "You'll be the laughing-stock of the whole town."

"You mean you will be," said Brook.

Then Will exploded for fair. He ran out from behind the counter. He grabbed Brook by the back of his coat collar and began boosting him with his knee to the door. But Brook shook him off and walked out of the store very dignified.

He walked clear up to Shady, to the Justice of the Peace. It was a good four miles. In the afternoon he walked back into the store and went right up to Will Longyear. He handed him a paper. It was a legal paper to come to the court of the Justice at 10 a.m. on September 25th. Will just snorted. Then he pitched the paper in the wastebasket.

My father was on his weekly trip to Kingston that day with the week's butter and eggs, and to do the banking and run any errands for the customers. He heard about it as far away as West Hurley on his way home. Everybody knew Brook Romer and Will Long-year, and the thing had spread like wildfire and everybody thought it was great and wondered how it would come out.

My father's patience was awfully strained. He told my mother and Linnie about it at suppertime.

"Well, is it that important?" asked my mother.

"Well, it has the whole county laughing," said my father. "That makes it important, I guess."

"Oh, pshaw," said my mother. "Just give him his dollar and the whole thing will be settled."

"It's gone too far," said my father. "You forget the court."

"Go up to Shady and pay the costs," she said.

"This is an affair of honor," he said. "Will Longyear says over his dead body. He's a partner with as much to say as I have. He won't pay the dollar. He won't go to Shady. He won't pay the costs. I am in the middle. I can't afford to have trouble with Will and yet some way has got to be found out of the mess. Somebody is liable to land in jail and it won't be Brook."

"Just keep out of it," said my mother. "If worst comes to worst, let Will Longyear pay for his stubbornness. Let him go to jail."

"The trouble is," said my father, "Brook sued the firm. Not Will alone. I'm head of the firm."

Linnie was listening and, of course, she is a woman, too, and she saw it just like my mother did. "Looks to me as if it will have to be turned over to the Lord," she said. "He will provide a way."

But my mother looked stormy and glared at Linnie. She didn't believe in fooling around about the Lord. But I saw my father smile. He raised his eyebrows to make his eyes big and looked at Linnie.

He made out that he was thinking hard. "Maybe the Lord would send a messenger," he said. "First, there is Will Longyear. He certainly needs to be born again and that won't be easy. That's a job for the Lord. Second, there is the greed of Brook Romer. For an hour's work he is charging the going rate of a dollar a day. I suppose he sees a way to get a quart of rye. Only the Lord would know how to stop that."

"Oh, Abe," said my mother. "Why do you be so!"

Then my father got firm. "We can't just pay the dollar and costs and fold our tents and steal away," he said. "The Orientals call it saving face and I guess there's a lot of Oriental in Will Longyear and Brook Romer. I am sure the Lord can provide a way if He thinks it's important enough."

"Oh, Abe, do be still," said my mother.

All that had been a week or ten days before. Will Longyear

went around acting like a wet hen all that time. My father argued
and argued with him, but it didn't do any good. And Brook Romer
just sulked and even told us boys to leave him alone.

Then it had started to rain day after day. So when my father
stood looking out the window at the freshet after breakfast I began
to do a little figuring.

"What day is this?" I asked him.

"You've guessed it," he said. "This is Saturday, September 25."

"This is the day of the lawsuit," I said.

"Yes."

"That reminds me," said Linnie. "I take it the Lord's messenger
didn't show up yet."

"If he did," said my father, "he didn't see Will Longyear or
Brook Romer. So I've got to go to Shady. It will be a tough trip
with the roads swimming with water holes and deep mud. I even
hate to put a horse through it."

"Can I go along?" I asked.

"Are you out of your mind?" he asked.

"I am not out of my mind," I said. "I am more in it than out
of it. I have never seen a court case and, well, maybe you would
like some company. Besides, Brook is my best friend and I can't
understand why he acts so. Maybe I can find out."

"Well, bless your heart," he said. "But it won't be fun."

With the bad going we started right away. My father had Grove
hook up Carrie single and the top buggy and put on the side curtains. And he had a rubber lap robe put in. It was cold and it was
wet and the rain kept pouring down. But we bundled up and
started out. My father did not have much to say. He just sat there
and drove.

Going past the M.E. Church I asked, "Didn't the Lord do anything at all about this?"

"What's that?" he asked. "Oh yes, now I remember. That Linnie
is a great one. No, I guess the Lord's been too busy to get around

to us. All I know is abide by the law and appear as ordered and take the consequences and let the people laugh. I suppose we can wear it out in time. But the Lord could have brought us an easier trip. I keep wondering about the Bearsville bridge over the Saw-kill."

It was as if some giant stood on the top of the Overlook trying to drown the whole Woodstock Valley at one time. About all that Carrie could do in the mud and water was walk, and there was always the danger of a washout and floundering. My father was watching the road and studying the harness all the time.

I saw a man up ahead slipping and sliding and not getting along very fast. "Who's that, do you suppose?" I said.

My father looked up and saw the man. "Don't know," he said. "But he must be crazy to be out in this."

"He looks drowned," I said. "Could we ask him to ride?"

"We wouldn't be human if we didn't," said my father.

When we came up to the man we saw that he was Brook Romer. He didn't have any raincoat and the water was dripping off his hat and down over his face and shoulders in a steady stream. His pants legs were mud up to his knees. He got off to the side of the road but kept right on trying to plough ahead.

"Good morning, Brook," said my father. "Here. For heaven's sake, get in and ride."

Brook paid no attention.

"Come on, Brook," I said. "Come on and get in."

"William," said my father, "you could get up and let Brook get in on your side. Then you can squeeze down between us."

But it was no use. Brook wouldn't listen. He just sloshed ahead. We kept alongside and my father kept talking to him but Brook wouldn't even look up. I guess we had gone a hundred feet this way when I couldn't stand it any longer. "Brook," I said, "now you are getting me mad. This ain't like you. Not anything at all. Now cut out this damn foolishness and get the hell in here."

My words slipped out before I thought and I wondered what
my father would think. I knew the words to get action all right,
but he didn't know I knew them. He looked surprised but all he
said was, "Well, bless my soul."

Brook was jolted, too. He stopped and looked up and said, "I
didn't teach him that. To use those words, Abe."

"No matter," said my father. "Get in. This is no place to discuss
words."

Brook climbed in. Clumps of mud dropped off his feet when
he lifted himself up. He was dripping all over. He squished when
he sat down. He was shivering. I squeezed in between them and
handed Brook's side of the rubber lap robe to him. I had to sit
partly on his hip so as to leave my father free to drive Carrie and it
was only a minute until I could feel the seat of my pants getting
wet.

We drove on and nobody said anything for a while.

Then Brook said, "This is a hell of a note. If I had ploughed
through this rain and mud all the way to Shady I'd have been
fierce as a hawk. Now I wish I was a kid and could bawl. Why
couldn't you have been Will Longyear? Then I wouldn't be in this
fix. Let's turn around. Let's call the whole thing off."

"It will be better if we go through with it and wind the thing
up," said my father. "You see it your way. Will sees it his. That's
what courts are for. And so let's do it like decent Americans at
least."

None of us said anything more about it. We just struggled on
through the rain and mud.

The Sawkill under the bridge at Bearsville was almost up to
the planks. My father stopped Carrie to take a look at it and judge
whether it was safe to cross. He decided it was. In about an hour
more we came to the house of the Squire. He was waiting in his
sitting room with a big tomcat asleep in a chair beside him.

"I thought maybe you boys wouldn't show up," he said, "seeing as how the weather is. "But just on a chance I built a fire in the stove. You boys better warm yourselves."

"Young William and I are in pretty good shape," said my father. "The seat of William's pants is pretty wet. He had to sit partly on Brook. Maybe he had better back up to the stove for a while. But Brook. I'm worried about him. He's wet clear through and chilled to the bone."

"I walked to about Chris Winnie's," said Brook, "and then Abe picked me up and brought me the rest of the way."

"Well, wait a minute," said Squire. He was an old man I'd never seen before. He had white whiskers and a pink and white face and twinkly eyes. He went to a closet and came back with a bottle of whiskey.

"I know you're temperate, Abe," he said. "But Brook here. Any objections?"

"Not under the circumstances," said my father. "He needs it."

Brook took a big drink. He shook a little and said, "Ah." He smiled at the Squire and my father.

"Now," said the Squire, "let's get down to business." He asked Brook all about the job in the feed room and the dollar. Then he asked my father if Brook told it right.

My father said Brook had.

"Did Brook do a workmanlike job?"

"Yes," said my father. "Even Will Longyear said he did."

"He didn't do any damage of any kind? Nothing that would make a countercharge?"

"No," said my father.

Brook leaned forward. "Wrong," he said. "I dropped a quarter sack of flour on a plowshare. Ripped the bag too much to save. I threw it out. Just remembered it."

I saw the Squire and my father look at each other. And then they looked at Brook.

"You really did, Brook?" said my father.

"Yes, I did."

"Something's come over you, Brook," said the Squire. "The day you come bustin' in here you was madder than my old tom here when he meets up with another tom on a soft spring night. I recall you said you'd make them pay in spite of hell and high water. And you was cold sober that day, Brook." He thought a minute and his eyes twinkled. "Well, you got the high water but you would know best about the hell."

"I got the hell, too," said Brook.

"Well, anyway, you started the law and the law will have to take its course."

"Why?" said Brook. "Why does the law have to take its course?"

The Squire laid down his pen he was using to make notes in a big book. He thought a minute. "Well, now," he said, "you've got me there. Never thought about it. Never had anybody in here that didn't want it to, as I recall. Tell the truth, I don't know. Just seems as if it's the only way to deal with ornery people, I guess."

With that the Squire shoved his spectacles up on his forehead and leaned back and put his hands back of his head and studied the wallpaper on the ceiling.

Brook closed his eyes and fell asleep by the stove. The big tomcat was snoring on a pillow in the rocker.

"The Ten Commandments," the Squire said to himself. "Seems as if they're about all the law we need. Trouble is, folks squirm this way and that. There's never been but one man who handled it easy—Moses. But he had help. The Lord don't break out of burning bushes and mountain tops any more."

"I wonder," said my father.

I don't know how long the Squire would have sat there looking at the ceiling if my father hadn't done something. He waved his hand at the rain outside and winked at me. I knew what he meant. It seemed to me that the law took an awful lot of time and talk.

"Well, Squire," said my father, "you have a very comfortable place here. But we will have to be getting along, I guess."

"Why don't you all stay to dinner?" asked the Squire. "Got a good Dutch dinner. I'm up for election again and it's the best way in the world to get votes. No obligation, of course," he laughed.

"That's mighty friendly," said my father, "but I'm afraid that it's not in our hands. The water is almost up to the Bearsville bridge. We better get back across it while we can."

The Squire reached over and shook Brook by the knee. "Wake up," he said. "Hate to disturb you, but this is a court of law. The court has to render a decision."

"Let's forget the whole thing," said Brook.

"That certainly might be the best way," said the Squire, "but the law don't permit it. I can't just write down here that the whole thing was a mistake. If I did that, the sheriff would be up here to jail me for monkeying with the law. You might say he would have to charge me for using common sense. Besides, I'd lose my fee. While I am strong for 'Forgive and forget,' I am a very practical man yet. But the law can handle it. You'll get justice, Brook, and Will Longyear won't have to hide in a hole, either.

"So," he went on, "I find as follows: Defendant, that's you, Abe, that is, the firm of Rose, Longyear and Elwyn, and because Will Longyear was the authorized agent of the firm and the firm received the benefit whereas Will Longyear did not, except that he didn't have to clean up the feed room himself; well, to get on, the firm must pay the whole dollar to Brook Romer, the plaintiff.

"But," he raised a couple of fingers in the air. "The quarter of flour ripped on the plowshare must be accounted for. Therefore, the plaintiff, you, Brook, must pay the defendant six bits. That leaves you two bits, which is fine pay for an hour's work seeing as how a dollar a day is considered good wages.

"And now the costs. Defendant pay the costs.

"I might add," he said, "but I won't include it in the record, that part of the costs really had ought to be paid by the plaintiff except that he can't pay them. He could be put in jail for them but that would only cost the county for his keep. So I think it is good law to put the costs where they will be paid in cash. After all, the court is worthy of its hire."

He looked up first at my father and then at Brook. "How's that?" he asked. "Satisfactory?"

"Perfectly," said my father. "A highly judicial decision."

"Suits me," said Brook.

My father took out his wallet and gave Brook four quarters. Then Brook handed three of them back to my father. My father paid the costs to the Squire and we started back to Woodstock. My father and Brook joked about it all the way.

We were late for dinner, but my mother and Linnie were used to that with my father. He always said the store came first. Meals were important, he said, but under the circumstances they couldn't be any more than second.

Linnie and my mother wanted to know how the lawsuit came out and my father told them all about our trip and Brook and what the Squire decided. "It was a miracle," he said.

"How do you mean?" asked Linnie. "A miracle?"

"Both sides won," said my father. "That's a miracle in a lawsuit."

"Humph," said my mother. "Foolishness. Nothing but foolishness. Half a day's time and you might have caught your death of cold."

"And the messenger of the Lord?" asked Linnie. "Did he appear?"

My father smiled. "You are going to be disappointed, Linnie. But yes, he did."

"What did he look like?" asked Linnie.

"Well, now, Linnie," said my father. "You saw him. Anybody with eyes to see and ears to hear knows he appeared. Stop and think. Suppose it had been a nice day so that Brook could have walked to Shady by himself? The messenger was the freshet. It never lasted this long before."

"No," I said. "The messenger was you. I'm hungry. Can we eat now?"

❧ Waiting for the Evening Mail

. . . and stunts and tricks and races and Mrs. Dan Sully

The artists may bring changes and improvements, but it does seem that they wouldn't want to change the summer evenings in front of our store. I hope they won't because it is the best part of the whole day. When a small boy says that, you can bet it's got to be good because the rest of the day for us boys ain't bad.

Daylight stays on until after eight o'clock in the summer. Folks are done with work; the men, I mean. The last mule stage with the mail comes from West Hurley around seven o'clock, and the post office is in our store. Mail attracts the men and the summer boarders but it is not only that. Something is always going on. There is the bicycle circus, of course. If something unusual happens it is the place to see it or hear about it, and it is the right time to be there. You can even hear the older men arguing about this or that, and it is a great place to learn about a lot of things if the men know what they are talking about and are not just talking to hear themselves.

Sometimes I am a little late. That's because of the rules in our house. One rule is about supper, and other meals, too. We all sit down together, and none of us can leave until everybody is finished. Then I go out into the lower yard under the locust trees.

Most always Fred Elwyn is waiting for me, so I guess the Elwyns have the same rule about meals. Then we go up in front of the store.

One night we stopped by a group of young men to overhear them. They were big enough to be loose from their mothers' apron strings. You could tell that from their talk. First off, Don Schoonmaker and Jack Terwilliger were telling about dances at a dance hall outside Kingston Point Park on the Hudson, and how they had sparked some girls there. Then Jim Plass broke in and said that he'd been reading about Cuban girls and that if there had been anything that would have made him enlist in the Spanish-American War it was to go to Cuba.

Just then George Lasher drove up with his black colt and a sulky. George had this colt pretty well trained, but he always lets himself in for something because he brags so much about it. Last night he was bragging about the colt's reach. "It's like a man's stride," he said, "the way we reach out in front with our feet as far as possible when we have sprint races."

"Looks like any old colt to me," said Harry Short.

"Why don't you show us?" said Jim Plass.

"Yes," said Jack Terwilliger. "Take him up the road past Hyp Bovee's. And then bring him back this way."

"We'll come down in front of Larry Elwyn's house away from this crowd," said Jim. "You can pull him down after he passes us and before you get up here."

"Well, I'll show you," said George. And he started off. Fred and I followed along down in front of his father's home. When we got there we could see George turning the colt around up by the second bridge, and then he started coming. And he was coming.

"Well, by George," said Jim Plass, "he does reach pretty well."

You could see George holding a tight rein and leaning forward against the brace of his feet. He had the colt up to speed when he hit the bridge so he would be going past us best on the other side.

He was almost over the bridge when it happened. The black colt turned a somersault and the sulky lifted enough to throw George up in the air, spread out like a frog taking off from a rock. He landed on the colt's belly. But he rolled off fast and onto his feet. Funny thing, though, the colt laid there quiet without thrashing his legs. Jack, Jim and Harry were used to horses, too, and they ran to help loosen the harness and get the colt up on his feet. The colt trembled some but they went all over him and he didn't seem to be hurt. George wasn't scratched. Men had come running down from up in front of the store, but George walked the colt around some. One or two straps had broken, but somebody got some cord. Then George put the colt back in the sulky and drove off.

But there wasn't any more doubt about the colt's reach. Coming out of the dust of the road onto the planks of the bridge had fooled the colt. One hind foot had reached so far ahead that it had caught a front foot coming back.

Everybody drifted back up in front of the store. They were talking about reach and Jim Plass said that it was the same with a man. If he had the longest reach he would always win a foot race. This brought on an argument and nothing would do but that they try it. They marked off about a hundred yards from the Woodstock Hotel to in front of our store and eight or nine young men were going to race it. Ed Harder, my father's oldest clerk, went in the store for his revolver, and he got ready to shoot the start. A man who was a summer boarder said, "Let's have a pool." And so he wrote the names of the runners on slips of paper and put them in his straw sailor. He went through the crowd and every once in a while a man or one of the summer girls or women took a slip out of the hat and put in a dollar bill.

One of the summer girls got Jim Plass on her slip. She squealed and called out, "I got Jim Plass. Might as well give me the money now. He's got the longest legs. He'll win."

They got about ten feet of cord from the store and then they called Fred and me. Fred was to hold one end of the cord at the finish line and I was to hold the other end. They told us to keep it tight. I felt pretty important and I guess Fred did, too.

Everybody lined up on the sides. The runners were up at the start toeing to a line in the dust. Some crouched and some stood up but leaned forward. Ed Harder raised his gun and then he shouted, "Get ready," and then the gun went bang.

You never can tell about a race. Norm Elwyn, Fred's oldest brother, was in the race. He is not tall like Jim Plass and does not have long legs, but he can move them faster. He is wiry. He got off ahead of Jim and almost right away both were out in front. Jim and Norm kept gaining so the others began to laugh and quit. Jim and Norm were neck and neck until almost three quarters, but then Norm put on extra speed and he hit our cord first. A pretty summer girl, who had been with the one who had Jim Plass but had drawn Norm, ran up and threw her arms around Norm and kissed him. The crowd shouted and kidded Norm and Norm got as red as a beet.

After it had quieted down a bit the young men tried standing on their hands and doing handsprings and the running broad jump. Jim Plass was the best, but none of the girls hugged and kissed him. Maybe it was because there wasn't any bet on these things.

The mule stage with the mail was late, so to kill time Jim Plass got up another stunt. Fourth of July was coming and the store already had fireworks and firecrackers on hand.

He went into the store and bought three of the biggest firecrackers and two of the biggest skyrockets. Then he got three water pails all alike from down in the barn.

He lined up the pails upside down in a row and he put one of the firecrackers under each pail. The firecrackers were about a foot long. "Who will take a dare?" he called. "I am going to set on one of these pails when the firecracker goes off, and who dares set on the other two?"

"Better not," said a summer man who had a chin whisker and looked like a professor. "Nobody knows the force in one of those giant firecrackers. You could be injured."

But you couldn't stump some of the summer boarders. They saw what it was. Nobody said anything about it, but here was a country chap testing their nerve. Two young chaps from Aaron Riseley's boarding house stepped up and said they would take the dare.

One of the summer girls from Riseley's screamed, "Don't do it," she called. "Henry and Spencer. Don't do it."

But Henry and Spencer did. Jim took one of the giant fire-crackers and handed two to them. "Now," he said, "stand by your pail. Light the firecracker when I say Go. Put it under the pail and set down on it. Then wait for the boom."

Jim Plass is always playing tricks. Sometimes they turn out funny but sometimes they don't. And sometimes everybody likes him and sometimes they don't. I had an idea this was another of his tricks.

They lighted the firecrackers and sat down on the pails just as he said. It was quiet all of a sudden. Nobody was saying anything. You kinda hold your breath when something like this happens.

The pails were not tight on the ground because the ground was not flat. You could hear the fuses sizzling and a little smoke come out from under each pail. Just when you expected the booms, Jim jumped up from his pail and ran off laughing. But it was too late for the others. The firecrackers went off. The pails under Henry and Spencer lifted off the ground and Henry and Spencer went sprawling in the dust. But the pail Jim had been on flew up and off to one side right at some summer girls. They screamed and lifted their skirts to their knees and scattered. The pails stopped but the girls had showed their limbs, and they put their heads together and giggled.

Somebody yelled, "That was a dirty trick!"

"But the girls put on a delightful show," said the man who looked like a professor.

Henry had picked himself up and dusted himself off and now he started for Jim Plass. He swung on him and Jim swung back and they had at it hot and heavy until Harry Short and Norm Elwyn got to them and held them.

What would have happened was that Jim and this Henry would have left the crowd and gone down back of the store. Nobody could see anything there from the road, and Jim and this Henry would have had it out with their fists.

But that didn't happen because the man who looked like a professor said, "What's the skyrockets for?"

"I'll show you," said Jim Plass, and so this Henry got so interested he forgot to want to fight.

Jim got about fifty feet of strong cord from the store. He tied one end to one skyrocket and the other end to the other. Then he strung out the cord so it would not snarl. Next he got two wooden boxes and set them about a yard apart, and he leaned one skyrocket against one and the other against the other. But he placed them so that the skyrockets leaned away from each other.

"Now we will set them off," he said. "We will see what they can do when they get up in the sky."

He was pretty smart to get this Henry to light one rocket while he lighted the other. But before they did, they moved everybody way back so that nobody would get hurt if something went wrong.

The skyrockets were the biggest ones and they were good ones. The fire rushed out of the lower ends. The rockets took off. The string ran out fast and followed them into the sky. The rockets were traveling away from each other until the string tightened and then they raced toward each other. Then they exploded together. Nobody had ever seen that and everybody clapped.

Just then there was the sound of a fast team and a wagon hitting the bridge across the tannery pond down by our woodshed and everybody turned to look. It was the big sorrel team of Mrs. Daniel J. Sully and her surrey. Mrs. Dan was driving and when they rushed up to a stop in front of the store you could see that Ben Johnson and three fashionable young actresses were in the surrey. Ben jumped out to tie the big sorrels, and Mrs. Dan jumped out and swept into the store. Ben helped the three fashionable young actresses out of the surrey and then stood talking to them while they looked around.

Mrs. Daniel J. Sully was a very interesting woman. She was the wife of Dan Sully, who had a summer farm up in the mountains in Mink Hollow and raised Ring Neck pheasants and peacocks.

Daniel J. Sully was an actor. He had a play about a priest and he was the priest. Every fall, winter, and spring he traveled this play all over the United States. He looked like a very roly-poly, happy man on the Irish order, but he didn't come to the village much. It was Mrs. Sully who came to the village and she always came fast with her sorrel team. When you heard the bridge thunder more than ever you knew it was her. Folks said she was a very lively woman. She talked quite loud and laughed a lot, and Ed Harder, who was handsome and tall, always waited on her. Because Ed was a regular daredevil and she was big and handsome, too. Once I saw her buying some pointed shoes on sale and Ed had on a pair of the men's and was showing her how the toe was so pointed that if you stubbed it against anything, maybe a chair leg, it glanced right off. She said that was cute and she bought a pair. They were high-laced shoes and when Ed fitted them she lifted her skirt to her knee, but Ed put the shoe on her and laced it up and was kidding her all the time. She patted his head but you couldn't beat Ed.

Fred and I edged over to overhear what Ben Johnson was telling the three fashionable young actresses. He was telling them about the time the whole Overlook Mountain was afire and how it looked like a big red streak across the sky at night.

First off, they wouldn't believe him, and one of the girls said "Twenty-three skiddoo to you" and giggled. But when Ben told how the whole rim of the Overlook was a long red streak against the black sky at night, and how nearly all the men in the Woodstock Valley and in the valley on the other side worked day and night for three days with shovels and axes and backfire, and some of them got too close and had to be rescued, he had the actresses shivering a little and they looked at the big mountain so near and right on top of them and gasped.

Fred whispered to me that Ben wasn't afraid to talk to actresses because he was maybe the best-looking young fellow in Woodstock. The best build and he knew how to dress up.

"Look at his wonderful upper legs and his big calves," whispered Fred, "and how tight his black pants are on them. Style. Right up to the minute."

Ben stopped talking and we saw that he was looking toward the bend in the road by the Woodstock Hotel. Others were turning to look, too. Fred and I looked and we saw what it was right away.

"Harry Riseley," said Fred. He had his mouth open and there was admiration in his eyes. "There goes success," he said. "It must be wonderful."

Harry Riseley had a beautiful young woman with him and he was driving by in a rubber-tired runabout with Aaron Riseley's two-year-old bay Morgan in the shafts. "Bride and groom," I heard somebody say in a low voice.

Everybody watched as they drove but they looked straight ahead and did not seem to notice. They had on slate-colored dusters and this was something new. All the dusters in Woodstock were tan colored. Harry had on a brown derby, and he had light tan gloves on his hands with the tops rolled back from his wrists.

"Pretty fancy rig," said Jim Plass when they had gone on down

over the bridge and up the road toward Bearsville. "That runabout. See the red wheels and the narrow cane seat? He had that
made special in a carriage works in Kingston. Neil Riseley was
telling me. Harry sure has hit the jackpot."

Everybody knew all about that. Hitting the jackpot, I mean.
Harry was the son of Aaron Riseley, but Mr. Riseley had an older
son named Neil. Neil was a wonderful man but folks told as how
he had stayed with his father on the farm and in the big boarding
house. Harry had gone to Spencer's Shorthand College in Kingston, and then had gone on to New York City to get a job. He was
so good at shorthand, folks said, that he was private secretary to a
railroad president. His salary was very high, they said, some that
it was as much as twenty-five dollars a week.

I had overheard the men talking about this staying in Woodstock or going out in the world around the stove in my father's
store. It was the old problem, they said. Whether a country boy
had better stay with his father or go away.

It was like Byd Snyder and his sister, they said. Except that,
of course, his sister was not a boy. Byd would have the Snyder
store, they said, and probably the best house in Woodstock. But
his sister had married Will Lake from Rhinebeck across the Hudson and Will took her off to New York City. Years ago he had
joined the New York police force.

"And look at him now, and at Byd's sister," I heard Larry
Elwyn say. "Will is a police captain now. He is able to send his
family to Woodstock for two months every summer and he comes
himself for a month. Pay goes right on. And when he is old
enough he retires on a pension."

Then I heard Chris Winnie speak up. "Yes, that's all right.
But what will he do when he retires and gets that pension? He'll
make a beeline for Woodstock."

The men laughed and slapped their legs. Then I heard my

father's voice. He was writing a letter or something at the book-keeping desk, but he must have stopped.

"You never see more than a little patch of sky at one time in New York City," he said. "You never see the wind sweeping down over the fields of grain with their different colors. Even the air is polluted, and dirt everywhere. Of course, the lights are sensational at night, and the little spunky brass engines on the elevated, and waking up on the nightboat in the harbor. There is the Battery with the Aquarium, the Fifth Avenue buses, Weber and Fields at Tony Pastor's, and John Drew at the Empire. There is Dead Man's Curve and the penny arcade at Fourteenth and Broadway. There is tony Fifth Avenue and Riverside Drive and Grant's Tomb. There is Central Park and the zoo. And I don't think there is a bigger thrill in this world than landing at Weehawken on a West Shore express at night. You cross the harbor on a ferry while you listen to the boat whistles and watch the buildings and lights on the New York City side. The ferry slip even has its own smell and you remember that smell all your life. Salt water and old wood and engine oil and steam and sweat and horse manure all mixed up together in a real smell. It catches hold of a man. It makes him dream big dreams."

"Stop, stop, Abe," cried old K'Neal Hogan. "You're breaking my heart. God, how I'd like to be twenty again."

"But do you know something?" my father went on. "All that's only for New York visitors. It's something that people who live there never know anything about. It's sort of hidden from them. It's all the reward of the man who lives somewhere like Woodstock and only gets to New York once in a while. The man who lives in New York is on a treadmill like one of Cal Short's horses at threshing time. Or, like an ant. Very busy, moving fast here and there, but all he has to show for it is an ant hill just the same. Except for the few millionaires, of course."

"Damn few of them," said Larry Elwyn.

"But we have this fertile valley filled with fruit," my father said, "the sight of the planted fields in spring and the smell of black buckwheat in the fall. The majestic Overlook Mountain behind us. The open sky above us that stretches as far as the eye can see. The thunder and lightning of storms and the calm of the sun. The association of patient animals. Homes big enough for companionship or solitude as the fancy strikes us. And everything we do of the greatest importance and interest because it is our own business. All of us are individuals.

"No matter how big you are in New York City you're just one of a crowd. You have to be gigantic or you're just a nobody in a big crowd. I once heard Alva Staples, of Kingston, say it. Alva's father, you know, sold out his cracker bakery to the National Biscuit Company for a fortune. Alva inherited and he's rich. Now he just runs a cheese, butter and egg business in Rondout to have something to do. I was buying a cheese one day. He took out a plug to let me sample it. I forget how the subject came up. He said, 'I feel like I'm quite a man until I step off the ferryboat in New York.'"

"Well, guess that's about the ticket, Abe," I overheard Chris Winnie say, and my father must have gone back to his books or whatever he was doing at the bookkeeping desk.

Now, after Harry Riseley had driven by in his tony outfit, I was thinking about what I had overheard in the store that night about New York City and Woodstock.

"He'll be back," I told Fred.

"Who?" he said.

"Harry Riseley."

"He'll be back where?"

"Harry Riseley. When he's through in New York, he'll head for Woodstock."

"Like hell he will," said Fred. "Are you crazy?"

Maybe I am crazy like Fred said, but I don't think so. I know I won't ever leave Woodstock and I bet Fred Elwyn won't either.

Somebody yelled, "Here comes the mail stage." Johnny Saxe was running his mule team around the corner at the hotel. He was late.

❧ The Catskill Mountain Storm

. . . and Rip Van Winkle and thirteen cows

I was up in the front entrance of the store in the afternoon, swinging on the awning rope, when I heard the thunder. But it sounded far away and I didn't pay much attention.

When you can swing on the awning rope at the store you don't pay much attention to anything else, except to be sure that your heels or some other part of you won't swing back into the entrance and hit the glass in the show windows.

Maybe you could bump into the glass with some other part of yourself and the glass wouldn't break, but if your heel comes back and strikes the glass there is trouble. Your father or Will Longyear, your father's partner, and anybody else in the store will come a-running, and you'll find that you won't be swinging on the awning rope any more.

Then I heard the thunder again and this time I did pay attention because it was closer and the windows shook a little. It sounded like some giant rolled a big wooden ball on a big floor up toward Bearsville.

The sun wasn't shining any more and it was getting dark. The sides of white buildings looked gray. The big plate-glass windows in Will Elwyn's store across the road looked yellow.

Ed Harder came out and took the awning ropes away from me and raised the awnings. "You better run home or get the seat of your pants inside," he said. So I went inside with him.

"The funny little sons of bitches are starting to roll them again," he called out inside the store.

No customers were in the store and the men left what they were doing and came to the front windows with Ed and me. Gusts of wind were bending the trees toward Snyder's store and the Woodstock Hotel, and the dust was flying thick.

"It's coming down from Yankeetown and Bearsville," said Grove, the barn man. "Down through the valleys. They're the worst kind. It's gonna hit us, I guess. Hope no damage is done."

He had no sooner said that than one of the lightning bolts shot right down out of the sky back of Will Elwyn's store and almost before you saw it a big crash sounded as if every building in Woodstock was falling down. I went and stood by my father. But the crash wasn't all. It bumped and banged around town and up into the mountains for a long time.

"Well, they're rolling them," said Ed Harder.

"What does Ed mean?" I asked my father.

"Oh, it's just a story," he said, "Ed means the echo. Folks who have been all over the world say that a storm in the Catskills sounds different than it does anywhere else."

"There was a writer," said Ed, "who grabbed hold of that and made quite a story out of it. I forget his name."

"His John Hancock was Washington something," said Will Longyear.

"Washington Irving," said Dickey Short, our newest clerk, who had been to high school at Kingston Academy.

"You tell him, Dickey," said Ed.

"The story is there was a bum," said Dickey.

"Like Brook Romer," I said.

"Well, not exactly. His name was Rip Van Winkle. He had a

wife and she nagged him. And he was a hunter. So he went out
hunting to get away from her. Up in the Catskills he ran across a
lot of little old men with beards who wore things like your tobog-
gan cap in winter with a tassel on it on their heads, and they
played ninepins all the time. This is a game where you roll big
balls at a lot of big wooden pins to knock them over, and that's
the thunder that you hear."

"Is that all?" I asked.

"Ain't it enough?" Ed said.

"I mean, what's the end? What happened to this Rip Van
Winkle?"

"Oh yes," said Dickey. "Well the story goes that he fell asleep.
Probably got too much for once. It's a little foggy whether all this
happened or he dreamed it. Anyway he didn't wake up for twenty
years. By that time he didn't know anybody and everything was
changed. He almost wished he had his nag of a wife back. The
story goes to show, I guess, that you better be satisfied to live in
your own time."

"Either that or don't get stinking drunk," said Ed.

"I don't think you told it just right," said Will Longyear. "But
it will do to explain how a storm around here sounds."

"Have you got the story all printed out?" I asked Dickey. "I
want to read it for myself."

"I don't have it," he said. "But you'll get to read it. If you stay
in school you will. They'll shove it on you."

All this time the thunder was rolling and bouncing around and
there were flashes and flashes of lightning. It was getting awfully
dark for the afternoon.

"Dickey, you better light the Welsbach lamps," my father said.
I followed Dickey while he did this because it was interesting and
it took my mind off the storm. The light these Welsbach lamps
made was a lot brighter and whiter than the old kerosene lamps
that hung from the ceiling. My father had just put them in and

they were the only ones in the village. They had little iron tubes
running along the ceiling and down the walls to a big tank
in the cellar. You filled the tank with some black-looking stuff
and poured water on it. That made the gas and the gas went up to
the lamps. When we had finished we went back to the men looking
out the window.

Just then another bolt of lightning came down back of Will
Elwyn's with a crash and the windows rattled and the thunder went
bouncing away through the mountains. And then the rain came in
buckets.

"Are you afraid, Willie?" asked Grove.

"I don't mind the thunder," I said, "but I don't like the lightning. Was anybody ever hit in Woodstock?"

"Not that I've heard of," said my father.

"Trouble is," said Grove, "I'm always afraid I'll be the first to
have the honor. Some bolts come so close it curls your toenails.
Take that last one right back of Will Elwyn's store. That singed
my hair. Of course, it could have been a quarter-mile away."

"It's just nature making an adjustment," said my father. "That's
the theory."

"If that bolt didn't hit something more than a theory I'll eat
my shirt," said Grove.

"It's nature and it's necessary," said Will Longyear. "And I
guess nature is God. If there's one thing He has to do it's to keep
things in balance. Just line up with it and you won't get struck.
Don't get under trees. Don't go near a stove or a chimney. Things
like that."

I said when I was in Libby Riseley's Sunday School class she
gave us a picture of God. "He was an old man with a long beard
and a fierce look, coming down out of a cloud. But He didn't look
big enough to make a storm like this out there."

"That's the trouble with Sunday Schools," said my father, "trying to put everything on a human basis. Folks think of God as a

judge but He's more like the legislature. Folks have to learn the rules and do their own judging."

"I wonder what that bolt struck," said Grove. "I've seen a lot of lightning in my day. From out in the hayfield. From the barn door. From the middle of the Hudson down around Storm King Mountain when I worked on the *Mary Powell* one summer. I've seen only one other like that one. Straight down. Zip and a crash and bump, bump, bump like that."

"What did the other one strike?" asked Dickey Short.

"It struck a tree. A big bastard of an oak on Charley Riseley's place just as you're starting up the Ohio toward Wash Elwyn's. Must have been four hundred years old. Split it wide open."

"I remember that," said Will Longyear. "Charley was in here a short time after and he said he got 152 cords of 36-inch wood out of that one tree."

"It wasn't any sapling," said Grove. "Did he tell you how easy it split? Seemed to be all loosened up."

"I don't remember," said Will. "But it was a lucky strike at that. Charley said he needed a hundred dollars quick for another horse and the wood just made it for him."

"There," I thought. But I didn't say anything. God was nature and nature struck the tree with lightning. And it was Charley Riseley's tree and he needed another horse and he got his horse. And so things kept in balance.

The storm went on and on. It was all right for awhile to watch the sheets of water blow in the wind and to see how the road and the sidewalk from Mower's to the Dutch Reformed Church and the whole village green had big and little rivers running this way and that. But there was an awful lot of the storm and it was about the same for a long time. I got tired of it. I went to the bookkeeper's desk and got some paper and a pencil and drew houses and things.

The clerks and Will Longyear stayed up in the front of the store looking out the windows at the storm. Will Longyear leaned against the counter with Dickey Short. Grove had his foot up on a chair and his elbow on his knee and his chin in his hand. Ed Harder would stand one place for a few minutes and then take a few quick steps to another place. Ed was high-strung, they always said. My father was busy straightening up the stock.

Not much was being said now except, "Where do you suppose that straw came from floating out there?" or "There goes that limb on Lown's first maple. I was wondering how long it could take it," and maybe it would be a minute or five minutes maybe between times when anybody said anything.

Then all of a sudden Ed Harder said, "Look," and pointed, and everybody came to life. Will Longyear and Dickey Short bumped their backsides against the counter to push themselves up straight and looked out toward the hotel. Grove took his foot down off the chair and tried to see where Ed pointed. I ran to the front. My father stopped with the stock and called out, "What is it?"

"Brook Romer," said Ed. "Something must be wrong. Running this way through the water. Looks like a drowned rat. Looks all peaked out. Came running around Snyder's corner."

Brook got to the door and took hold of the awning rope so that his arms could help out his legs to lift himself up on the step. He looked as if he had run a long ways and didn't have much left. He was panting hard.

Ed flung open the door and reached out and pulled Brook in. He helped him onto a chair and said, "What's the matter?"

Brook tried to get his breath and pretty soon he said, "Aaron Riseley's cows." Then he couldn't say any more till he could get more breath.

"What about them?" said Ed.

"Struck by lightning," said Brook.

"A cow struck by lightning?"

"Thirteen," said Brook.

"All at once?"

"All at once."

"My heavens," said my father.

"Thirteen. It's an unlucky number," said Dickey Short.

Nobody said anything then for a minute. They just looked at Brook trying to catch his breath.

Then Grove said, "Well, I guess Aaron can stand it."

"Probably never knew what hit them," said Will Longyear. "Probably never felt it. And all in all, better for them, I'd say. Better than slaughter."

"Wonder how it happened?" said Grove.

"I wonder why it happened," said Brook.

Ed took hold of Brook's shoulder and shook it. "Come back to earth," he said. "Where is this? How do you know it? Riseley's pasture is beyond the bridge over Sawkill Falls. Half a mile from here."

"It's no use thinking I'm fuddled, Ed," said Brook. "I saw it happen."

"You saw it happen?"

"I'd been over to West Hurley. I was walking back when the storm struck. I don't follow the road, you know. I walk cross lots. It's shorter."

"Yes. Well, what about it?"

"I was back to that slant field where the big black rocks poke out of the ground. Some hickories in that field. It's just above that pasture lot of Aaron's. I'd been watching the storm and when it broke I speeded up. I had in mind a ledge that hangs over. A big jutting rock ledge in that slant field. I got there all right and sat underneath to wait out the storm. Just then there was a hell of a clap of lightning that blinded me for a second. My head tingled and I could have sworn that my hair stood on end."

"Your hair? You don't have any hair," said Ed. "But go on."

"Well, that's it. I looked down in the pasture and there they were. Thirteen cows dead. I got out of there."

"Thirteen cows with one bolt?" asked Ed. "Damn good aim."

"Under a tree," said Brook. "It hit the tree."

"Why didn't you stop and tell Aaron?" asked Will Longyear.

"I did. But Aaron wasn't home. Only boarders. They wouldn't know a cow from a bull. I ran on up to Jimmy Lasher's. Jim's away again, I guess, and Ceily's out. Pepper's blacksmith shop was closed, and the hotel barn looked like it was, and I didn't stop at the hotel bar. Not this trip. There's always somebody here, and so I came here."

"I'll hitch up," said Grove. "Soon as the storm quits we'll drive down to that pasture."

"There won't be much trade for awhile after the storm," said my father. "I can look after it. So you boys might as well go along with Grove."

"I'm not particular," said Will Longyear. "I'd a little rather stay here, in fact. Brook, you better go up in the feed room and take off your clothes. It's hot up there. They'll dry faster."

"Well, I guess *I'll* go then," said my father. "Want to go, William?"

I said yes and I said it as if I meant it.

The rain and the storm stopped almost faster than they started. Grove drove Carrie and Jim around to the front of the store and they all piled in and took me along. Going down the long grade past Pepper's and the old sawmill the ditches were full of rushing water, and some places holes in the sides of the road were torn out. When we got to Aaron Riseley's boarding house and turned right to cross the bridge Grove stopped the team for a minute while we watched the water roaring over the Sawkill Falls.

It was only a little way now. A little to the left and up a rise and downgrade around a bend. But we saw them from the top of the rise. Some men were walking around them and looking at them. As we came up I saw Charley and George Riseley and Jack Moran. All of them lived on the other side of the Sawkill just a little way up from Boice's new sawmill. I wondered how they knew about it so quick.

When Grove pulled Carrie and Jim up by the side of the road they had their heads in the air. Carrie snorted once and our men all sat still in the wagon for a minute looking the thing over and nobody said anything.

Then Grove, who had been a farm boy, said, "God." And when he said it the men all moved out of the wagon all at once on both sides like it was a signal or something, only it wasn't. I climbed down and followed them. I don't think Grove saying "God" meant anything. He wasn't swearing. I just think he didn't know what else to say and maybe didn't know he said anything. But I thought of what the men said in the store about the storm and Sunday School and God and nature and keeping things in balance. Then I looked at the cows. Something bigger than men had certainly been here.

It looked like all the thirteen cows were huddled under a tree when the storm came roaring down. But how could dumb animals know enough not to get under a tree when there was lightning?

"They were all touching," said Charley Riseley who always knew quite a little about everything. "Lightning struck the tree," he said. "All of them wet, of course, and water always helps electricity for some reason. Only one of them moved after going down, see? That one over there. She had enough life left to put one front foot on the ground and bend her knee trying to get up."

Jack Moran was down on one knee to study the cows and was breaking little sticks and throwing them aside. "So you think they was standing, Charley?"

"Yes."

"I don't. It was hot. It was late in the afternoon. They had grazed enough and were chewing their cud. They could have been lying down when she struck. The whole caboodle was touching each other. It's a small tree. Not big enough for all of them to get under out of the rain."

"I hadn't thought of that," said Charley Riseley. "Yes, it could be that way, Jack. Don't make much difference now, though."

"It's a bad loss for Aaron," said Ed Harder.

"Maybe not," said Jack. "He has more cows in another pasture. Enough for milk for his boarders. He aimed to sell some to the drovers when they come through, he told me the other day. His cows are insured. This saves him the trouble of dickering. There's one thing sure as hell though. Too bad cows can't be taught to stay away from trees in a storm."

"Did you hear that, William?" my father whispered.

"Yes," I said.

Then my father took hold of my arm and pointed to the sky. I looked, and there was a rainbow just like the pictures of Noah coming out of the Ark after the Flood that Libby Riseley gave us when I was in her Primary Class.

❧ Libby Riseley's Primary Class

. . . and the mysteries in the Ten Commandments

Even if you happened to be little folks you got to know the wonderful stories in the Bible in Libby Riseley's Primary Class, in Sunday School in the Dutch Reformed Church. It was all pictures and Libby telling about them. But when we got into the Ten Commandments it wasn't so easy for Libby because of Roy Harder, son of Levi, and to tell the truth, two of the Commandments puzzled me when we got to them. But I am not the kind that would say anything about it.

But Roy Harder is a farm boy and even when he was little folks he got to know some things about nature and what nature does to cows and bulls and rams and ewes and roosters and hens that the son of a country storekeeper like me would not know about in the tender age. And Roy is always full of mischief anyway, and so he was the one that made Libby the trouble.

It all started out when Libby said one Sunday that now we would go into the Ten Commandments and she would explain them. We would have one Commandment each Sunday, she said, and that there are ten of them and so that would take ten Sundays. Well, everything went all right except maybe for that one "Thou Shalt Not Covet," but we had only nine Sundays and when nine was over Libby said, "Well, that winds up the Ten Commandments and next Sunday we will go on to other wonderful things in the Bible."

Roy wasn't too good in school but it was only because he did not like to study and got more fun out of cutting up, but he could count to twenty. When Libby said the Ten Commandments was all over Roy was next to me that Sunday and I saw him counting the picture cards Libby gave us for each one of the Commandments. He whispered to me that he had only nine picture cards for the Ten Commandments. I didn't know one way or the other because I didn't have all my picture cards. But Roy always put his in the pocket of his Sunday suit on Sundays and did not wear it till the next Sunday, and so he had all of his and he had only nine for the Ten Commandments.

I told him that he had lost one but he said not.

"Well, tell Libby," I said. And so he did.

Libby looked at him blank. Then she began to talk in that way of hers. Fast, and with laughing all mixed in with her talk, and her voice going up and down and up and down. She said yes, she had left one out. It was "Thou Shalt Not Commit Adultery." She had left it out, she said, because it was not a Commandment for little folks like we were but only for grown-up people. Anyway, they sent her only nine pictures to go with the Ten Commandments and that was why she didn't have any picture for us.

And then she stopped talking and laughing and her eyes got big, like she was surprised at something. Then she said time was up and we would sing our closing song.

Then there was that other Commandment that Libby couldn't seem to explain. She did give us a card on that one. It was the one that says, "Thou shalt not covet thy neighbor's wife, nor his ox, nor his ass, nor anything that is thy neighbor's."

The picture card she gave us to show this covet business wasn't much help, Roy told Libby. It showed a man on a broken chair in a lower corner. His coat was torn and a whiskey bottle lay on the floor beside him. The devil was whispering in his ear and the man was looking up at another man higher up on the card in a nice home with his wife, and petting his ox and his ass. The Commandment was printed down below. "Thou Shalt Not Covet," and so forth.

Libby tried to explain to Roy that it is all right to want nice things but that we should work and save to get our own in a Christian way. We must not just wish for things that Christians have and then to go on doing what the devil wants us to do. If wishes were horses, beggars would ride, she said in her fast talk and laugh. No merriment, though. Just her way. I didn't see what beggars and horses had to do with it but I didn't say anything. I figured I would find out all about it sometime.

But Roy wanted to know now. He asked Libby how you go about working to get a wife in a Christian way but all Libby said was that it was time for our closing song and to all rise and sing.

So here was adultery and covet that we didn't know much about from being in Libby Riseley's Primary Class. In cases of ignorance like this I can always go to my father and ask him and he can straighten me out if it is a safe subject. But Roy told me what he figured adultery was, and if he had it right I could see that it was not a safe subject. So I left it alone. But the covet business was different and I asked my father about it. It was not hard to explain, he said, and he would do it. He started out to say that it is wrong to want something somebody else has, but then he said well, that wasn't exactly right either, because if you never wanted anything hard enough to go after it you never would get anywhere. He tried another tack but that got kinda mixed up, too. And so he said he would look it up in his Pellet's Notes that he used so the men in his Men's Bible Class could not stump him. Pellet will know, he said, and then he would go into it with me.

But I found out before he got around to it. And with a bicycle.

As everybody knows, the bicycle has turned out to be a success even if lots of folks said they were too high-priced for the average and that they made a circus monkey out of a man and that they were not ladylike for a woman and that the roads are not suited to them and that they are too dangerous for youngsters.

Will Elwyn got them started in Woodstock when he took on the Columbia agency and has made more money out of this side-line than out of his ginseng patch. They have been going great guns. Almost everybody has one, even the kids. Even the summer boarders don't bring theirs along with them from New York City in the summertime any more. They don't have to. There is a business in used and rented bicycles in Woodstock, and in repairs and so forth, and Russell Cronk has come to Woodstock to run this end of the business. He has his shop across from the village green this side of Snyder's store.

Russ Cronk is a wonderful man. He is a bicycle racer and is the champion of Ulster County. Things seem to turn so that I am the boy in the Village who has got to know him best. He likes me. It was his bicycle that brought me to my senses on this covet Commandment. Of course there is a sad part to it because it raised what they call a veil between Fred Elwyn, who is my best friend, and me. All this came about this way, and the first time I ever saw Russ Cronk.

One day my father told me I was elected to take the grass

clippers and clip the long grass under the white picket fence around our home that had not been reached by the lawn mower. There is an easy grade down past our house, from the center of Woodstock to the first bridge. I was lying on my side clipping the grass when I looked up and saw something that just could not happen. A man was riding a bicycle down the grade. He had his feet on the pedals but the pedals were not going round. At first I thought he had lost his bicycle chain but then I saw that the chain was there. What was more, when he got to the bottom of the grade he turned into Larry Elwyn's barber shop and he began to move his pedals backward just like Ed Harder does when he shows the trick of riding a bicycle backwards. But this bicycle didn't move backwards from going ahead all of a sudden or the man would have pitched right over the handlebars. All that happened was that the bicycle slowed down and came to a stop. The man stood the bicycle up against the side of Larry Elwyn's barber shop and went in.

I left the clipping and strolled across the road as if I had not seen the bicycle at all. I kicked at a couple of stones in the road and threw a couple of them into Tannery Creek just as if I was a boy just happening along. But I was getting closer to the bicycle all the time until I was there and I studied it. It looked just the same as any bicycle to me as far as the chain and wheels went, except that the hub of the back wheel was bigger than any other bicycle I had seen.

But the big thing was that it was nickel-plated all over. It shone like a watch. It was the most beautiful bicycle I ever saw.

Of course I wanted to touch it.

I was reaching out when the man came out of the barber shop. I yanked my hand back and he laughed. He was a young grown-up man, and good-looking.

"Do you think it's a beauty?" he asked.

"Yes," I said. "It's a beautiful bicycle, all right."

"I am a sucker for bicycles," he said. "This is the finest bike I could think of. I had it made special."

"You did? My gracious," I said.

"It is my advertisement," he said. "I clean and polish it every day. I don't want a spot or a nick on it."

"How do you mean, your advertisement?" I asked.

"I am opening up a bicycle shop across from the village green," he said. "Bicycles, tires, repairs, saddles, punctures, everything. When folks see this bicycle and know it's mine they will know that I know bicycles and will come to me for anything they need."

"What's your name?" I asked.

"My name's Cronk. Russell Harrison Cronk. What's yours?"

"William Palen Rose," I said.

"They call you Bill?"

"Yes. Bill," I said.

"Do you have a bicycle?" he asked.

"Yes."

"Well, Bill," he said, "come up to the shop and see me. I'll show you a lot of things about bicycles."

"There's one thing I would like to know now," I said.

"What's that?"

"How do you hold your pedals still while you're riding?"

"Oh, that." He laughed. "That's something new. It's a coaster brake. Greatest invention yet."

He told me how the coaster brake was in the axle of the back wheel so that it slipped when the pedals held still. It caught again when you pedaled ahead. If you moved the pedals backward it put on a brake. It didn't brake when you stood beside the bicycle and pushed it backward either.

He told me that the bicycle did not have tubes in the tires. "Come up to the shop and see how easy it is to fix a puncture in these tires," he said. Then he took his handkerchief out of his pocket and wiped a speck of dust off the nickel-plated frame and got on and rode off.

I went to Russ Cronk's shop a lot after that. Of course it was no time before all the boys in Woodstock knew about that nickel-plated bike, and of course we all yearned to ride that bicycle. But it looked like I had the best chance. Fate had thrown Russ Cronk and me together and he acted like he knew me best. He always called me Bill this and Bill that, but with the other boys he would say "Hey, you" or something like that.

One day I ran an errand for him and he wanted to give me a nickel but I wouldn't take it. So he thought a little and then he said, "Tell you what. How would you like to ride my baby for an hour or so?"

I jumped at that and got all excited.

"There's just one thing," he said. "Take it easy until you get used to that coaster brake. Don't jam it on all of a sudden or you'll go head over tea kettle. I don't mind if you bust your own head, but don't hurt my baby."

Then he laughed. But it was easy to see that he was scary about letting me ride the bicycle and I made up my mind right then and there that I wouldn't get a scratch on it.

I rode up to the Methodist Hall. Then back through the Village and on up past the cemetery past Cal Short's blacksmith shop. Then I rode down to Aaron Riseley's boarding house and back. The bicycle was such a beautiful thing and so far ahead of anything that even the people from New York City ever saw, that when I went past people stopped and it took the eye. The boys in the village stopped whatever they were doing and looked. I was the first one to ride Russ Cronk's bicycle, and just a Woodstock boy at that, and I admit that I felt proud as one of the peacocks on Dan Sully's place up at Shady.

Being proud was a sin, of course. But it is funny about sin. You are not likely to think about it when you're doing it. I wasn't thinking about Libby Riseley's Sunday School Primary Class or the Commandment that says other people must not covet your wife nor your ox nor your ass nor anything that is yours. But it was all there just the same.

I rode through the village and up to the cemetery again and then I noticed that there was a splash of mud on the nickel-plated frame of the bicycle. I got off and got out my handkerchief and I rubbed off that mud and shined up the frame. It was time for me to take the bicycle back to Russ Cronk's and I wanted it to be shiny.

But when I got to the shop and was giving the bicycle to Russ, Fred Elwyn stood there. And right in front of Russ he said, "What did you do to the bicycle?"

Russ looked up quick with a worried look.

"I didn't do anything to it," I said.

Russ had started looking over the bicycle. He lifted up the front wheel and spun it and then he lifted up the back wheel and tried the coaster brake with the pedal. Then he got down on his hunkers and looked over the frame inch by inch. But he couldn't find anything wrong.

"What does he mean?" he asked me. "Is there something I don't see?"

"He don't mean anything," I said.

"Then why did you get off the bicycle up by the cemetery just now," said Fred. "And why was you squatting down by it like there was something wrong with it?"

"I was just dusting it off with my handkerchief," I said. But I didn't say anything about the splash of mud. Maybe it would have been better to leave the mud on so that Russ could wash it off and not to take a chance on a scratch. But I got it off without a scratch and so there wasn't anything to worry about.

"So you was just dusting it off," said Fred. "Is that so?" He said it in a way to make trouble for me and so that Russ wouldn't be dead sure yet that there wasn't something wrong. He said it in a way to make Russ think that maybe Fred saw me do something else.

So there you see is what covet means. It is not just your wife

or your ox or your ass. It is anything. Fred wanted to ride that bicycle, instead of me. That was the covet in him. It made him act
mean and it raised a veil between him and me that lasted three
whole days.

The next winter I saw another covet acted out, and that helps
you know about it better than having it explained in words in
Libby Riseley's Primary Class or by Mr. Pellet of Pellet's Notes
my father studies for Men's Bible Class. It was the pony business
and it was a lot worse. It could have killed Lewis Harder, son of
Ellie, and me, and if that is not bad enough it cost me a pony
and a cart.

Lewis' mother and my mother made it up that Lewis would
come down to Woodstock from their farm near Bearsville and
spend the day with me that winter. It was a good day and cold.
There wasn't any snow on the ground but there was skating on a
big pond that Cal Short had dammed up on his farm. I forget what
Lewis and I did most of the day, but in the middle of the afternoon my mother said we could get out of the house for awhile if
we harnessed up the pony and took a drive. The pony had not
been out all week and she felt good and it was no trouble to have
her spank right along.

We decided to drive up to Rock City and then go around a side
road that went past Short's pond to see how many were skating and
come back to the main road by Cal Short's barnyard and blacksmith shop. Lewis was a great talker but he stuttered some and we
always laughed at his stories that happened on his father's farm.

We were just coming around toward Short's pond and he was
telling me how one of the city girls that summer had chased their
hired man with a pitchfork and kept sticking him in the behind.
We were laughing hard, but just then a crowd of boys spotted
us and started to skate fast toward us, yelling at the top of their
voices.

It scared the pony and she took off. I was driving and tried to hold her but it was no use. Lewis was stuttering and asking if he could help. Just then the pony took to the ditch with a rail fence. One wheel hit a rail sticking out of the fence and one side of the cart bounced up high. Lewis and I flew out into the road with me on top of Lewis, and the pony went on down the ditch kicking at the cart to get free of it. She smashed the cart to pieces and broke the traces loose and went galloping off home with the harness flying all around her.

I was crying by this time because I was hurt and I was mad, and I knew it was terrible to have the cart and harness smashed up that way. Lewis and I got up and ran after the pony but of course we couldn't even gain on her, let alone catch her.

My father was out of patience with it all but when he learned how the boys and girls had skated at us and shouted he didn't wonder, he said. But he said he knew the pony and cart would cause trouble sooner or later when he bought it for us boys, because none of the other boys in the village had ponies. Jealousy can be pretty ugly sometimes, he said.

I asked him if jealous was the same thing as covet and he said, "Not exactly, but it is next-door neighbor."

So that is what covet is and the Commandment has it about right. It is bad. In one case a veil came between Fred Elwyn and me for three days and in the other case I lost a pony and a cart. Because nobody could drive the pony after that. She balked. If you touched her with the whip she backed up. Even my father couldn't drive her without getting into trouble. Grove the barn man said he would like to try it but my father said no because he knew what Grove would do. Grove would try to beat it out of her and my father said that would be wrong because it wasn't her fault and she was just a dumb animal. So my father led her behind his buggy up to Shady one day and had her turned out to pasture to get over what he called her sickness. But she must not have, because I never saw her again.

❧ The Wisdom of Jack Moran

. . . and Hyp Bovee's iron tie-post

The men around the stove in the store got into a fist fight only once. One night in the winter when it was zero and the snow was deep, Jack Moran had been drinking and came into the store for a little visit with the men. He found Charley and George Riseley there and Larry Elwyn and Jim Plass and Stanley Longyear and a drummer from Eddyville, where the dam is on the D & H Canal. Everybody called this drummer Barney Solon and he always gave Clifford and me a nickel when he was in Woodstock if we could catch up with him. He owned a saloon in Eddyville and sold goods for Edward D. Depew & Company.

This Barney Solon belonged to the Catholic Church and he was always laughing and was full of stories and had a red face. Everybody knew this red face was because he was cured of consumption. He did not smoke or drink and he was always chewing on sassafras root.

When Jack Moran came in, Barney was telling about a fine and strict old Catholic lady in Eddyville who wouldn't gossip herself but she kinda hoped that other folks would. "I hope men and women won't carry on," Barney said she said, "but if they do I want to be the first to hear about it."

But he stopped telling stories about this old lady when Jack came in. Jack came in singing little snatches of an Irish song and he clapped the men on their backs.

"Why hello there, Barney, me boy," he said. "When did you stumble in?"

"I see you are full of good spirit," said Barney and he winked at the others.

"Just a drop or two for my health," said Jack.

"How old are you, Jack?" asked Barney.

"I've sort of lost track," said Jack. "Forty-two or forty-three I guess."

"Well, then you are old enough to be full of wisdom," said Barney and he winked at the men again. "I will now give a little lecture on wisdom, gentlemen. Every generation has a little more wisdom than the one ahead of it. Ever notice that? And so wisdom grows down through the ages. Five or six hundred years ago everybody got soused. And everybody was fighting everybody else. But not today. By the time my grandmother was eighty years old she had a lot of wisdom. She smoked a pipe and used spirits. She said anybody was a fool to drink before forty, but if they didn't drink after forty they were damn fools."

"So you see, Jack," said Charley Riseley, "you are past forty and you are not a damn fool."

There is one funny thing about a man who has been drinking. He can change awful quick. Jack could figure he was getting kidded and maybe the heat of the stove was getting into him. And Barney Solon had made a bad mistake to say anything about fighting, and the men said later that Charley Riseley had ought to have known enough to keep his trap shut. That was because Charley Riseley was road supervisor and Jack Moran was driving the team to West Hurley over the roads for Eulie Boice with barrel heads and spindles to ship on the railroad.

"But *you* are a damn fool roadmaker, Charley," said Jack.

That started it. They began to slam words around hot and heavy. The men tried to break in to ease things a little, and Barney Solon started another story, but Jack and Charley paid no attention. Pretty soon they were both on their feet and George Riseley jumped up, too, to help Charley. Fists flew for a minute, but my father and Will Longyear rushed out from behind the counter and grabbed Jack's arms and pulled him to the front door. Somebody opened the door and my father and Will shoved Jack out into the snow. He didn't come back.

I felt sorry for Jack and I could tell from the way my father acted that he was, too. His patience was strained with Jack, of course, but he wasn't happy with himself either. He was too quiet and stern. I don't think he liked Barney Solon much right then and anybody could see that Charley and George Riseley had not handled it right. After all, Jack had been drinking and they were not born yesterday. To make it worse, the men around the stove said they guessed they had better be getting on, and left. I went home to bed.

I thought about it a lot before I went to sleep and I figured it out. Charley and George Riseley had tempers, too, and they were just as much to blame as Jack Moran. But Charley and George did not drink and they were active in the Dutch Reformed Church and that made them what my father calls solid citizens all the time. And I guess you would say that Jack Moran was a solid citizen only part of the time. I guess that's the way it always is in this world. You can get in fights but if you don't want to be thrown out of stores you had better get in the church and be thrifty and keep away from drinking, and not swear.

Because when you clear everything away and come right down to what caused the fight, it was the roads. All roads are pretty tough in thaws in winter, of course; but I had gone with Grove, our barn man, on deliveries that fall enough to know they were not too good then, either.

My father went down to Eulie Boice's sawmill the next day to talk with Jack when he was sober. But Jack said, "It's all right, Abe. I had it coming. But come spring I wish Charley'd get after the roads better."

"Maybe he will now," said my father. And Charley Riseley did.

As soon as the dust flew the next spring he went after the roads harder than any other supervisor by a long shot. Everybody said the road to West Hurley was like a barn floor.

And another funny thing about it was that the stock of Jack Moran in the wisdom business went up. Jack came in the store and sat around the stove a lot after that and the men listened to him when he opened his mouth.

Then came his wisdom with Hyp Bovee's iron post and that settled it. This was in Jack's job the next September after the rush of summer boarders was over, when he was helping Hyp Bovee with his new undertaking building. An old worn-out building without paint had always stood on Hyp's land the other side of the big bridge next to our house. Hyp tore this down and put his new undertaking building in its place. It had a big plate glass in the front so that you could see coffins, and satin linings for them, and silk pillows, and rough boxes, through the windows. He wanted things nice, inside and out, for this building, and so he laid a flagstone walk with a curb next to the road in front of it. He got Brook Romer to help Jack with this sidewalk and curb and I went over to watch and I overheard the whole thing about Jack's wisdom with the iron tie-post.

Hyp Bovee stutters, so you have to wait a little to know what he has on his mind. He brought out a long solid piece of iron about two inches thick and handed it to Jack and Brook. It was bored through at the top and a ring was placed through this hole.

"What the hell are you going to do with this?" asked Jack.

Hyp started to explain in his stuttering way. He was surprised by Jack's question; besides he knew that everybody would think that what he had in mind was a little fancy for Woodstock, what with the flagwalk and curb and now this. But after a while he managed to get it out what he had in mind.

This long piece of iron was his idea of a hitching post. He

wanted Jack and Brook to put it between the curb and the side-walk.

Jack told him that a nice painted wooden post would be better and safer. He pointed out that the post would be so close to the sidewalk and so thin and hard to see that anybody at night could run into it. "This iron post business goes all right in the city," Jack said, "but they have street lights. This is Woodstock and so dark at night a bat has trouble. Wood wouldn't hurt anybody much, but this damn iron!"

But Hyp said he guessed Jack knew who was boss and to fix the hole for the post and to cement it in and stop talking about it. People would soon get used to it being there, he said.

"You better put a lantern on it at night," said Jack. But he went to work as Hyp said, with Brook helping him.

I heard Jack tell Brook how men always think backwards and not frontwards. "It's a wonder all of us don't kill ourselves with our own mistakes," he said. Then he told Brook about old one-legged Zeke Whipple up near Cooper's Lake whose stock was bothered by a wildcat. So he set a bear trap. He didn't get the wildcat and after a time he forgot about the trap. One day he had a half-grown calf on the end of a rope and the calf got ornery and began to run. He ran so many ways and so fast that old Zeke's long white beard kept flying up across his eyes so that he couldn't see where he was being dragged and one of his leather boots went flying off his foot. Next thing he knew he set his sock square down in the middle of that bear trap. He was there three hours before his boy came looking for the calf and found him. His leg was so bad that a sawbones had to take it off, Jack said.

"Sure as hell," he said, "this iron tie-post is going to be one of the best things that ever happened to the business of Doc Downer."

That night, when the men were visiting around the stove in my father's store, Hyp Bovee rushed in and asked Ed Harder to get him a gallon of lamp oil. He handed Ed a glass kerosene jug with a swing handle on top.

"Run out of oil after dark, eh?" said Ed. "Bet you're popular with Martha tonight." Martha was Hyp's wife.

But Hyp told him to stop talking and to get the oil and to hurry.

Ed had him fixed up in no time and Hyp started out as fast as he had come in.

The talk around the stove stopped while Hyp was getting his oil but it started up again after he rushed out. Jack Moran began to tell the men about the new flag walk and the curb and had just come to the iron tie-post and how close it was to the flag walk, when the door flew open and Hyp rushed in more full of stutter than ever.

His overalls were all wet and dripping and he stunk to high heaven with kerosene.

When they got him quieted down so that he could be understood it turned that he had been rushing back to the house in the dark. He took to the new flag walk and forgot all about the iron tie-post. Swinging along he had slammed the glass jug into the post and darned near broke his arm and covered himself with oil.

Ed Harder and my father and Will Longyear took him to the back of the store behind the high drug counter. They got his old overalls and long underdrawers soaked with kerosene off him, and Hyp told them to get him new ones. He needed them anyway, he said, and besides he didn't want Martha to know he had been such a gosh-darned fool. Then he bought a new oilcan of tin and had it filled and went his way.

After he went out, the men around the white-bellied stove started to laugh like all getout. And Jack Moran slapped his leg again and again and kept saying in a loud voice, "I told him so, I told him so." Then he told what he had told Hyp Bovee about the danger of the tie-post and he went into the story again of how old Zeke Whipple up near Cooper's Lake lost his leg in his own bear trap.

The men laughed and laughed. Then Charley Riseley spoke up. "Jack Moran can think ahead," he said. "That's the greatest thinking there is."

The next day the iron tie-post in front of Hyp Bovee's fancy new undertaking parlor was gone. Hyp rooted it out himself.

❧ The Coffin Trimmer

. . . and Brook Romer four sheets in the wind

It's a funny thing, but when Brook Romer got a lot more than three sheets in the wind one night it put Hyp Bovee over the top in the undertaking business. Hyp went into the business two or three years ago and he was doing good, but I heard my father tell my mother that he wasn't doing good enough. Of course this was a secret. My father was helping Hyp with his books and borrowing. My father always said there are two bees in business and when you hear them buzz look out.

"I didn't think Hyp would do a quarter good against Nelson Lasher," said Jack Moran in the store one night. "Nelson was in the driver's seat with his fine big home and lawn and new hearse and black team and stock of coffins in that fine coffin building of his."

"All that prosperity can be a handicap," said Will Longyear. "They always say that nothing succeeds like success. But you can't let it look expensive. On the other hand, it's queer about funerals. The way folks go for the best. What is it? Pride?"

"Hyp's hearse and not having any coffin buildings looks like a saving to the customer, though," said K'Neal Hogan.

"But cheaper isn't all there is to it," said Charley Riseley. "Hyp needs equipment and he will have to figure out some way to get a showroom for fixing coffins."

"I guess you're right," said my father. "And Hyp is working toward that. By the way, now that Kingston has bought up Cooper's Lake for a reservoir what's this I hear—that there's no swimming in the Sawkill any more? Not allowed?"

"Kingston can't do that unless they buy up both banks all the way down," said Charley Riseley. "I know enough law for that. Besides, it's foolishness. If they know as much about water as they think they do they would know that swimming don't hurt. The Sawkill tumbles around so fast under the sun that it purifies itself in just a short distance anyway."

And so the men were off on the Sawkill.

That was my father's way to start the men off on another tack and leave Hyp's undertaking business rest. He didn't want them to talk about that and lots of other things they got to chewing over. I heard him say one time that if everybody would put together all the interest they take in other people's business and put it on their own, just about all the problems in this world would be solved overnight. The thought has great possibilities, he said, and he wished that some of the experts among the summer boarders who deliver lectures in the M.E. Hall and the basement of the Dutch Reformed Church would take it for a subject sometimes, instead of always lecturing on "Looking Ahead" or "Looking Behind."

My father thought that Hyp's undertaking business was too much of a favorite subject for talk. I heard him say that to my mother and Linnie.

"But what can you expect?" said Linnie. "Taking an interest in the undertaking business is different from other things. Sooner or later everybody finds himself right up front in it."

I have heard this Hyp Bovee thing talked in the yards outside
funerals. I have heard it talked in the Woodstock cemetery after
the rough box is down and folks take up visiting before going
home. And, of course, around the white-bellied stove, and almost everywhere.

Some would say that it wasn't right for Hyp to go into the
undertaking business when Mr. Lasher was already in it and
taking good care of all the trade as a general thing. Of course,
they said, there were bound to be peak loads because nobody has
found a way yet to make everybody give up and quit on anything
like a sensible schedule. On the other hand, some said that competition was the life of trade. Nobody thought that Frank Lasher
was cashing in on unfortunate deaths or even fortunate ones, some
said, but if the spirit ever moved him to do so he wouldn't be so
able to give in to the temptation if Hyp Bovee stood by ready
and willing to offer cheaper funerals. And some others said that
Frank Lasher didn't need any sympathy because look at his fine
place.

"It's like a man I knew once," said Jack Moran. "He was making big money but made me promise I wouldn't tell anybody.
Maybe Frank would be smarter if he let a weed or two grow in
that fine lawn."

But everywhere people always wound up thinking that it was
all right for Hyp Bovee to go into the undertaking business if
enough people died and he could make a go of it.

At first Hyp Bovee's hearse didn't measure up to Frank Lasher's
and the only place he had for fixing coffins was a loft over his
barn. If folks didn't know this there was no difference, but if
they did it was too much like tough times before modern ways.
Besides, Hyp didn't have anybody to help but his daughter
Flossie, but Mr. Lasher had his father to dress up with him
and be on hand for funerals. Two dressed-up undertakers at a
funeral make it seem more important than one dressed-up man, or

one dressed-up man and a dressed-up daughter, even if Flossie had dressed up and helped her father at funerals, which she didn't.

But Hyp got funerals right from the start from the poorer people and ones with big families where death was nothing to get excited about. With poorer families nobody was leaving anybody anything anyway, so that funerals didn't matter so much, and with big families there were too many other ways for money to go without spending it on somebody it couldn't do any good.

Ed Harder had it about right. "People got into the way of thinking," he said, "that once you are on your way to the cemetery it didn't matter much who was driving the hearse."

A day came when Hyp asked my father how to go about borrowing some money from the Kingston National Bank so that he could put up a special undertaking building with plate-glass windows and plenty of room for stock and getting coffins ready. My father knew the men at the Kingston bank and was able to take Hyp to the county seat and show him around.

Hyp figured that this new building would set him up in just enough of a different way so that he would get funerals from farther around, in such places as Van Dale, Mink Hollow, and over toward Shokan and West Hurley. And it did. But still he had gone into debt and his business went on being a life-and-death matter until the night when Brook Romer got four or five sheets in the wind and rushed into the store just as they were closing up. He called out that Flossie Bovee was dead.

Everybody stopped in their tracks to look at Brook in surprise before anybody could get words into his tongue. Shawn McGee muttered something and crossed himself. He was a new clerk in the store who drove all the way to the Catholic Church in Stoney Hollow every Sunday to go to what he called Mass.

Then they got over the shock and it came to them that nobody else had said anything about Flossie Bovee being dead or even sick and that Dr. Downer was in the store only an hour before.

They also knew that Brook was likely to lie down and go to sleep anywhere when he was full and have nightmares and then come running to tell some awful happening.

"You've been drinking and dreaming again," said Ed Harder.

"Well, I'm cold sober now," said Brook. "And you would be, too, if you had seen what I saw. I admit that I got a quart tonight and that I had been asleep. But when I woke up I was coming down this way and I noticed that Hyp Bovee's new building was all lit up. I stopped and looked inside and then I looked over in a corner and there was Flossie Bovee laid out in a coffin. I ran all the way up here."

My father and Will Longyear and Shawn McGee paid no more attention to him and went on closing up. But Ed Harder had to have his fun.

"I'll tell you what, Brook," he said. "You know Flossie and how different and independent she is. I'll bet she was lining a coffin and laid down in it to try it for fit. She's a hard, steady worker and no fooling about anything. You know how she is. Strictly business. I'll bet she has been working hard since five this morning and was dead tired. So when she laid down in the coffin it felt comfortable and she rested awhile and she fell asleep. By God, that would be good, wouldn't it?" And he went into a laughing fit and the others had to join in in spite of themselves when they thought about it. All except Brook.

He just stood there, looking sober as a judge. "You're certainly a cute fellow, Ed," he said. Then he leaned against the counter and stuck out his arm and watched to see whether he could hold his hand steady. It was as steady as a rock. "I am not drunk," he said. "If I didn't see Flossie Bovee laid out in Hyp Bovee's new building just now I must be out of my head. But I am not drunk. Look at my hand."

"Go back and look again," said Ed.

"Not me," said Brook.

"I'll go with you," said Ed.

They went out but Ed was back in no time. "Brook must have been in a trance all the time he was in here," he said. "Hyp's building is dark. It's as black as your hat down there. When Brook saw that, he lay down in the doorway and went sound asleep. Just as if he'd never been awake. I shook him but I couldn't wake him. So I left him there. He's used to it."

The story went all over the valley in no time. It was all vision, my father said. But the story changed and changed until people said it as a fact that Flossie Bovee lay down in all of Hyp Bovee's coffins to try them and make them more comfortable. Folks said they were bound to be better just like everything is better with personal attention.

That ended Hyp Bovee's life-and-death struggle to get into the undertaking business in Woodstock.

糸 The Substitute Undertaker

. . . and the "best damn funeral in town"

Hyp Bovee came down with lumbago and folks said that when Hyp got lumbago everything had to give. It wasn't just an ache with him. It was a spasm. This time he had bent over to lift a coffin up on a sawhorse to line it when the lumbago hit him. He went down on the floor and howled for help. Flossie helped him ease himself flat on his back on the floor, and he lay there until Dr. Downer came. The doctor gave him a big dose of black medicine and told him to stay flat for an hour and try to relax. Then the doctor came back and poked his finger in Hyp's back for awhile and then they managed to get him on his feet. Hyp could just manage to nip his feet along and was bent over.

This happened Thursday and the Grazella funeral was on Saturday. Flossie Bovee was in the store late that afternoon and she said Hyp fought the lumbago all day Thursday but the lumbago turned out to be a pretty good fighter, too.

This Italian that was dead was an older brother of Tony Grazella. He had come to Woodstock and settled down with Tony and his wife and ten children and had gone to work in the California bluestone quarry up on the side of the Overlook.

Everybody liked Tony. He had a place up toward Bearsville and didn't live in the shacks of Little Italy down near Van Dale. The Holland Dutch families of Woodstock Valley were ready to like his brother, too, until they learned that he was just a load on Tony. He drank up most of his wages and was no great help in the Grazella home. He brawled around the barroom of the Woodstock Hotel and the stables. Jake Wurts had to run him out of the barroom two or three times. He came into my father's store to eat a can of clams on a day when he was drunk. But he poured whiskey into the can of clams and slopped them around and he wasn't allowed in the store again.

On Wednesday, after he quit work in the quarry, he was rushing down to the barroom when he slipped and fell off a cliff and killed himself. It was kinda tragic but everybody was happy about it after they thought it over. And that went for Tony and his wife, folks said. But, of course, he had to be buried. After Dr. Downer looked him over he called Hyp Bovee because Dr. Downer was Dutch Reformed and so was Hyp. They got a priest from the Catholic Church in Stoney Hollow, and, of course, everybody wanted to do everything they could for Tony.

Things were going fine until Hyp got the lumbago. He tried to get Frank Lasher to take over. Folks said Frank said he would be glad to any other time, but he had a funeral himself on Saturday over at West Hurley. The priest was too busy on Sunday, folks said, and it was awful hot weather and it just wouldn't do to postpone to Monday when Frank Lasher would be free. So there was Hyp in a terrible fix.

Then on Friday my father was late for dinner again. He didn't come and he didn't come. Harry kept saying he'd rather eat alone than starve and Clifford teased. The patience of my mother and Linnie got more and more strained and my mother said there is reason in all things. She told me to run up to the store to see what on earth was keeping my father.

"Or above the earth or under the earth," said Linnie.

When I came back I told them it was under the earth. "He is talking to Hyp Bovee," I said.

"Hyp stutters," said Linnie. "His talk takes a long time."

So my mother said we would go on without my father and eat ahead. "I will ask the Blessing," she said.

We finished dinner and my father had not come yet. Linnie told my mother that this was baking day and they would have to get at it. "Why not have Willie run up to the store again to hurry things along?" she said. I knew it wouldn't do any good but I went anyway.

Will Elwyn hadn't come back from dinner yet and so my father was back of the high desk with the cage around it doing some figuring. He kept right on figuring but glanced up once in a while at Hyp Bovee. Hyp was standing in front of the cage leaning against it and doing most of the talking, but doing it the hard way with his stuttering.

My father never stopped doing what he was doing when people talked to him. He told my mother that this was because people could get to him in country business and were always talking to him and if he didn't go on with his work he never would get anything done.

"It is suicide to have a private office in the country," he told her. "Lots of men who make some money and get to feeling high and mighty make that mistake. A man has got to be right out in the open all the time where folks can get at him. And country people are great hands for visiting."

He didn't look to be done with Hyp Bovee yet and so I tugged on his coat and said that my mother and Linnie had to do baking.

"Yes, yes, yes," he said. "Go sit down and we will go in a minute."

Hyp went on with his stuttering again but my father did not wait for him to get it out.

"I suppose I could do it," my father said. "But why pick on me?"

Hyp stuttered that he wouldn't ask it but there didn't seem to be anyone else. One of the ministers can't be at the funeral because it is Catholic, he said. He said that my father had a top hat and a Prince Albert and the d-d-demeanor that nobody else in the village had unless Dr. Downer, and it didn't seem just right for a doctor to be burying his own dead. It was very exacting to be an undertaker, he said. Just enough of all religions, just solemn enough, just enough quiet to show respect for the dead. Tender with flowers, strong enough not to cry during the hymns, able to keep things running smooth but not a show-off, able to smile just right. And you have to have the respect of the people even though you are the only one making any money out of it.

My father said he certainly wouldn't be up to it as a rule. Then he thought for a little while. Then he said he saw an Italian funeral in New York City once and if he could help Tony Grazella he would want to, of course, and Hyp, too. So he said he would do it.

Hyp Bovee left then and we started down to dinner.

My father explained to my mother and Linnie about Hyp Bovee and the lumbago and how Frank Lasher was tied up and how it was too hot weather to postpone. "A country storekeeper has got to do a lot of things for folks," he said, "but this is the limit. I'm worried sick."

"Don't try for sympathy," said my mother. "You don't fool us a bit. You know you sort of like the idea to see what you can do with it. Riding up high on the hearse and a procession. Watch out you don't take a fall."

"They talk about Italian finesse," said Linnie. "Does Hyp have any Italian in him? Maybe this Italian funeral puts him in over his head in the undertaking business. How do you handle an Italian funeral anyway?"

"That reminds me," said my father. "I'll have to make a quick trip to Kingston this afternoon. Hyp says Tony says his brother wasn't much good, but after all he is dead. That makes a difference. Hyp says that Tony says he wants to give his brother the best d-d-damn funeral in town. His words. Not mine. So I am going to Kingston and borrow a pair of the fancy nets the Italians put on horses in a funeral procession."

"Oh, pshaw," said my mother.

When my father sat down to eat he said the real reason he decided to be a sort of temporary undertaker was to help Hyp. He said that Hyp needed all the help he could get. For one thing, he said, Hyp did not look like an undertaker because he was built like a churn. Slim on both ends and bulging in the middle. And, of course, the stuttering. And he was Dutch Reformed. "We are brought into this world and baptized by Dutch Reformed," he said, "and our own people had ought to take us out of this world."

My mother didn't say anything to that. So a twinkle came into my father's eye.

"This is nothing against Frank Lasher," he said, "because competition is the life of trade."

My mother said she didn't see what competition had to do with the undertaker business and to say there was any life in such competition was downright foolishness. "You can't sell people on death," she said.

Us boys followed my father back up to the store after he had eaten because we were going to try to get to go to Kingston with him. But it didn't work. He would be too busy, he said, and that was all there was into it. But we did see him talking to Ed Harder, with their heads together on the sly. Ed was listening hard and nodding his head and when my father finished his talk I saw Ed look at my father and close one eye in what was a long wink.

When my father went out to get in his rig, Ed followed him to the door. "Try Arthur Carr in Kingston," he called. "He's the kind will ketch on quick. Hope you get them." My father did not get home for supper and it was late when he drove in.

On Saturday morning after family prayers, my father said the Catholic funeral had to be in the morning and he got himself dressed up all in black pants and the Prince Albert. He put on the high hat and looked at himself in the long mirror in the sitting room. He looked fine, but he looked like an undertaker just the same. Linnie tried to joke but he wouldn't joke back and kept looking solemn. "I have to get in the mood," he said.

I asked him when the funeral would be coming past the house, and he said a little after ten if he could get them started. Italian families always have a barrel of relatives he said, and there would be some from Little Italy. He supposed there would be lots of visiting and that all took time.

So I hung around the house. I wanted to be up on the front porch when my father came through with his funeral. But I didn't want my mother to know I was hanging around just for that because I knew this wasn't a show or a circus parade. A funeral is a funeral and folks must feel sad. Or anyway they must look as if they feel sad by showing it in their faces and maybe hanging their heads. Clifford had a chance to go with Grove on a delivery and Harry said funerals were old stuff and went to the store.

So I pretended to be looking for a book or putting the fire-engine puzzle together or anything just to be around. But I seemed to worry my mother. She kept saying, "Why don't you run along outside somewhere and play?" And once in a while she made excuses to go out in the yard and I knew that she was watching for the funeral too and how my father looked and not because she was sad about Tony Grazella's bum brother. But she didn't want me to know that.

So when I was still around and my mother had been out in the yard a few times, Linnie said, "Oh shucks anyway, Mrs. Rose, what difference does it make if both of you want to see him as an undertaker?" So my mother gave in.

"You go up on the porch, Willie," she said, "and when you hear the wagons coming down over the first bridge you come and tell us. But don't shout about it because even if I do I don't want the neighbors to think I care how your father looks."

So I did that but it took a long time. The sun beat in on the front porch and it was like an oven there, but I stuck it out. Then I heard them coming and I ran to tell my mother and Linnie.

They came out on the porch and sat down and rocked. My mother had a book and Linnie had *The Ram's Horn* and they made out as if they were resting and reading. But I never saw Linnie read *The Ram's Horn* before so I knew her heart wasn't in it. They didn't look up except with their eyes until the procession was coming over the iron bridge right at the corner of our woodshed.

"Oh my days," said my mother and grabbed Linnie's arm. They both stopped rocking and stared. Because Ed Harder and four or five of the village band was leading the procession all in their uniforms and walking slow. Just then Ed gave a couple of toots on his cornet and the men started playing while the procession went through the village. But the tune was not like the *Star Spangled Banner* on the Fourth of July. It was low and moany and slow.

I had a good place. I had climbed up on the porch railing in the corner and had my feet and arms wrapped around the post. The grounds of our house sloped down to the bridge and the porch was level with the upper part of the slope. I was fifteen feet or so up off the side of the slope and quite a ways out into space.

Behind the band the funeral procession was coming faster than it ought to on such a hot day. This was because the team hitched to the hearse did not seem to be used to a band, and was nervous. They kept prancing and had their heads most of the time over into the top of the buggy where the priest was riding behind a very lazy horse. To keep out of the way of the team the priest kept urging his horse faster, but then he would have to jerk him back because the band was walking so slow. The driver of the hearse kept holding his team back but things just did not jibe.

My father sat on the other side of the hearse seat, up high. His back was stiff as a ramrod and he looked as if he would rather be someplace else. Back of the hearse came Tony Grazella and his wife in a rig, and back of them came a surrey with all his kids. Tony was showing his teeth and looking around pleased. The dust was deep and clouds of it drifted over into our yard and on the porch and we were coughing and so was everybody in the procession. When the band started up everybody came running out to see. They stood in yards and they stood in front of our store and other business places and the Woodstock Hotel and everywhere.

The procession was a good one. It was long, just like my father said it would be, with rig after rig after rig and some people walking. And black nets covering the team on the hearse from their ears to their tails made it look awfully important and solemn. I had seen lots of funerals but never with nets on horses. They looked just like horses in a book I had that showed pictures of Ye Olde Tymes in England.

We watched the whole thing go past the house. Up by the Woodstock Hotel the band stopped playing but we heard it again about the time they would get to the cemetery.

When my father came home he was so weary and white with dust that his black pants looked like he had come from Hugo Dish's gristmill. Even his moustache and eyebrows were white. With the funeral over, he had taken off the Prince Albert and was carrying it over his arm. He had taken off the top hat and was carrying that in his other hand. He got washed up and then my mother made him some cold lemonade and he stretched out and sighed and sighed.

Linnie praised him. "You looked fine on the hearse," she said.

"That might be," he said, "but I would have been more comfortable if I had been in it."

"The procession was wonderful," she said. "The horses looked grand. You are a born undertaker."

"Just so I don't die one," he said.

"I want the horses to have nets like that when I'm buried," said Linnie.

"The reminds me," said my father. He turned serious and looked at my mother. "I sold the nets to Hyp."

"Oh, pshaw," she said. "You didn't own them. You borrowed them."

"No," he said. "I couldn't borrow any. So I bought a pair. Ed said Arthur Carr would have some but he didn't. I hunted all over Kingston and Rondout. At last I found an Italian undertaker in East Kingston down by the brickyards. He had an extra pair. I bought them for twenty dollars."

"And what did you sell them to Hyp for?"

"Oh, just a reasonable mercantile profit. He gave me forty."

"Abe Rose, how could you do such a thing. A hundred per cent profit!"

"Well," said my father, "you've got to consider a lot of things. First, it was rare merchandise. I spent half a day finding the nets.

Second, I didn't charge Hyp anything for today's work. Third, he can charge more for funerals with the nets and I won't be surprised if a lot want them after today. And fourth," he said, getting up and stretching himself, "I wouldn't be an undertaker again for five hundred dollars. So there."

⚜ A Dog's Life

. . . and the first telephone and the discovery of coal

The day the telephone came to Woodstock I learned two very important things. One was that if progress is all that folks want, Woodstock did not have to get it by having artists come in and change everything all around. Because if the men would sit up and take notice, Woodstock could have big coal mines. And the other thing is that boys lead a dog's life.

The day of the telephone was in February before the trees had new leaves. I saw some men tacking a long wire to the trees from out Rock City way, but that was interesting for only a few minutes and the men acted so important and busy that you didn't dare to ask questions. So I didn't know it was what they call a telephone until my father was so awful late for dinner that day.

This strained the patience of my mother and Linnie because they had lamb stew and dumplings for dinner. "The dumplings are a soggy mess," my mother said, "not fit to eat. I think that country storekeeping is a dog's life. We will all ruin our digestions with such queer hours."

"Well, I'm sorry," my father said. "But if you're going to have progress you have got to be willing to put up with such things.

Will Mead's telephone line got to us just about noon. They wanted to hook it up in the store right away because they were anxious to see if it worked. You can't blame them. This is the first telephone for Woodstock. There is a box halfway up the Overlook at Mead's and one in our store. If it works steady, Will Mead and his boarders will be just as good as right in the Village all the time. It's a mighty wonderful thing, I can tell you. Just before I came down to dinner I stood behind Will Elwyn's bookkeeping cage and said 'Hello' and 'How is the weather up there?' to Will Mead, and Will was behind the desk in Mead's Hotel two miles up the mountain. He said 'Hello, Abe' and 'It's cold up here,' and I heard him almost as plain as if he stood right beside me."

But my mother was thinking about the soggy dumplings yet. "What's so wonderful about that?" she said. "You knew it was probably cold up there already just like it is down here."

"Well, take a fire. He could let us know in a couple of seconds."

"Suppose he did? What good would it do? Mead's is halfway up the mountain. If it was a fire you would see it and know it from down here anyway. And what could you do about it?"

"Well, suppose Mead's needed a doctor?"

"Yes, I can see that. But how many times do they have a sickness at Mead's? Especially when there isn't time for Will Mead to come down and get the doctor?"

"If I was the victim I would think once would be enough," said my father.

"Just like boys with a toy," said my mother. "Look at the dumplings. I still say country storekeeping is a dog's life. There's no end to it. You expect to close up ten o'clock and somebody keeps you open till midnight. Some farmer who went to bed with the chickens routs you out five o'clock the next morning and asks if you want to sleep all day. You come back to breakfast late. And to dinner. And to supper. Just a dog's life."

"Have you ever thought what a dog's life is like?" asked my father. "Take the life of a well-rounded dog. Never forgets how to play. Never has to. Sleeps when he feels like it. Leaves when other dogs or people bore him. No hours when he must do this or that. He goes where he wants to, through back yards, along the brooks, over the fields and into the woods. I don't have much fault to find with my life, and the more business the better. But I think a dog has it all over me."

"Oh, pshaw," said my mother. "I guess you're glad you're a human being and not a dog. You are just talking to hear yourself talk again."

My father laughed and chonked down the soggy dumplings just as if he liked them and went on back to the store. "I want to telephone to Will again and ask how the weather up there is now," he said, very sober, to my mother and Linnie when he left.

I had never thought about a dog's life before but now I could see there was a lot in what my father said. I could see that I had a dog's life pretty much and so did Fred and Ira and Willie and Johnny Pepper and my brother Clifford and the Boice boys. We wandered over back yards. And got into the grape arbor back of Snyder's store, and sat up in the oxheart cherry tree and ate cherries right above the kitchen door of the Woodstock Hotel summer nights without being caught. We did not plan these things. We happened on them. Something new all the time. Like when we stumbled on the little pond on Abe Deyo's farm that he kept stocked and saw some big fish in it and rushed home for our fishing poles and caught thirteen bass as fast as we could drop our hooks in the water, and didn't get found out. Or like we happened on K'Neal Hogan's best chestnut tree just after he had thrashed it but we did get found out when K'Neal came down to district school next day and pointed us out.

And sometimes dogs and boys find something that is important and they come running and trying to tell people about it but people just don't pay any attention. That's the way it was with the coal mine.

We were playing shinny in a quarry hole that was frozen over. It was over back of the cemetery where nobody ever went. Nobody had worked any stone out of it for maybe fifty years as far as we knew. The sides had lots of brush and some moss on them.

We had been playing for quite a spell when Lancy Boice caught the can out in the open and gave it a real clout. Lancy is big and heavy. The can sailed through the air and hit the flat side of the quarry down at the other end from us. And it stuck there. An edge of the battered can had caught in a crack in the stone.

I was nearest so I went to get it and throw it back on the ice. But when I pulled it loose a part of the rock came with it and dropped on the ice at my feet. It looked like a big piece of flat rock and yet it didn't. For one thing it was too black.

I looked up at the quarry wall where the black piece had been and it looked like it was a piece of a layer. The solid bluestone came down to it and under it the solid bluestone began again clear down to the ice.

"Come on," shouted Lancy. "Throw out the can."

"Wait," I said. "Come here. All of you come here."

"What's the matter?" called Fred Elwyn.

"Come here and tell me what you think about this," I called.

They all skated over and I showed them the piece of black rock. I pointed to the way it was a layer three or four inches thick in the solid wall of bluestone.

"I've got a hunch," I said.

"I know what you think," said Willie Pepper.

"What does he think?" asked Delancy.

"Coal," said Willie.

"Coal?" said Egbert Boice. "Coal? It couldn't be. Let me see that."

Egbert was older and he knew about as much as anybody in

school. "Looks like coal," he said. "But coal don't come from here. Coal comes from Scranton. It's over in Pennsylvania. Comes through the Delaware and Hudson Canal to Rondout." He grabbed hold of my arm. "You've seen the big piles of it," he said, "when you take the yacht at Rondout to go to your grand-mother's at St. Remy."

"I know," I said.

"Do you know what this means?" Egbert said, all excited. "This is what they call a vein of coal. Maybe it leads to big mines of it all under the Overlook Mountain. Why, somebody could make a million out of it. And I'll bet we would be rich, too, because we found it."

"Let's run and tell the men what we've found," said Delancy. That seemed to hit the nail on the head and we all sat down and started to take off our skates.

Then Fred Elwyn spoke up. "Wait a minute," he said. "Let's do this thing right. If we run down to the Village and shoot off our mouths to every Tom, Dick and Harry about this stuff they will think we found it where there had been a coal pile or some-thing and won't pay any attention. And we will lose a fortune. Now, who is the man with the most brains in Woodstock? Let's go to him and find out if it really is coal. And if it is we will make him keep our secret till we make some plans."

"Dominie Park," I said.

"He's just a preacher," said Fred.

"He has been to college," I said.

"If you are going to a minister," said Delancy, "what's the matter with our Methodist minister?"

"Because he did not go to college," said Fred. "He only learned to preach. That's what my father says and he had ought to know because he goes to the Methodist church."

"How about Doctor Downer?" asked Egbert. "He has been to college and doctors have to study science. This coal business is science."

"I still think Dominie Park," I said. "Dominie Park went to two colleges. He must be the one with most brains."

"There's only one way to settle this," said Fred. "We'll draw cuts. The one that gets the shortest stick names the man."

So he got the sticks ready, eight of them, and we drew with our backs turned to him.

I got the shortest stick.

So it was Dominie Park and we set off to the Village and down the lane from the village green to the Dutch Reformed parsonage.

Dominie Park came to the door when we rapped and was surprised to see eight boys standing there. He had an open book in his hand and he took off his nose glasses when he saw us. He wanted us to come in but we didn't want to and we showed him the piece of black rock and told him where we had found it.

"We want to know if it is coal." I said.

He looked at it and turned it over and over.

"It looks very much like anthracite," he said.

"Is that coal?" asked Fred.

"Yes," said Dominie Park. "What they call hard coal. The other kind is soft coal. It is used in steam plants; but this is hard coal for heating houses, because it is cleaner. There is a very interesting story about this hard coal. Folks knew about soft coal and were using it. When they found this hard coal they tried to burn it but it did not seem to light fast like soft coal, and so they went away to eat or something. When they came back this hard coal had had time to make a very hot fire and they were very much surprised. But delighted, of course. This hard coal is a very interesting study. If you boys will come in we will look in the books and find out all about it. It comes from Pennsylvania, which is a good thing for us."

How much longer he would have talked about this coal I don't know. But Egbert broke in.

"What shall we do about it?" he asked.

"Do about it? How do you mean?" asked Dominie Park.

"Maybe there is lots and lots of it under the Overlook Mountain," said Egbert.

"It might be possible," said Dominie Park.

"It might make millions of dollars," said Egbert.

"Yes, I suppose that is true," said Dominie Park.

"So what shall we do about it?" asked Egbert. "Nobody knows it is there. We just happened to find it."

"Oh, yes, I see," said Dominie Park. "You want to know how to find out how much there is under the Overlook. Well now, boys, that means engineering, digging, maybe a tunnel or a shaft. And money. Lots of money. Those are things I don't know anything about."

There was more talk that slowed down more and more. Dominie Park wanted us to come in again and he said he would have Mrs. Park make us some coffee or something. It was a big temptation but we had got pretty low by that time and we left.

I was pretty disgusted with Dominie Park after all the work to get him selected and my saying he had the most brains.

"Your brainy man didn't turn out to be so much," said Willie Pepper.

"Maybe a Dominie wouldn't want to make a million dollars," I said.

"Do you suppose Dr. Downer would know what to do?" said Egbert.

So we went up to Dr. Downer's house but Mrs. Downer said he wasn't home.

Then we went to my father's store. Men around the white-bellied stove were talking about cows, but we butted in. The men there just looked at the coal and said, "Hmmmm."

"Don't you even want to go to the quarry hole and see?" I asked. But nobody said anything. Then they went back to the cows.

Then we went out. Just then Bent Bim was going past with his bobsleds and a load of logs from the woods. Delancy said let's climb up and straddle the logs and ride to his father's sawmill down by Riseley's Grove. So Egbert chucked the piece of coal away and we climbed on.

I did not think about the coal again until my father told about a dog's life. It's just like the life of boys in Woodstock. Nobody cares about the important things you try to do and so you might as well have a good time and let the coal mines go hang.

✿ Brook Romer's Temporary Conversion

. . . and the bear discovered in the hut

Delancy Boice didn't have anything for us to do at his house, so we started toward the school ground to build some more on the hut in the corner where the stone walls come together. On the way we had to go by the Test in the old sawmill. Delancy was riding on the seat of my bike while I pedaled and he said to stop.

"I might as well pass that Test right now," he said.

I stopped but I ho-hoed. "You're only ten," I said, "and only sixteen days older than I am. Nobody's every passed the Test until they are twelve anyway."

"None of them's ever been Delancy Boice," he said.

"Big talk," I said. "You're big, yes. But your imagination is bigger. But if you do and you should just happen to lose your balance and jump without breaking your big fat head, don't figure that I am going to try it, too."

"I've been thinking about it," he said. "It might be easy if you just walk out to the end of the beam and jump without stopping to wonder about it."

"That's what Clint Shultis did," I said. "Three or four years ago. He broke his leg, remember?"

But Lancy was already climbing up on the beam. He reached the top and straightened up and flung his arms out for balance. He started to walk out to the end of the beam fast but lost his balance and had to drop his hands down to hold on while he crooked his legs around the beam. I had been that far myself and I looked for him to turn around and slide back. But he stood up again and got balanced and went on. At the end of the beam he lowered his hips a little and bent his legs to spring off. I closed my eyes. I heard a thud and then a groan. I kept my eyes closed. I couldn't bear to look.

Then I heard him yell. He was calling my name.

I opened my eyes and looked down. I expected to see him down in the old tangled planks where you land if you don't jump far enough, and I thought he was hurt bad. But he wasn't there. Then he called again from up on the beam. He was straddled on it.

"Climb up here and help me," he called. "My pants are caught on a nail and I can't get loose."

I climbed up and crawled out on the beam as far as I could. I told him to move back a little so there was slack in his pants and I could unhook the nail.

"Didn't you jump?" I asked.

"Do you think I bounced back up here?" he asked.

"But I heard you strike and I heard you groan."

"You sure didn't see it."

"I closed my eyes when I saw you ready to jump. I couldn't bear to see you break a leg or something."

"And you heard me strike and groan?"

"Yes."

"You sure got a hell of an imagination, too" said Delancy. "I lost my balance and set down hard on the beam. It hurt. But I'll pass that damn test before I'm twelve years old. You see if I don't."

"You better wear old pants then," I said. "And now come on if we're going to do anything to the hut."

Some of the boys must have been to the hut before us because when we got there a lot more work had been done. It had three turns to crawl through on your belly now to get into the hut.

"We will try the entrance," said Lancy. "Two corners were hard enough to crawl around. Now three. Maybe we don't need another."

So we got down on our knees and started to crawl into the dark of the den. We had crawled past the first two turns. Delancy was ahead and me behind, but all of a sudden he stopped quick and I banged my head into his butt in the darkness.

Just then I heard it, too. It was a sound from inside the hut like a growl. The back of my neck kind of prickled. It must have been the same with Delancy because I felt his butt jam against my head again. He was trying to back up.

"What's that?" he whispered.

He started backing up against me and I started backing up, too. We backed out around the corners of the entrance as fast as we could and we got clear out into the open before anything happened. Out in the open you could move and move fast if you had to. Of course, that was pure instinct, but a pretty good instinct at that. But once outside and with nothing following us we felt better about it and our instinct went away. So we stood there and puzzled about it.

"It might be a bear," I said.

"That's right," said Lancy. "Remember last summer when the Italian came down from the Overlook Mountain with the two trained bears and had them together in front of the hotel? They sounded just like that. Maybe you wouldn't call it a growl but they forced the air out of their noses like they were disgusted and a little sore at the Italian because he kept at them with that long stick."

"Maybe they *were* disgusted," I said.

Delancy looked at the hut and thought a while. This calls for the council to meet," he said, "if we're going to get what's in there out. I wonder if we can find the other boys."

We ran. We ran up the dusty road to Pepper's blacksmith shop and found Willie and Johnny. Fred Elwyn was mowing their yard and didn't know whether he could leave, but he did. Ira Elwyn was working somewhere with his father because it was vacation time. We couldn't find my brother Clifford, and Roy Harder was driving team for his father's haying up at Rock City. But we were enough to decide, we guessed. We told them there was a bear in our hut.

We took them down to the school ground and listened outside but you couldn't hear anything. Fred Elwyn said we were crazy about a bear being inside. Besides we were all 'fraidy cats, he said, and he would crawl in through the entrance and prove there wasn't anything in there.

"Well," said Delancy. "It could be that whatever it was has left while we were hunting you."

"There's nothing in there now, anyway," said Fred.

We went around to the crooked entrance. Fred got down on his hands and knees and crawled in. We waited.

All of a sudden he came backing out in a rush.

"I heard it," he said.

"So now you believe it," said Delancy.

"I know how to get it out," said Fred. "Whatever it is. Anybody got a match?"

"What do you mean, anybody got a match?" said Willie Pepper.

"Lookit," said Fred. "Do you want to get it out or don't you want to get it out? What good is the hut with a bear inside? Maybe you would like a bear to be a member of our club."

Well, it took a lot of arguing, but Fred won.

"When that roof blazes," said Willie Pepper, "if it's a bear it will come bounding out right at us."

"I'll throw the match," said Fred, "and then we will all run behind the corner of the schoolhouse."

Willie Pepper always had a match because his father asked him to light the forge in the blacksmith shop sometimes. He gave one to Fred. Fred tiptoed up to the hut and got ready to strike the match. Everybody got ready to run.

The match fell in some dry leaves on the branches that covered the boards in the roof. They blazed right up and we ran. But we peeked around the corner of the schoolhouse. The fire caught leaf after leaf and then the twigs. It spread fast. The center got higher and higher and redder and redder. It began to roar like quick fires do. But nothing happened.

"That's funny," said Delancy.

"Maybe it wasn't a bear," said Fred. "Could anything else make a noise like that? The wind maybe? But there's no wind."

Just then there was a howling yell. The roof went right up in the air and the flames scattered in a wide circle. It was as if there had been an explosion and a man had been blown right up out of the flames. He came out yelling with his arms and legs already working like he was already running before he hit the ground. When his feet struck he was already moving fast. He took the stone wall by the Baldwin apple tree alongside the boy's backhouse in one jump, and made off across the field between the school grounds and the Big Deep in the Sawkill. He mowed down the scrub and saplings along the bank and went out of sight. We heard a big splash.

Then we looked at each other and nobody said a word for a minute.

Willie Pepper pointed his finger at Fred and said, "Now you've done it."

"It was only his coattail on fire," said Fred. "Didn't you see that?"

"Well, it was a man. Not a bear," said Lancy. "But who was it?"

"Didn't you see?" asked Fred.

"No. He went too fast."

"It was Brook Romer," said Fred.

"We don't have to be afraid of Brook," said Delancy. "He'll know we didn't know it was him."

"Let's go see," said Fred.

We climbed the stone wall and ran across the field to the Big Deep. It was Brook, and he was just climbing out on the bank. He stood up with the water pouring out of his clothes. He coughed and snuffed the water out of his head and spit, but before he could say anything Fred looked stern and said, "Brook, this is a pretty queer business."

Brook wiped the water out of his eyes and off his bald head and sniffed and spat again, and then he looked at Fred. "That's beginning to be my impression, too," he said.

That Fred just knew how to be top man. I don't believe he had to think it out. It was just natural. I could see that if we had let it go and tried to make out we didn't know anything about it Brook would probably find out. And then it would be our fault and Brook would be mad for two reasons. One would be that we set him afire and the other would be that we tried to lie out of it. But Fred wasn't giving him a chance. He was throwing the fault over on Brook right off.

That was an instinct Fred had that was different from the rest of us. Like in the spring, when all of us carried little bottles of maple sap in our hip pockets. I just happened to find the sweetest and reddest sap on Cal Short's tree across from the cemetery one day and was just ready to fill my bottle when Fred showed up from nowhere. "Stop," he said, "that's mine. Cal told me I could have all the sap from this tree." I didn't think fast enough but by the time I figured out that Cal Short had not told him any such thing Fred had the sap in his bottle.

So now he said to Brook, "What business did you have growling in our den and scaring us? We thought it was a bear. You made us burn you out. Now the den is ruined."

Brook looked himself over. He pulled his coat around and looked at the tail burned off. "Do you mean that you boys started that fire?" he said.

"Yes," said Fred. "It's our den."

"So it is," said Brook. He ran his eye up and down Fred and then he looked at the Big Deep.

"How would you like a bath?" he asked.

"You're in bad already," said Fred. "Don't try to do anything that will make it worse."

Brook said, "Yes. I guess you're right. I was in a dead sleep and must have been snoring. It's my fault, I guess."

Delancy came up closer. "Brook," he said, "you take off the wet clothes and let's build a fire and dry them."

Fred thought that was a good idea and so did Brook, and so Fred took charge. He said to Willie Pepper, "You've got a match. You get a bunch of leaves and twigs and be fire-tender. Johnny, you go out into the clearing and be sentry to let us know if anybody is coming. Maybe boys can be in their birthday suits in swimming, but a naked man would get us in bad. Lancy, you and Willie Rose find some dry wood and bring it to Willie Pepper. I'll help Brook to get his clothes off."

It looked to me as if Brook could get his own clothes off and Fred wouldn't be doing much. But then I guess that's the way it always is with bosses.

Brook must have been dead drunk and crawled into the den to sleep it off out of sight. But running across the field with his coattail on fire and jumping into the Big Deep all over sobered him up some. When his clothes were dry he was sober enough to put them back on, but he looked terrible. His coat was a swallow tail and where the fire had burned it away it was charred and showed so much of his seat you could see his suspender buttons.

"This ain't good," said Fred.

He looked over the coat and rubbed his chin. Pretty soon he said, "Lancy, remember when you tore that rip in your pants up at the cider mill and you didn't want your mother to know it and ask where you had been? Remember how you sneaked a needle and thread out of your house and we fixed it?"

"Now wait a minute," said Delancy. "I may get caught."

But Fred didn't pay any attention to him. "And you," he said to me, "here's where you can really do something. You know the little pieces of cloth they have left over at your father's store? What do they call them?"

"Remnants," I said.

"That's it. You go up and get one of them."

"What? A whole remnant?"

"Just a small piece, dummy."

Well, that wasn't so hard. These littlest pieces they had left over beyond a yard the clerks just measured long and let them go to the customer without cutting them off. But once in awhile there was a customer so hard to please that the clerks gave them just what they bought and no more, even if it was the end of a bolt. They knew my father wouldn't like that, so they sneaked the ends into a barrel with the rubbish down back of the store. I could get one easy.

"And Lancy," said Fred. "Bring along a scissors, too."

"What are you going to do?" asked Brook. He yawned. He was dressed now except for his coat. He lay down on a grassy spot by the fire.

Fred didn't answer him. He sidled up to the rest of us and whispered out of the corner of his mouth, "Let him go to sleep." Brook did, right away, and began to snore.

Delancy was back before I was, because it was only a little ways to the Boice house across lots. But I got back pretty soon, too. Fred said I made a good selection. It almost matched the coat.

One nice thing about the remnant was that it was big enough so that Fred could double it before he cut it into the shape that Brook's coattail had been. Then we took turns sewing up the edges and sewing it onto Brook's coat. Fred put on the coat and you could hardly notice it had a new tail.

We told Fred his idea was wonderful and what a big success it was. But he just said, "Well, I'll tell you how it is. There are men in this town, even the ministers, who mean a lot to us boys when they find some time to spare for us. Even our fathers. Maybe they lick us sometimes but I guess we have it coming. But Brook is different. He's always got time for us. Not a one of us can remember far back enough to the first time Brook picked us up when we fell down and were hurt and put us on his knee to tell us stories. He always understands and never bawls us out. Look at the two clubs he helped us form, and our Anti-Cigarette badges. He even saves his empty whiskey bottles for us so we can take them back to one of the hotels and get pennies for candy. And yet he needs pennies more than we do. Of course, he gets drunk, lousy drunk, but he is perfect except for that and we can't do enough for him."

We heard a noise behind us and turned. It was Brook. He had come awake. He had heard what Fred was saying and was getting to his feet. Brook picked up his coat and saw the new tail on it. He looked over at us and smiled. We smiled back and came over to him. We knew that he could see we had gone to quite a lot of trouble for him.

"Boys," he said, "thanks." Then he looked at Fred. "I heard what you were saying. Especially that drunk, lousy drunk business and about it's being bad. It is bad, boys."

He stopped talking because he was filled up. He waited a minute until he could trust himself to speak. "It has been a peculiar but a wonderful afternoon," he said. "The healthful touch of nature and contact with the heart. I'll tell you how I feel right now. I feel like swearing to you boys that I'll never get drunk again as long as I live."

But he did, of course.

✿ First Business Deal

. . . and what the Devil finds for idle hands

"Your father didn't hurt you much just with one slap of the daybook on your bottom," said Linnie. "You may hurt inside but I'll bet he hurts worse."

"And maybe it was the best way to teach you a very important lesson," said my mother. "I could preach and preach to you boys without doing as much as one little slap of that daybook. I have told you time and again that the Devil finds things for idle hands to do. So why don't you get busy raking up the twigs and leaves from the locust trees in the yard? Then you won't be tempted."

What had happened was that the mule stage from West Hurley had dumped off a big bale of raw peanuts in front of the store that morning when Clifford and I were hanging around. It was the first day of school vacation and it was once when time was not of the essence.

Clifford and I knew all about raw peanuts. They are no good until the man has carried the bale down into our kitchen and my mother and Linnie have roasted them in the big oven of our wood stove. But just the same we noticed that the weave of the bale was pretty loose and we began to work it open big enough to get out a few of the raw peanuts. We thought we stopped quick enough when Will Longyear came out of the store and said he didn't want to see any more of that. He came out twice more and he could see, of course, that the hole was bigger and we had not stopped. After he went in the third time my father came busting out of the door all of a sudden with the daybook in his hand.

Clifford and I took off down toward the barn and I don't know where Clifford got to but I rounded the back of the house. I was older so I guess that's why my father kept after me. He caught up with me in the front yard under the locust tree and grabbed hold of my shoulder and slapped me on my behind once with the daybook. And he said I would get more if there was any more of that peanut business. It was the first time my father ever slapped me with anything. He went right back up to the store and I went into the house bawling.

After my mother and Linnie made me believe that my father would not stay mad at me, I went out under the locust trees and looked around at the ground. The twigs and leaves were pretty bad, just like my mother said, and I decided to try out that idle-hands business and got a rake and started to rake them up. Where I had raked began to look so much better that I was kinda proud of what I was doing and got interested, and I guess it was true that the Devil wasn't anywhere around.

Somebody said, "Hello, there," and I looked out over the white picket fence. It was old Aaron Riseley with his white beard and his cane. He had come along the path outside the fence and stopped to watch what I was doing. And that's when my first business deal and I came together.

"Did your father tell you to rake up the yard?" he asked.

"No," I said. "I didn't have to do it. In a way I just wanted to do something so that the Devil would not find something for my idle hands to do."

"Do you like to rake?" he asked.

"I don't like it and I don't not like it," I said. "But my mother

says the Devil finds things for idle hands to do and I'm finding
out it is not just a fancy saying."

"Well, well," he said. I went on raking and he just stood there
and watched me. Pretty soon he said, "How would you like to do
that kind of a job for money?"

"I'm just a boy," I said. "I wouldn't want to work all day raking things up. This is school vacation. I want to have time for
what us boys do when something is going on."

"I understand that," he said. "This job of mine you can do
when you want to and you can stop and do what the boys do when
you want to. Vacation is a long time. There will be times when
your hands are idle and you know now what the Devil can find for
them. I am Aaron Riseley."

"Yes. I know," I said.

"I own Riseley's Grove."

"Yes, I know."

"I want the Grove raked out. Not so much the pine cones and
not the carpet of needles, of course. But the wind blows down a lot
of the dead limbs. I want them raked up and old picnic boxes
and papers I want dumped down over the bank of the Sawkill,
but not in the water. Think you can do it?"

I thought about the grove. It was big and raking it up would
be a lot of work.

"I don't know whether I could do it alone," I said.

"You could get another boy to help you. I'll give you and the
other boy—well, let me see—I'll give you and the other boy
seventy-five cents."

I had never earned any money and so it was a temptation. Well,
not exactly a temptation, I thought, because my hands would not
be idle and I didn't see how the Devil could sneak into it.

So I said, "I will do it."

"Fine," he said. "Get started any time. The sooner the better."

He went on and I dropped my rake and went looking for Fred

Elwyn. Larry Elwyn has boys of all ages but Fred is my age and he is the one I go with. Fred is very smart. He always has ideas about doing what when.

I found Fred oiling his bicycle in the part of their barn that Larry Elwyn does not use for a barber shop.

"We'll start at the Big Deep end of the Grove," he said. He was all steamed up. "That way we can stop and take a swim when we get sweaty and tired. Why, it won't be any harder than to have some little thing to do when we are resting between swims. Tell you what. We will rake in circles. You on one half of the circle and me on the other. When we meet in the center we'll carry the pile to the creek bank and throw it over. It's like engineering," he said, acting important. "You have to plan these things. And boy, think of jingling seventy-five cents in my pocket!"

It didn't look like much when we started in but there was a funny thing about that grove. It got bigger and bigger as we went along. When we first looked over the job we figured we could do it in about a week. But the first week went by and the second week went by and pretty soon the first month went by. There was an awful lot of that grove to do yet when it got into August. Fred and I got terrible sick of that grove and the only thing that kept us going on it was two things. We said we would do it; and the seventy-five cents apiece. I guess it was mostly the seventy-five cents. I got so tired I chucked the job one day and Fred couldn't get me to come back. Then he had a bright idea. He said to come back because he wanted to show me something.

"How many times does five go into seventy-five?" he asked me.

"It goes fifteen times," I said.

He broke up little sticks until he had fifteen of them. He laid them out on the pine needles. "Now," he said, "just say that each one of these little sticks is a nickel. You have got fifteen in your pocket. Fifteen. If you went into Mower's and got a dish of home-made vanilla ice cream every day you could do it for fifteen days.

If you went in every other day you could do it for a whole month and that would take you to cold weather when you wouldn't want any ice cream. No more begging for a nickel and not getting it sometimes when you do. Just walking around independent as a hog on ice. Ice cream or candy or spare wire or a jew's-harp or a mouth organ whenever you wanted it and not having to kiss anybody's ass for the money."

"A hog on ice is not very independent," I said. "If he is dead and on ice he's dead and is not moving around very much. And if he's alive on ice he'd slip around all over the place."

Both of us started to laugh because we could see a hog slipping and sliding on one of the quarry holes in the wintertime and squealing all the time and not getting anywhere.

So I went back to work. So when you come right down to it the pay was what kept us at it. I wouldn't wonder if that's the way it is with a lot of work in this world. People keep at it because of the pay. I know I heard my father say one time that the finest feeling in the world is to feel bought and paid for.

We didn't get that grove finished until after school started. But we worked at it afternoons after school and on Saturdays. And one day it was done.

"When do you think old Aaron will pay us?" asked Fred.

I wondered too. He didn't seem to come around and both of us did not dare to go and ask him for the pay. Aaron Riseley was very stern. I didn't know about him but it could be that he was very proud of his credit. I have heard my father say that some men are so proud of their credit that they do not pay up for a long time. And so we waited.

The thing ran along and it ran along so that it raised doubts in Fred. One day he said he guessed I never had any business deal with old Aaron at all. "What did you do, dream it?" he said.

He saw that he had hurt me and so he said, "Well, hell, forget it." He took on a look of being very wise. "But the grove looks nicer and we did it and that's something, even if we won't be independent and will have to ask for any little thing we want."

That sort of ended it and we quit straining about it and went on to other things.

Then one day, late in the fall, after the frost had opened the shucks of the walnuts and chestnuts, I was on my way down across Riseley's bridge over Sawkill Falls. I was bound for two walnut trees in the lot where Riseley's cows got killed by lightning and where I was pretty sure nobody had been for walnuts.

Who should I meet on the road across the bridge but Aaron Riseley! He was walking with his cane, and his long white beard made him look fierce, like pictures of Moses. He looked at me when I went by but he didn't seem to know me. He seemed to be lost in thinking. But after I passed a little I heard him call to me.

I went back and he pulled some money from his pocket. "I was in the grove the other day," he said. "Are you Abe Rose's boy?"

"Yes," I said. "I am. I am the boy you made a business deal with."

"I don't think I ever paid you," he said.

Then he counted out seventy-five cents to me and said, "You can pay the other boy." With that he went on and I just stood still in the road and looked after him. There was an awful mistake, of course, but I didn't dare tackle him about it.

I didn't go after walnuts that day but went to find Fred. I told him what had happened and said that when Mr. Riseley made his business deal with me he must have meant that he would give seventy-five cents to have the grove cleaned and not seventy-five cents to each of us.

"He said I was to pay you," I said. "Half would be thirty-seven and a half cents. It is seven and a half dishes of Mower's ice cream, and not fifteen. But you can't split a cent. So you take thirty-eight cents and I'll take thirty-seven. After all," I said, "you figured out all the engineering. I only worked."

For once Fred didn't say anything. He just narrowed his eyes at me. He took the thirty-eight cents and walked off. I knew he was thinking that Aaron Riseley paid me twice seventy-five cents and that I was just trying to be too big a businessman.

I told Brook Romer about it and the Devil and idle hands. "I guess you'll find out," he said, "that the Devil is hanging around all the time. No matter whether your hands are idle or busy. But what I can't understand is why you didn't tell Aaron Riseley the bargain was for seventy-five cents for each of you."

"What, argue with Aaron Riseley?" I said. "He's so old and stern that he was in the Civil War and got through Andersonville prison alive. If you are a boy you don't tackle Aaron Riseley."

"No, I suppose not," said Brook. "Come to think of it, that wasn't when you made your mistake in the business deal. You made it when you took the job. Right then is when you had to have your eyes open. You will find that you have to be wary in a business deal. I made the same mistake in that lawsuit. You remember that lawsuit, don't you?"

I got Fred alone after about a week and I explained the whole thing to him and told him what Brook said. I explained all about idle hands and busy hands and the Devil. And that in a business deal you have to have your eyes open and get everything settled right at the start.

"Well," said Fred, "I can see that Brook is right about it. The Devil didn't have anything to do with it, though. It was because you was dumb, dumb, dumb. If you will admit that, we will be good friends again."

"I admit it," I said, and so that made it all right with Fred.

❧ Willie Pepper, Inventor

. . . and it's how inventions are used that counts

Willie Pepper always talks like he is going to be an inventor when he grows up. He is around his father's blacksmith shop all the time when he is not doing something else and he has a lot of ideas that he talks about that just pop into his head. The only trouble is that most of them pop right out again. And there is another thing about inventions. Some look all right when they are used right, but when they are used wrong they can be worse than if they had never been invented at all.

That's the way it was with Willie Pepper's invention for sliding downhill in the summertime.

The way it came about was this. We were playing marbles one morning until Fred Elwyn won all the marbles. Nobody wanted to trade him anything for some of the marbles, not even Ira Elwyn who had two snare wires and needed only one. And so we had to stop marbles and didn't have anything else to do.

All this was down in Pepper's front yard, where the walk to the front door is level and you can draw a circle on the walk to put the agates in, and the cracks between the flagstones make perfect lines to shoot from so that nobody can creep nearer to the circle without being caught.

But nobody but Fred had any more marbles and that ended it. We didn't have anything else to do and so we flopped down on the grass in the shade of the big horse-chestnut tree in Pepper's yard and waited for something to turn up. We had done this before and something always turned up.

"If Kingston Water Works would let anybody go near the Sawkill we could go for a swim in the Big Deep," said Fred.

"Maybe the drovers with a herd of cattle will come along," said Ira Elwyn, "and we can earn a dime by watching them while the drovers eat dinner."

"Maybe," said Fred.

"I wish the Italian with the trained bears would come down out of the Overlook," said Delancy Boice.

"That happened only once," said Fred. "It won't happen again. Because people only watched and did not pitch him enough nickels and dimes."

"If it was fall we could go for chestnuts and walnuts," I said.

"Yes, if," said Fred.

All this time Willie Pepper had his head propped up on his hand and his elbow on his knee and was looking at the side of the blacksmith shop. He wasn't saying a thing and I knew that he was thinking. All of a sudden he said, "We could ride downhill."

Fred Elwyn sat clear up. "Are you crazy?" he said. "Sliding downhill is for wintertime. You have to have a crust on the snow and sleds and bobs."

"And colds and sniffles in the head all the time," said Willie Pepper. "That's the trouble. You have to be all bundled up. The wet mittens freeze. Your nose runs all the time. You have to go home and get warmed up too much."

"Well, you can't do it without snow," said Fred.

"Maybe we can," said Willie Pepper. "Come on."

We got up and followed him to the blacksmith shop. There was always a lot of old iron, rusty bolts, boards, planks, wagon wheels, and almost everything else around the outside of the blacksmith shop, and Willie Pepper can mosey around in these old things without anybody stopping him and telling him to get out, because Henry Pepper is his father.

Willie went in the shop and told us to wait. He came out with a brace and a wood bit about an inch wide and we went to the back of the shop.

He told us to find four old wagon wheels the same size and asked Delancy, who is big for his age, to stay with him and help him. When we came back with the wheels, they were boring holes in each end of a long plank. Then Willie hunted up two old iron axles and two big bolts, and when we bolted them in we had a pair of wheels at each end of the plank. You could see right away that if we straddled the plank and if the boy in front steered by taking hold of the front axle and the boy behind took hold of his axle and kept the back wheels in line, we could ride down any hill like a bobsled, even if it was the summertime.

It took quite a while, and we had to be home for dinner and come back before we were finished. But along late in the afternoon we were ready to go and we pushed Willie's invention up in front of the Woodstock Hotel.

We headed the invention down the long grade that runs all the way from the hotel down past the Lutheran Church and the old sawmill and almost to Jimmy Lasher's house. Then we got straddle of the plank and started off. Willie Pepper was in front steering the front wheels and Delancy was in back to keep the back wheels in line; but, of course, he had to reach back of himself to get hold of the back axle.

We went fine and faster and faster. Everything would have been all right but there is a thank-you-ma'am in the grade about where the old sawmill is. Teamsters use it with heavy loads to partly hold the wagon and let their teams rest. We were going fastest right there and Delancy wasn't ready for it. The back wheels jumped up over the thank-you-ma'am. Delancy lost his hold on the back axle, and flew up in the air, and when he came down on the road we had gone on. With nobody holding the back wheels in line, they skewgeed off the road and into the ditch and the bank across the ditch, where we stopped after bumping around for about a hundred feet.

Delancy came running. He wasn't hurt, only scrubbed a little on his backside where he hit the road. Willie Pepper got off the front end and said, "Something about this invention is wrong."

"You don't say," said Fred. He was excited and I guess all of us were.

"I think I know what it is," said Willie. "The hole in the back end of the plank is in the wrong place. That end of the plank had ought to go far enough behind the back axle so that the boy behind can set back of the axle and take hold of it in front of him."

We pushed the invention back up the hill and stopped at the blacksmith shop to make that change. Then we went up in front of the Woodstock Hotel and started again.

This time everything went fine until we got almost to the bottom. But nobody had noticed that Johnny Saxe and his mules with the mail stage from West Hurley was coming up the road from Aaron Riseley's. We didn't see him till after we had started and couldn't stop. We figured that he would get out of the way but he must have been musing and looking at the rumps of the mules. He heard us yell just in time and yanked his mules to one side with a cut of the whip. "What the hell," he shouted as we went flying past. Except for that it was a good ride and it was plain that Willie Pepper had another good invention.

We got in one more ride before suppertime. It was perfect because we waited until nobody was on the road all the way down to Aaron Riseley's boarding house. This time we coasted all the way to the little bridge over that tiny brook below Jimmy Lasher's.

We hustled back after supper and had one ride but some of the young blades saw what we were doing and began to take an interest. Hazel Stanley was there too, of course. She is a city boarding girl who is quite a tomboy. She is a big girl and sometimes when the evening is chilly and she rides her bicycle to the village just to hang around and see what's doing, she wears a turtle-neck sweater which is strictly for men and boys and not for girls. This makes her look too much like a girl and I have heard some of the young blades make remarks on the QT, and some of these remarks are not very nice.

And, of course, Jim Plass was there and so you could expect some kind of trouble before very long.

It was like Jim Plass that he didn't ask if he could take over Willie Pepper's invention. We heard him talking about how he guessed he would try it out and would some of the young blades like to go along. He was joshing with Hazel Stanley, too, about taking a ride with them and she said nobody could dare her. So he just came over with a bunch of them and with Hazel and he said, "Step back, infants. Let some real riders take her down once."

"What could we do about it?" Fred Elwyn said later.

They piled on with a lot of laughing and hollering and started off. Jim Plass was in front steering and Hank Vandenberg was behind ahold of the back axle. The rest were strung along the plank so the extra load that was more than boys made the plank bend down some in the middle, but anybody could see that this extra load would make it go faster downgrade. Hazel Stanley was about in the middle and she said for the boarder behind her to put his arms around her and hold her on. They were all letting out loud yells like a couple of tomcats in the middle of the night.

The trouble was that it was almost dark and nobody had taken a look at the road. They were flying down past the old sawmill when everybody saw that old K'Neal Hogan was walking up the middle of the road. He walks with a cane and he is another one that looks like pictures of the prophets in the Bible that Libby Riseley used to give us when we were in her primary class in Sunday School. K'Neal moves slow and he wears a coat longer than most on a chilly night. He looked up and saw this contraption coming down the hill right at him and the way he made for the ditch with his long coat flying out and forgetting to use his cane had everybody laughing for a minute in spite of themselves. But the laugh stopped as sudden as it began and changed to a gasp.

Jim Plass had tried to steer away from K'Neal Hogan but he lost control and this made Hank Vandenberg lose control of the back axle. Willie Pepper's invention went into the ditch and struck something and jumped into the air. The riders flew up and away from it like sticks when you put a giant firecracker under a pile of them on the Fourth of July.

We ran down the road. Everybody was getting up by the time we got there and brushing off and shouting different things, except Hazel Stanley. She didn't get up but just lay there as if she was dead. But it turned out that her limb was broken and she had only fainted.

Willie Pepper and Fred Elwyn and the rest of us boys hung around until they got Doctor Downer down for Hazel Stanley. Then we went and got Willie's invention and set it up straight on its wheels. We were starting to push it back up to the Village when Jim Plass called out, "Never would have happened if you boys hadn't brought that damned thing around."

Henry Pepper was waiting for us when we got to the blacksmith shop. He didn't say much except to tell us it was too bad and that we must put Willie's invention back of the shop and leave it there.

That was the end of riding downhill in the summertime even though it had all the fun of a bobsled in the wintertime and without wet mittens and the sniffles. But it was like a lot of other inventions that are wonderful. If they are used wrong they can be terrible things.

❧ God and Will Elwyn's Store

. . . and rifles and blisters and red pepper

It was the middle of the night, of course, when Will Elwyn's new store burned down. Somehow if you have got to have a big fire in Woodstock it is in the middle of the night. That's when we had the big fire at Dr. Smith's boarding house and so it was when we were having the Will Elwyn store fire.

Our house was not in so much danger as when Dr. Smith's fire was right across the road, but my father's store was in danger because Will Elwyn's new store was right across the road from it; and there was just as much danger to Mr. Lown's house and to Mower's Ice Cream Parlor right next to my father's store. But if my father's store caught, our home would be in just as much danger, of course, because our home was right next to it. So my mother woke me and my brothers and told us to get dressed and to get out of the house and to be careful.

When I got out I could see that the men were handling this Will Elywn fire in a different way from the Dr. Smith fire. In Dr. Smith's the men formed long lines down to Tannery Creek and handed buckets along. They had six or eight buckets. The full buckets went from hand to hand and the last man splashed just the one bucket full up against Lown's house or against ours. No use splashing any water on Dr. Smith's boarding house, of course, because it was a goner anyway. When the bucket had been splashed it was handed back empty along the line of men to the creek. Oh, they used wet blankets, too, up against the buildings they were trying to save, and kept them soaked as best they could.

But after that Dr. Smith fire the men got to talking and they
decided they needed a better way. In the first place, some buildings were too far away from the creek for that sort of thing. Of
course, there were pumps but pumps are slow and you can't have
a line of men to three or four pumps anyway. There are not that
many men.

So it was Larry Elwyn, as I recall, who suggested keeping empty
hogsheads on hand. These could hold almost as much as three barrels. The store got them with molasses and turpentine and things
like that.

"If there is a fire," Larry said, "we will wheel these out as close
as we can and keep them filled. If it is near a pump we will use a
hose. Or we will form a line to as many pumps as we can and keep
the hogsheads filled with buckets. Then the men splashing water
can dip in fast. If the level gets down, a man can get right in the
hogsheads to dip and hand out the buckets. And we can spot some
around the Village before there is any fire and have them filled
already with a top over them."

So that's how the men were saving Lown's and my father's
store and Mower's, in the Will Elwyn fire. You could see that the
hogsheads helped some.

About Will Elwyn's new store burning down I didn't care. It
wasn't any news to me anyway. I can't say that I knew it would
burn down but I knew something would happen to it when God
got ready. You couldn't be a graduate from Libby Riseley's Primary Sunday School class and not know that there would be an end
to Will Elwyn's new store some day. The picture cards Libby gave
us every Sunday proved that. Some of them showed the queer
ends that kings and princes and wives and husbands came to in
the old days when God was more active. Like Absalom, who was
so vain about his wonderful hair, but it was the thing that caught
in a tree and made him powerless and he was killed.

It wasn't that Will Elwyn was bad although you could say that his new store was a little too vain. He was one of the finest men in Woodstock and had been my father's partner until he pulled out and built this new store. You couldn't say that it was his fault that God ended his new store. But he had too many bad people working in the store.

I watched the fire and the smoke shoving way up into the sky until the best part of the sight was over and you could see that all of the other buildings would be saved, and then I went and sat on our veranda and thought about it.

I remembered when I had overheard my father tell my mother that Will Elwyn had got a crazy idea and was going to build a big new store right across the street from our store. "It is a shame," my father said, "because he is giving up a partnership with me where he is keeping the books and doing just what his talents had ought to do. But his friends have money and have influenced him. That is a big group around here and I suppose they figure on giving all their trade to Will. They have seen how I got along starting with nothing and it looks easy to them, which it isn't. It's work, of course. Anybody can do that if he will. But it's knowing how, and being able to control yourself, and knowing that people are human, and glorying with some and sympathizing with others, and paying the same for everybody's butter when you know you'll have to bury some of it. And it's being strict about paying your bills on time, and doing that before you take out a cent for yourself, and knowing merchandise and the sixth sense of knowing what folks will buy and close attention all the time, and taking care, care, care. Yes, and it's being a church man and a lodge man. It is building a reputation for the real values in life, never too strict and never too slack."

"I know," my mother said. "But now it don't do any good to worry. I guess if you just go on doing the right thing it will come out all right. We used to get along on very little. We can get along on very little again. Why, my days, when we first started out we lived in a few rooms on the second floor in Rondout and carried every drop of water from a city hydrant a block away."

"But we were young," said my father. "And only ourselves to look after."

"Yes, it was easier then."

"You see, this is going to take a big slice of the trade," my father said, "and there's just so much. Clerk hire, horses, light, heat, insurance, losses, they all go on just the same in a big store. Good heavens, I wonder how many stores people think can get along in Woodstock. It isn't Will. I know Will. He's listened to a lot of bad advice, that's all."

"Of course, folks have a right to go into the store business if they want to," my mother said. "You had a right when you came here even though Snyder's was well established and had built up a good solid business. I don't suppose Ed Snyder liked it very much. But you had a right. You knew it and they knew it."

"But I started in a small way," my father said. "I had to inch my way along with a lot of worry and hard work. The Snyders had that comfort at least. They had years to get used to the idea and time to scale to it. But Will Elwyn is starting out with almost as big a store as Ed Snyder and I have now. When I started in, it was just Snyder's and me and I was scrawny. Now it's Snyder's and me and Will Elwyn and none of us are scrawny. There just won't be enough to go round."

"It's you and Snyder's and Will Elwyn," my mother said. "You have the biggest and you are free of debt and you know how. God has looked after us because you have looked after what He put in your hands to look after. And I believe He will go right on doing it."

"You can't leave everything to the Lord," my father said. "The Lord helps those who help themselves."

"The Lord helps those who work and save," my mother said, "but not them as do nothing but worry. You know what you always say. All things work together for good to those who love the Lord."

"I believe they do," said my father. "But sometimes it takes a long time. In the meantime I could go broke."

"If so, that would be God's will," my mother said.

"Well, it isn't my will," said my father. "I can see that sales will go down. I will have to find a way to cut expenses and keep on giving as much service. I don't know how I'll do it but it's my job, not God's. There's just one thing I know and that is if I can make it better for the customers to trade with me they will trade with me."

They didn't know I was listening and I didn't say anything because children don't know anything anyway and they never say anything when their fathers and mothers are talking serious like that.

But I thought my mother was right and that God had ought to do something about this thing because my father did work hard and he had a good store, and where two things are joined together like that it is not going to help God or anybody else very much to wreck them.

So after I said my prayers and got into bed I said something more to God without their knowing it because I said it in my mind. I asked God to do something about Will Elwyn's store and to help my father with his. And so when they said Will Elwyn's store was burning down I remembered what I had asked God to do and so it didn't surprise me.

After I cooled down from the first excitement and was on our veranda watching the fire and thinking, I could see that things had been working right along. In a way it wasn't God that had started the fire at all. It was God's rule that started it. If Will Elwyn had been there all the time and had paid attention and had worked like my father said you have to in the store business this fire would not have come along. But the trouble was that Will didn't, and so there you are.

Right from the start Will Elwyn's store was interesting to the young blades who fool around with horseplay and stories, and he hired a couple of these for clerks. All this attracted the boys and I remembered that I seemed to be there a lot. I remembered now that I heard stories there that I knew my mother and father wouldn't like. The horseplay and the stories would not have happened if Will Elwyn had been there but Will wasn't there a good part of the time. He was young and he liked to hunt and fish and be in politics and such things.

And then a lot of other things happened that seemed to be in connection with the store. Such things as troubles for other people who didn't mean any harm but were caught just the same.

Two of them caught my older brother Harry. One day he came running home with his feet full of blisters. It was summer and my mother had let him have his feet bare. He was up around Will Elwyn's store like a moth around a flame, I suppose. The clerks had been burning rubbish out in the road in front of the store but too close to the store, like anybody careless will do. Harry came along shoving his bare feet through the dust and when he came to the pile of ashes they looked burned out and gray and cold.

Some of these young blades who hung around the store were on the front porch of the store and they could have called to Harry and warned him, but they didn't. So Harry came shoving his bare feet through the dust which gives you a wonderful feeling when you have your feet bare. With each shove of a foot he would say "choo" in a slow way so that he sounded to himself like a steam engine coming along. He "choo-chooed" right through the pile of ashes and he was so busy choo-chooing that when his feet struck into the live ashes underneath it was a second before he came to himself.

Then he screamed and lit out for home and the young blades on the store porch laughed and laughed and slapped their legs because they had been watching Harry come choo-chooing along and had been waiting for the surprise when he struck the ash pile. And when Harry's sudden change was so much more than they expected, they like to have died with so much laughing. When I saw Harry's feet I could have killed them; and I believe my mother and Linnie could have, too, for all my mother's Methodist faith.

Another time Harry teased my father so much for a rifle that when my father came back from one of his weekly trips to Kingston he had a Flobert rifle for Harry's birthday. Harry was almost beside himself with pride and joy, and it was a good thing that he was so happy because it turned out he had only a day to enjoy the rifle.

Afterward my father said he ought to have had sense enough not to give Harry a rifle. But I didn't think it was that way. My father is not a hunter and he does not know about shotguns and rifles or he would have given the rifle to Harry just the same; but he would have done it the way Larry Elwyn, who hunts foxes, gives shotguns and rifles to his boys. And that would be to go out with Harry and show him things he could do and could not do with a rifle. For one thing, if somebody wants to look at the rifle you have to be sure that it is not loaded.

This Flobert rifle was just for a boy. It was not the best rifle in the world, like maybe a Stevens rifle is, that you can get by selling subscriptions to the *Youth's Companion*. You cocked this Flobert rifle and slipped one bullet into it. Then you let the hammer down easy on the shell to carry around and be ready to shoot at a rabbit or whatnot. If you wanted to shoot you just pulled the hammer back and aimed.

The day after he got it, Harry went up through the street and in the road between my father's store and Will Elwyn's store. Jim Plass saw him with the rifle and came over to him. Jim Plass was always trying to be smarter than he was, and he wasn't very

smart or even anything much, when you came right down to it.
But, of course, Harry was feeling pretty big with his rifle and it
pleased him when Jim Plass took notice that he had one.

Two old men were sitting on the porch of Will Elwyn's store
and they were arguing about politics. One was Jonathan Whispel
and the other was Henry Lasher. Jonathan Whispel was a Demo-
crat, so he was an active talker with his hands and arms.

Just then he flung his hand out at the end of his arm and held
it there while he was probably damning Republicans, and there
was the crack of a rifle. A bullet crashed right through Will Elwyn's plate-glass window in the exact spot where Jonathan
Whispel's hand would be, right then, if he hadn't moved it. He
thought he was hit but then he and Henry came to and saw that it
was only the plate-glass window which, of course, was bad enough.

There was excitement and loud talk. People came running out
of both stores and Mr. Whispel and Mr. Lasher jumped up and
ran out to Harry and Jim Plass, and they were mad.

Jim Plass was calling Harry a damn little fool and Harry was
holding the rifle by that time because Jim shoved it right back
in his hands when the rifle went off.

But Harry said Jim Plass wanted to see the rifle. Jim took it and
put his thumb on the hammer to cock it and it must have slipped.

It could have been very serious, of course. As it was everybody
was mad and my father's patience was very strained. He scolded
Harry and took the rifle away from him and then went into Will
Elwyn's store to pay for the window.

A few days later, men around the white-bellied stove in my
father's store seemed to remember only how surprised Jonathan
Whispel and Henry Lasher were when they thought they had been
shot. Ed Harder would say, "Old man Whispel had just said he
didn't want to live any more with Republicans in power but that
shot changed his mind." Then they would laugh.

But Harry didn't laugh for a long time.

It was in Will Elwyn's store, too, that I first learned that there is any sin in our family. My father smoked a Peter Schuyler after dinner every day, but smoking a cigar or a pipe or even a little chewing for some of the older men is only a little off from being perfect. So our family was about as perfect as a family can be. Besides being strong in the church and family prayers every morning, we didn't play cards and didn't bet and there was never any cider in the house. My father kept out of the bars in the Woodstock Hotel and Sam Elwyn's, and he voted the Prohibition ticket unless there was some great issue like 16 to 1, he said, when a man had to be practical and make his vote count.

But in Will Elwyn's store one day the young blades were talking about drinking, and laughing about some of the funny things that what they called "soaks" do. I was listening and I had ought to know enough to keep my mouth shut sometimes. Most always I do but that time I didn't. I knew that being a "soak" was a sin and so I said that was one thing about our family. Nobody in our family ever was a "soak," I said.

They laughed hard at that and the laugh sounded mean. Then they said that I had certainly pulled a hot one. It happened that one of my cousins who was a wonderful grown-up young man was visiting at our house just then. They told me that the night before he had been so well soaked that they had carried him to our veranda because he couldn't get there himself.

I didn't believe it and said they were just making it up. But they said I was a pious little stuck-up skunk. I slammed into them with my fists but they held my hands behind my back and slapped my face hard and shoved me out the door. "Go over to your father's store," they said, "where it is holy." And that's just what I did do. My father was not there because it was his day in the county seat in Kingston, but I told Ed Harder. I thought he would praise me but he didn't. He just said, "Well, maybe it serves you right. Why don't you keep away from there?"

I didn't understand why Ed was that way until that night, and then the worst of it all happened. I woke up with a noise of loud talking and when I listened I was almost sick. It was my father talking to my cousin. He was telling him not to be a fool and to go to bed. But if he wouldn't he could take his things for all he cared and clear out and never come back again, and he didn't care whatever became of him. I heard my cousin talking too and it seemed he was so drunk that he didn't know what he was saying. Then I heard my cousin stumble down the stairs and out the front door. I suppose Ed Harder knew all about my cousin and that's why he scolded me and didn't pat me on the shoulder and say I was all right and to run along and play.

The next day I heard my father tell my mother he had a telegram from Kingston and he would go there and get my cousin out of jail and see that he got to his home. I could write down the name of this cousin and where he lived but I am not going to because most always he is fine and plays the violin and sings hymns and other songs and I think it is better to think about that side of anybody.

And so I sat there on the veranda of our house and watched Will Elwyn's store burn, and I thought about these things. My mother came in from the gate where she was standing with some other women and watching and talking and she said, "Oh, here you are." She asked if I knew where Harry and Clifford were and I said they were around somewhere. She said the fire was about over, and the fire was too bad and she thought it was time to get back to bed again. She told me to find Harry and Clifford and bring them. I found them and Clifford came along, but Harry said he was going to stay up the rest of the night.

My last experience at Will Elwyn's store had been the most terrible of all for me. My mother said that nobody but the Devil could have thought it up. It was afternoon in the winter when all the summer boarders were gone and things were quiet and sleepy. I was in Will Elwyn's store again. I always seemed to be in that store when the Devil was around. Willie Pepper and Fred Elwyn were there, too, and we were just hanging around. Hank Vandenberg was the clerk in the store and Jim Plass was there with him just loafing around. Hank was taking the lid off a box of something in the center aisle of the store. He pulled the nails out with a nail puller and when the lid was off he was starting to turn back the folded paper. He was handing the lid boards to Jim Plass and they were talking and laughing about something I didn't understand. My mother said afterward that neither one of them had sense enough to fill a teaspoon.

My father said afterward that I was too curious, like a pup. Learn to keep your nose and tail out of things, he said. And I did pretty much, afterward.

I stepped up to the box to see what was in it and on the outside of the paper folds on top was some stray red sugar. I wondered if it could be a whole box of red sugar.

So I asked Hank Vandenberg if it was. He looked at me quick and stopped unfolding the paper on top. Then he glanced at Jim Plass. But they were smiling and I thought they wanted to be nice to me.

He said sure it was red sugar. A whole box of it.

I said, "Aw, it is not." I said, "What would you do with a whole box of red sugar when all that women do with it is to put it on top of little cookies and cakes?"

"All right," he said, "so Willie don't believe me. Put your tongue down there and taste what's on the folded paper."

I did, and when I did he blew as hard as he could. The red stuff flew up in my face into my nose and mouth and eyes. It was red pepper.

I screamed and ran for home and I heard them laughing as I went.

Well, I thought, that's God for you. There wouldn't be any

more Will Elwyn store. I was sorry for Will Elwyn because he
was one of the nicest men I knew. But the store was all a mistake
from the start and I knew that God knows best about His rules,
like my father said. His rule is that if you are going to run a store
you have got to know how and on top of that you have got to work,
work, work. I climbed into bed with Clifford and I thought, "Let
it burn."

☙ Research on Milk

. . . and how to become a famous student

Elijah T. Bovee was old and hefty and he took hold of the
teacher's desk with both hands and pushed and pulled himself
up out of his chair and kinda groaned with what he called his
rumatiz. He picked up his ruler and rapped on his desk to get
everybody's attention. This was what he always did when he was
going to make an announcement. I guess his going through all
these motions when he could just as well say what he had to say in
his chair and stay comfortable was his idea of showing that he
meant business.

The announcement this time had to do with us in the class in
advanced composition.

"We have reached the first day in June," he said, "and the
school term will end soon. Before it ends, I want each of the students in this class to turn in the best essay he is capable of."
("Where is his rule not to end a sentence with a preposition?"
I thought).

"I don't mean one that you do in a half hour or so," he went
on. "I want a real effort. I want it written on white paper with

pen and ink. I want it to show a complete knowledge of the subject. Research and your own thinking. I want originality. You will have three weeks to do this and, of course, you will have to put some work on it outside of school. Now I will assign the themes.

"Addie Johnson, babies. Salo Shultis, apple pie. Egbert Boice, barrels. Charles William Peter Reynolds, West Point. Willie Rose, milk."

I thought right away some of this was going to be easy, but not for me. Addie was a big, handsome, laughing girl and always helped with the little beginners at recess time because she liked babies. Salo made pies so good that she brought them to church donations. Egbert's father turned barrelheads in his sawmill. Pete Reynolds thought that General Charles William Peter Reynolds would sound great, and was crazy to go to West Point. But me? Milk, he said. All I knew about milk was that it was good on oatmeal. I raised my hand.

"Yes, Willie," said old Elijah.

"Couldn't I have another subject?"

"Why?"

"Milk is pretty—well—mysterious," I said.

"All the better for research," he said, "just go to the encyclopedia. Ask farmers about it. Draw on your own experiences with milk. Make notes. Cover the subject. You'll have no trouble with it if you dig. And now school is dismissed."

Outside I got ahold of Fred Elwyn and Roy Harder and Lancy Boice because I know them best and we always put our heads together on lots of problems. I asked them how much they knew about milk, and they didn't know any more than I did, except Roy. He is Levi Harder's boy and Levi Harder is a farmer and they have two cows. He said he knew quite a lot and if the chance came he would be glad to help me with some of my research. He said he would let me know when the chance came.

At supper I told my father about the essay and asked him what

he knew about milk. I told him Elijah T. Bovee wanted us to research and go to original sources and ask people and draw on our
own experiences, and such. "He wants it complete from A to
Izzard," I said.

My father looked puzzled and chewed away at his supper.
Linnie Jewel coughed and I looked at her and she was looking
at her plate.

"Elijah T. Bovee should have his head examined," my father
said.

"I know," I said. "It's too hard. Not like the others. Addie
Johnson, babies. Salo Shultis, apple pie. Egbert, barrels. Pete
Reynolds, West Point. I tried to have him change it and had a
mind to ask for storekeeping. But he wouldn't."

"If Addie Johnson covers her subject from A to Izzard," said
Linnie and then I saw her catch a look from my mother. "Well,
never mind," Linnie said.

"What's so mysterious?" I said.

"Stick to the encyclopedia," my father said, "and you'll get
along all right."

After supper I went up to the living room and took down the
encyclopedia book that had all the Ms in it, and I found out that
there is a lot of milk that Woodstock don't know anything about.
Like Milk River in Montana, that is 729 miles long; Milk River
project to water 140,000 acres; milk snakes; milk sugar; milk
powder; milk bacteria (which is germs); Milky Way, with thirty
thousand million stars; and a lot of other milks. And on top of it
all is the milk that we know.

I wrote down notes on all this, but the next day I asked old
Elijah if I was to cover it all. I felt a lot better when he said, "No,
just write on cows' milk. But make it complete."

Well, I kept working, all about fat and water and minerals and
amounts and customs in Africa and I don't know what all. It
seemed there was an awful lot to milk.

It was about a week later that Roy Harder called me and Fred and Lancy into a corner of the school fence and said that he was ready now to help with my research.

"Why, I've already got that done," I said.

He squinted his eyes at me and he said, "Not the real research. Don't you remember that old Elijah said he wanted original sources?"

"Yes, the encyclopedia," I said.

"No, not that. Do you know where milk comes from?"

"From cows."

"Sure. But why and how? Old Elijah wants it complete, remember?"

Well, this stumped me.

"So you and Fred and Lancy come with me. We are going to research right back to the beginning."

We went across lots up over K'Neal Hogan's farm and back of the cemetery and on past Levi Harder's barn to a meadow. Roy stopped us by a rail fence and pointed to their two cows in the meadow. "Now keep quiet and watch," he said. "This is old stuff on a farm. Watch Claribelle. That's the white one. Pretty, and a pure-bred Jersey. The brown one is Bessie. She is a grade."

"What's the difference?" asked Lancy.

"Claribelle gives richer milk. More cream in it. Bessie is a grade cow. That means not pure bred. She could be part Jersey or maybe part Holstein, or part two or three things. It's according to what her mother and the bull was. Now that's research, Willie, like Old Elijah wants you to do, if I know milk. Put it in your essay."

Just then Claribelle stopped eating grass and looked at Bessie and then she walked over to Bessie and she tried to jump up on her. Bessie paid no attention and kept right on eating grass.

"Why did she do that?" asked Lancy.

"That's instinct," said Roy. "That's the beginning of milk."

"I thought milk comes from what a cow eats," I said.

"It does but not till after."

"After what?"

"After the bull. And that's the next part of your research."

"You mean they don't take a cow to the bull any old time?"

"That's right. She's got to show her instinct first."

"When will your father take Claribelle to the bull?"

"I don't know. He don't talk to me about it. I have to learn these things by myself. There's only one bull, and that's King David of Aaron Riseley, because Aaron has to have a herd for a lot of milk for his summer boarders. Farmers don't have many cows. You know that. Just enough for their own use. Veal and beef and milk and cream for their own use, and butter and cottage cheese. Things like that. Aaron Riseley has the only bull but he's enough for the cows around here. He's a big son of a bitch. Pure-bred Jersey. Only they have to spell him. Claribelle is what they call ready and now it's just a question when King David will be ready. But it's got to be quick work for us. And secret. If they know this is research you won't get to do it. I'll keep on the job and try to let you know."

It was late on Saturday that Roy came running up to me in front of the store. "Pop just took Claribelle out of the pasture," he whispered. "Come on."

We ran down past the school and when we got past Jimmy Lasher's we cut over through the fields. We kept behind a rail fence with scrub bushes so as not to be seen until we got behind Aaron Riseley's barn and then we lay there and waited. Pretty soon Levi Harder came down the road leading Claribelle. He plodded along in the dust and Claribelle was fussy. When he reached Riseley's red barnyard with board walls so high that you couldn't see into the barnyard from the road, two of Riseley's farm hands were waiting for him. We knew them. They were Jim Scuttle and Steve Yander. They swung the barnyard gate open and Levi and Claribelle went in and then they closed it again.

"Come on," said Roy. "Keep low. Jim won't care. But that Steve Yander is mean. Don't let him see you."

We sneaked in the back of the barn and up to the haymow, and struggled across the hay to the wall next to the barnyard. There was a window there and we could look down and see what the men were doing.

Down in the barn, King David sounded like he was tearing things apart. He bellowed and pawed and butted his head against the wall. Every once in a while something struck against the bottom of the haymow so hard I thought it was coming right up through.

"That's an iron keg they keep in his box stall," Roy said. "He tosses it up against the bottom of the haymow with his head. It's for exercise, and so he won't be so ugly."

Levi had Claribelle quiet and was holding her up short in her halter.

Jim Scuttle and Steve Yander went into the barn and we heard them shouting and cussing, and King David snorting. We heard Steve say, "You'd think there is some stranger in here the way he's acting." Then they came out with him and it was a sight. Jim and Steve each had a long pole, one on one side of King David and the other on the other. They were at one end of the poles and the other end of the poles had big snaps that were snapped into the ring in King David's nose. He was a big brute and looked to weigh two tons. He rammed right ahead, yanking Jim and Steve and they were almost sliding off their feet in the barnyard dung and both of them were shouting and cussing like mad. It certainly was strong and fast work.

When it was over they had a job to get King David under control and back in the barn. Levi stood with Claribelle for awhile. Then he opened the barnyard entrance and started off up the road with her and now she was quiet as a lamb.

Jim and Steve seemed to get King David back in his box stall

all right, and then something happened. Roy started to turn around. His foot went down through the hay and through a space in the haymow floor until his whole leg stuck out below right above where Jim and Steve were.

Steve Yander saw Roy's leg and bellered and rushed for the haymow. He had a buggy whip in his hand. He floundered around in the hay right at us slashing with the whip and we rolled and shoved around in the hay as much as we could but it wasn't enough.

"Get your kid asses out of here," he shouted, "and get out quick." And he cussed and swore. We didn't try to get to the ladder. We jumped. But he was right on us with the whip and he kept slashing us with it until we were out the back way and over into the field. He quit then and went back muttering to himself, and after we had crossed the field we stopped. Fred looked at me and I looked at him. Our clothes had saved us pretty much from the buggy whip. I was always a good runner and I had on shoes. But Roy had leather boots and that slowed him some. I got away pretty good, but he had a pretty bad red spot on his neck.

It's a funny thing about boys. We both stung where the whip lashed us but we started to laugh.

"By God," Roy said, "this research business is pretty tough. I wouldn't want to do it all the time. But now you know *that* part about milk."

"You put milk on your oatmeal and you never think what goes on to get it," I said.

"Well, they never found out how to get it any other way. Now Claribelle will have a calf and she will have to have milk for the calf for awhile. But there will be more than enough and it will last a long time so that people can have it. A cow has got to be what they call fresh to give milk, and it's the only way to get her fresh."

We got home all right. My ankle hurt for a couple of days from landing on the barn floor when we jumped, but this time I didn't say anything around home about having a pain. And I didn't say anything about the research.

I was about ready to write my essay now, but Fred Elwyn said there was one more research. K'Neal Hogan's hired man, Dutch Bogert, was the one that sold milk around the village. Fred made it up with me to see if we could go with him one time and when we asked him he said, "Sure, you can do the running for me. Come down to the barn four o'clock tomorrow morning."

We didn't make it the next morning. It was seven o'clock when my father called me and Fred said it was the same with him. But Fred had it fixed for the next morning for sure. He said his father was getting out at four o'clock the next morning to drive to a paint job, and he would wake him. And I tied a cord around my big toe and hung it out the window and when Fred came out he tugged on the string and that woke me up.

Dutch Bogert was already in Hogan's barn when we got there. He had a lantern hung on a rafter above one of the cows and he was milking her into a pail he held between his knees. When we said, "Here we are," he said, "Oh, hello there. Say," he said, "I want to try an experiment. I'm the best damned tit man there is in Ulster County," he said. "You two go back there by the door and stand about two feet apart and open your mouths."

We did that but Fred said, "What's coming off?"

"I want to see how good my aim is." With that he shifted a little and turned a tit our way and he shot a stream of milk into my mouth. He did it so quick I wasn't ready and I couldn't handle it all. I swallowed fast but it ran down over my chin. Fred bust out laughing, and so his face was turned to me when the next stream hit his cap and knocked it right off his head and the milk splattered against his ear and ran down over his blouse. "My God," he said, and tried to jump away.

"Gosh," hollered Dutch. "Why the hell didn't you stand still and keep your mouth open?" He set down the pail and came over

and grabbed a rag off a hook and mopped Fred off. "It'll dry as
soon as the sun comes up, in a few minutes," he said.

Fred was a little mad but he got over it and we set about helping
Dutch to get to go through the village to deliver milk. He would
milk his pail full and then we took it outside and dumped it in a
big milk can that held maybe ten gallons and stood in a little shed
with a flagstone floor. This big can was heavy. It was sort of the
shape of a bottle if the neck was short. Close to the top it had two
metal handles riveted to the sides. The top had a riveted handle,
too, and it had deep edges that slid down into the neck of the big
can, and was pretty tight. Alongside the can on a shelf was a
metal milk ladle. It was about an inch wide and an eighth of an
inch thick and long enough to reach down to the bottom of the big
milk can. The end you took hold of was bent around so you could
take hold of it. On the other end was a metal cup.

Dutch explained all this to us. He said the cup on the ladle held
just a pint, and that was how he measured milk when he delivered
it.

Dutch said all this was scientific. "It's a cool morning," he said,
"but you notice how warm it is in the barn. That's the body heat
from the cows and horses. You see the openings up there in the
sides next to the roof? That's to let the heat out, or it would get
too hot in here. But it's nice on a cold morning and it smells
wonderful. You would think with all the dung it would stink.
But the cows and horses don't eat anything but hay and grain, and
the sweet smell comes from the clover in the haymow and the
breath of the cows. But it's too warm for milk and that's why we
carry it out and dump it in that cold milk can in the cool milk shed
with the stone bottom. That takes the animal heat out of the
milk and cools it. And it helps keep it clean. Oh, once in
awhile a straw or a little hay dust will drop into it when you're
milking, but you don't worry about that. Mostly it's used to cook

with, anyway. Us Dutch folks drink coffee mostly and a little tea, with our vittles. Even the kids. They don't drink much raw milk."

We helped Dutch hitch up one of the horses to the milk wagon. The middle of this wagon was built low. The milk cans are set on the floor, and there was a seat back of it. That was so you could step in and out, easy.

Then we were ready and started off. "This will be easy for me this morning," Dutch said, "because you little skunks will do the runnin'. I'll just set on the seat and ladle out the milk." And so we started off.

When we came to a house, if it was on Fred's side he jumped out and ran to the kitchen door and picked up a tin pail he would find there. If it was on my side I did the same. We would bring the pails to Dutch. He knew just how much each house got. Sometimes one ladle full and sometimes two. And he would ladle it out and we would run the pails back to the kitchen doors. When folks got up they took them in. When we'd been all over the village it was coming seven o'clock. I was tired and I guess Fred was too. "Just suppose you was me," Dutch said, "doin' all the runnin' myself."

"Yes," I said. "But four o'clock every morning. Why can't you deliver today's milk tomorrow, and a little later in the morning?"

"Because milk has got to be fresh," said Dutch. "Folks are not much of a hand for milk that ain't fresh."

I went home and had breakfast and then I lay down on the lounge in the living room and fell asleep. I would have missed school if Linnie had not found me and waked me up in time.

So now all my research was done and I started in on writing the complete essay on milk that old Elijah wanted. I started out by telling what milk is. How there are lots of kinds but the kind wanted in this essay is the glandular secretion from the breast or udders of animals that suckle their young, like from cows, mares, goats, ewes, camels, asses, zebras, reindeers and llamas, just as the encyclopedia said. But we do not have such animals as asses, camels and llamas in Woodstock, I wrote, or anyway, if folks did see them in their pastures their eyes would pop. And so we would confine our research to milk that comes from America's cow and bull. And I wrote that folks might think that bulls don't have anything to do with the milk, but they do, as I would show.

Then I went on to write that milk is a good food because it has water and fat and minerals.

From there I went into how we get cow's milk. It starts, I wrote, when a cow shows her instinct. She does this by jumping on another cow and letting a farmer see her do it. Then I described how there is only one bull for all the cows around Woodstock and so the farmer who has a cow with instinct must make an appointment with the bull just like is necessary with a big businessman who is very busy. The next step in getting cow's milk, I wrote, is very difficult to explain because this part of the research was very hazy in my mind although Roy Harder and I had done it at more trouble and danger and pain than it was worth, and if Mr. Bovee wanted more than that in the essay he had better do that part of the research for himself.

I went on to write that then a calf is born and the calf must have milk, but there is more than the calf needs and it lasts a long time, and so there is milk for people.

Next I told how Fred Elwyn and I went on into research with the help of Dutch Bogert and how Dutch is the best man with a tit in Ulster County and that he can aim a stream of milk into your mouth at twenty feet. And about cooling milk, and the milk shed, and the milk can and the milk wagon and the little tin pails outside doors, and delivering and measuring the milk. I even put in the sweet smell in the barn to make it very real.

It was a lot of essay when I got it all down in writing in ink on white paper and I handed it in to old Elijah and figured I was done with it. I had had all the research I wanted for awhile.

When school let out the next afternoon, Elijah T. Bovee stopped me going out and said he wanted to talk with me. I sat down and waited. When all the others had left, old Elijah picked up some papers from his desk and I saw it was my essay. First he leafed it over a little but then he looked at me and he was very serious.

"I read this last night," he said. "You went into a lot of research. I have assigned milk for essays for forty years but I never got research like this. Did you have any help from anybody? Let us say from the three worst scamps in this school, to wit, Delancy Boice, Leroy Harder and Fred Elwyn?"

"Well," I said, "they were with me on some of the research, just as it says there in the essay. But they helped. They didn't hinder."

"I see they didn't. Well, it's one or the other. Either very good or very bad. For once I don't trust my own judgment. I'll have to get some other opinions."

That's what he must have done, because all of a sudden I was the most famous student in Woodstock and all around. Men would pat me on the back and ask what I was going to research next.

The men around the stove in the store talked about it and very serious. I overheard Ed Harder say, "Well, that's what teachers say school's for. To make the kids dig and think for themselves. If teachers are on the level the kid's essay rang a bell."

Old Elijah gave me 100%.

But now, Addie Johnson on babies only got 72%. I was telling Ed Harder about the 100% and the 72% and he said, very serious, "Well, that's because Addie didn't do all her research."

I guess that must have been it.

Linnie Jewel's Accident

. . . and how a boy's interests seem to change

All of a sudden something happened to me that made me different than I had been while I was growing up into a bigger boy. And it was because of an accident that happened on our front veranda one Sunday afternoon.

It was like having a new interest in something I never thought about before, and it interfered with the interests I had before. I'm still interested in swimming, and playing shinny, and trying to get high marks in district school, and hunting chestnuts in the fall; but it's when I'm quiet, like reading Oliver Optic, that I don't have the same interest any more.

I used to get lost in Oliver Optic and people had to speak to me two or three times, and sometimes shout my name, to bring me up out of it. But now it does not seem very important what's going on in the story. I am fidgety and I would rather stop reading and run off to do something, like climbing one of the willow trees in the back yard, or digging up horseradish roots on the bank of the creek, or snaring suckers.

This is all since the accident on Sunday afternoon on our front veranda. The accident didn't happen to me. It happened to Linnie Jewel.

It was an awfully hot afternoon, and, of course, I had to have on my Sunday clothes with long stockings and shoes. I thought I would melt. It didn't help any when I overheard Linnie say to my mother that she had looked at the thermometer and it was a hundred in the shade. "I think I'll go up and take off my corset and bloomers and roll my stockings," she said. "I should think a body could be excused on a day like this, even if it is Sunday," I overheard her say.

"If I was young and slim as you, I would, too," said my mother. That gave me an idea. "I am young and slim, too," I said to my mother. "I could take off my stockings and shoes, and my coat."

"No, I don't think so," said my mother. "It's Sunday. Suppose somebody should see you. You'll be all right if you keep quiet. You have that new Oliver Optic book you're only half through. Go out on the front veranda and read it and you'll forget all about the heat."

I didn't think this was fair and I went into a pout even though I tried not to.

Linnie looked at my mother, and then she looked at me and smiled. "Don't you think he could just take off his coat?" she asked. "He would still look nice and clean for Sunday afternoon."

"Well, I suppose so," said my mother. "I wasn't giving it much thought, I guess. I wasn't meaning his coat. Only his shoes and stockings."

I stopped pouting right away and got my coat off in a hurry. And I was thinking that that was Linnie for you, always helping my father and mother to understand us boys. She smiled a lot and she was pretty, and she was always saying cute things that we laughed at. She never said anything cross to Clifford or me, even sometimes when we were mean and pouty and we knew it. Such times she just put her arm down over our shoulders and although we shook away from her and kept on being mean and sulky I know I liked her to do that. She was a grown-up girl but she wasn't big and broad like the girl we had before her when I was very small and whose name I do not remember. But she was full of health and color with her bright brown hair high on her head, and when she was dressed up with a high collar around her neck, and her little watch pinned on her white shirtwaist, and her gold bracelet on her wrist, and her skirt down to the floor so that you could see only the tips of her white shoes, she looked very slim and dainty.

I had heard my father say that she was well named because she looked to him like a jewel and she was a jewel in his opinion. This

was when my mother had complained to him about some little
thing Linnie didn't do to suit her. "Well, why don't you tell her
how you want it," he asked, "instead of keeping it bottled inside you? She will do it your way if she knows what it is you want.
You keep it bottled up inside you and someday the cork will fly
out with the pressure, and you will be sorry and hate yourself afterward. It's a funny thing about two women under the same roof,"
he said. And then my mother said that she would have to agree
that, all in all, Linnie was a jewel. They were alone when they said
this and, of course, they didn't know that I overheard. It didn't
make any difference to me except that I like Linnie.

So I got my Oliver Optic book and went out on the porch and
sat down to go on with the story. It was about a white young man
and a colored boy who would do anything for him and they had to
go across the Sahara Desert. I went with them into the desert and
they were just beginning to get lost when Linnie came down from
her room and came out on the veranda where I was. She had the
Youth's Companion and she stretched herself out in the hammock
and started to read a story.

I went back to my story and we did get lost good and real in the
desert. Worst of all, the thirst and the heat were terrible and the
water bottle was almost empty. It was agreed that each would take
a final drink and the white young man had the colored boy take the
first drink; but he just made out he was drinking without letting
the white man know that, so that the white man maybe could get
home alive. The colored boy died and I was struggling with the
white man to get out of the desert. So I was a thousand miles away
from our front porch when all of a sudden the accident happened.

I heard a gasp and a bump and I was yanked back from the
Sahara Desert a thousand miles away faster than you could snap
your fingers.

The gasp and the bump came from Linnie and my eyes jumped
up over the Sahara Desert to see what had happened. The rope at

one end of the hammock had broken and Linnie had been bumped down on the floor. It had happened so quickly that her limbs had jumped up in the air and she was on her back. She sat up quick, but her skirt had been flung up and there she sat with both limbs uncovered clear up above her knees. If my father and mother had been there, or some grown-up person, I suppose she would have had her skirt down first thing, even if she had broken her back, because I have noticed that keeping her skirt down to the ground is the first thing on a woman's mind no matter what she is doing or what happens. But I was just a boy and didn't matter, and so she just sat there for a long minute or so. I suppose she was figuring out what had happened and whether she was hurt.

But I don't know about that because I didn't see her face nor any of her except her limbs. I just kept looking at her limbs and I was surprised that there were so much of them under the skirt of such a slim young woman. Maybe I kept looking at her limbs because I knew they would be gone in a minute and I would never see them again. Maybe I tried to take my eyes off them to ask her if she was hurt. But if I did, I couldn't. I don't know what came over me, but I couldn't move and I couldn't speak because my breath was caught in my throat.

The white-laced kid shoes went up higher than I would have supposed. The feet were small and the ankles, too, but just above the ankles the laces in the shoes spread. The stockings were black silk and they spread out smooth as paint over the curves that went over the calves, and in again, and over knees that were round. The stockings were rolled just above the knees and above the rolls was the bare white skin of more beautiful upper limbs than I ever knew anything about. All in all, they were not like any limbs I had ever seen because all the limbs I had ever seen were my father's and those of Harry and Clifford and of the other boys when we were in swimming, and some of the very lower limbs of the little girls we chased at school to hear them giggle and squeal. And although I never had thought about Linnie having limbs at all, if I had thought about them I never would have thought that she had such big curves under her skirt. That's when I knew for the first time that women's limbs are wonderful.

She covered them up, of course, and I thought that it was such a pity. I don't know why it was, but I never had had anything happen to me that gave me such a thrill. Except that maybe it hurt Linnie a little, I thought that every Sunday afternoon would be the best afternoon in the week if I could be reading Oliver Optic out on the front porch and it could be so hot that Linnie would take off her corset and bloomers and roll her stockings and be in the hammock, and the hammock would always go down with her.

But it has happened only once, of course. I keep watching and hoping, and watching and hoping, and spend so many long afternoons on the porch that I have read my Oliver Optic books through three times, but the ropes my father put on the hammock are too good and I haven't seen Linnie's limbs again.

❧ Psychology Is Only Skin-Deep

. . . *Dr. Jekyll and Mr. Hyde at District School*

The sentence read, "So often in the course of life's few fleeting years, a single pleasure costs the soul a thousand tears."

This was the first sentence that had to be diagrammed. The double seat where Ira Elwyn sat with me was all mine, because Ira was in class reciting on the long bench at the front of the room along the right wall where old Elijah T. Bovee could sit at his desk and face them. That was a good thing because if I was to diagram this sentence right I needed lots of room to struggle in.

I took my ruler and drew a straight line so I could pick my subject, predicate, and object and write them down first. So far I wasn't bothered much. It was a tricky sentence and poetry at that, but only a dunce would have failed to notice that the sentence really began after the comma—"A single pleasure costs the soul" and so forth what and when. Before I went any farther I memorized the fact that it was written by somebody by the name of Francis William Bourdillon and that Mr. Bourdillon was born in 1852 and had not died yet because the place for the second date was blank.

I looked at the way I had divided the sentence and thought that if Mr. Bourdillon hadn't been a poet that's the way he probably would have written this great message to mankind that was now giving me trouble. Of course, he wrote it to be read and thought upon. He didn't figure that school teachers would hack it to pieces into parts of speech and have you put them in proper places on a diagram.

Oh, well, get the three main words down on the line and stop stalling. Subject "pleasure," predicate "costs," object "soul." The "cost" is to the "soul" and the preposition of the adverbial phrase which answers the question "where" is understood.

I erased "soul" as the object and wrote down "tears" in its place. "Pleasure costs tears." So it was a transitive verb taking an object. I made a note of that because old Elijah T. Bovee would be bound to ask about the verb in class. Elijah T. Bovee never missed anything. I put the brass edge of my ruler up to my lips and looked at him where he sat at his desk up front conducting the recitation. He was trying to get Roy Harder to tell him the opposing generals in the Battle of Quebec in the French and Indian War.

Roy was the kind that always said that history was dead stuff. It certainly was for him. He had started guessing with Howe and Jackson and had run through the generals of the Revolution and was getting close to the Civil War, after guessing Sam Houston

along the way. Old Elijah, in his black shiny suit and raspy temper-
ament, was getting tired of Roy's guessing and was getting sar-
castic. The attention of the whole room was attracted. It looked like
Roy was in for another of old Elijah's dunce caps. He didn't have
you wear the dunce cap and sit up front on a high stool because he
said it was a waste of time, and he wanted the dunce to go back to
his seat and put in the time he would have sat on the stool in real
study. School in the United States had improved a great deal since
the old days. But what old Elijah did was to take a sheet of paper
and make a dunce cap out of it and put your name on it and set it
on the window sill of the front window. Roy had three of them
there already with his name on them.

Elijah T. Bovee was a good teacher, as far as school books went,
for boys and girls who wanted to study. I know he was a good
teacher with me because I was only twelve years old and I already
could recite the battles of all the wars, the Declaration of Inde-
pendence, the Gettysburg Address, and the measurement tables;
and I could figure compound interest the short way, and fractions
and decimals; and could pick out all the parts of speech and diagram them; and tell you all the capitals and rivers of all the na-
tions; and tell you the organs and bones of the body and almost
anything else you asked me that they cover in school. But Roy
Harder wasn't dumb either. If there had been a class in horsetrad-
ing or birds, or trapping and hunting, or caring for cows and
horses, or sowing and reaping, or girls, or funny sayings, Roy
would have been at the top of the class. But, of course, those things
didn't count in recitations and examinations.

I was in the part of the room where Elijah T. Bovee almost had
his back to me. I was suffering for Roy. I have been up to his home
in Rock City and played with him a good many times, and been in
scrapes with him, and even stayed to supper. His mother makes
the most wonderful apple pie in the world.

I took a sheet of paper and printed on it in big words, "Wolfe and Montcalm." Then I held it up so that Roy could look past old Elijah and see it, and if I knew Roy he would.

He did but he didn't have sense enough to stall along a little with, "Now let me see," or "Oh, wait, now I remember" before he said the names. And even then he sort of asked them like "Wolfe and Montcalm?"

I barely had time to lower the sheet of paper to my desk before old Elijah looked around the room. I didn't think he caught on, and when he looked my way I had the brass edge of the ruler at my lips again and was studying that sentence I had to diagram. I didn't look up but I knew that old Elijah sort of had his squint eye on me for a second and was thinking it over. Then he turned back to the class and went on with the questions. I kind of made a face at Addie Johnson and Salo Shultis, two pink-and-white older girls who sat near me, and it looked as if they admired me in their eyes. I felt pretty good and went back to my diagramming.

The "often in the course of life's few fleeting years" didn't stump me. "Often" was an adverb (when), "in the course" was a phrase modifying the verb (where), and "of the years" was probably an adjective phrase modifying the principal word of the preceding phrase (descriptive). But that word "so" at the start of the quotation needed some thinking.

I put the brass edge of the ruler to my lips while I thought.

Suppose the word was "therefore" instead of "so." That would indicate something going before as if this sentence was only part of a fuller quotation. It could be a conjunction, or could it?

Victor Lasher, sitting behind me, tapped me between the shoulderblades. I turned around and he handed me a note. I put it down under my desk and looked at it and my heart jumped a little when I saw that it was signed Addie. Addie Johnson had written me a note!

It was the first time that I had a note from one of the bigger girls. They wrote lots of them and passed them along to the older boys, like Charley Reynolds and my brother Harry and George Elwyn. Addie and Salo didn't know it but I liked both of them very much. They had coloring and their eyes were full of mischief. They laughed a lot. They liked being the big girls in the school and the attention they attracted from the smaller girls and the older boys. You could tell that.

But what Addie had written to me was something else. "Wake up and stop the noise," the note read. "Old ETB don't know you're studying so hard you're unconscious." I looked around. All the students had heard the noise but me.

Then I realized I had been blowing against the brass edge of the ruler and it had been making a little, low whistle like a tea-kettle does if it has a small spout and is just getting going.

I looked over at Addie and she smiled and I smiled. And, of course, I took the ruler down from my lips. I looked at Addie as long as she would look at me but she went back to her studying. I went back to mine.

The next sentence to be diagrammed was, "For every inch that is not fool is rogue"—John Dryden (1631-1700). I memorized John Dryden and the dates and started in to pick out the parts of speech before putting them down on lines. I made it read, "Every inch is rogue that is not fool." Single subject, two verbs, and two predicate adjectives. Intransitive. And there was one of those extra words again, "for" which would have to be thought about a little.

All of a sudden old Elijah slapped the flat of his hand down on his desk and I jumped and so did everybody else. His eyes roamed around the room a little and then he shouted, "Whoever is making that noise stop it immediately!"

The thing that happened then will never be explained. I cannot explain why it happened and none of the students will ever be able to explain it. They know just how such a thing can happen because it has happened to them and maybe it has happened to everybody. Older people who don't have to keep quiet and do everything somebody else's way have forgotten that it probably happened to them when they were boys and girls, and old Elijah is the kind that would rather say it cannot happen than to have some decent explanation like "I didn't know I was doing it."

The thing that happened was this: Elijah T. Bovee had no sooner said to stop the noise immediately than I put the ruler to my lips and made the noise right while he was looking at me.

Now above all I wanted to be a good student because it always made me feel better and happier instead of making trouble all the time and never getting to know anything. Mixed in with it also was fear of old Elijah and the way he made a fool out of everybody who didn't answer right, and the way he beat up some of the boys with his hickory stick. Of course, I will admit that Addie Johnson and Salo Shultis were watching and it could be that they had something to do with it somewhere in my brain. But if they did, I didn't know it. I do know I was confused.

That's the only explaining I can do. I guess it was just what the school book on physiology has a chapter on and is called psychology. Of course, old Elijah knew that I was the one who had been making the tea-kettle noise.

He got up and walked down to where I sat and he stood there for a spell looking at me. He looked down at the sentences I was diagramming and there was a grin on his face. "I see that you and Mr. Dryden have been getting acquainted," he said. Then he read, " 'For every inch that is not a fool is rogue.' Well, now Willie. John Dryden had it about right, don't you think so?"

"I guess so, sir," I said.

He took hold of my arm and lifted me a little. "It will be my pleasure to have you with me up front until I get through with this class," he said.

I got up and he pushed me a little ahead of him in the aisle and we went up to his desk. He told me to sit on an extra chair there alongside him and he then went on with the class recitation as if nothing had happened.

I had nothing else to do so I followed the questions he was asking the class to see if I knew the answers, but I watched old Elijah out of the corner of my eye. He seemed to have forgotten all about what I had done and about my sitting there alongside him. I began to feel better. I felt sure that maybe he had me sitting there until the class was done just to impress me and that then he would send me back to my seat. Maybe with just a word or two, to be more careful. But it turned out that he had no such thing in mind.

And that's the trouble with old Elijah T. Bovee. He is great on book knowledge but he never seems to have enough sense to leave well enough alone so that folks will like him.

When he had dismissed the class he announced to the entire school that he would pause for a few minutes while he disposed of my case. He was very easy and intellectual about it and there was a grin on his face all the time as if he was enjoying himself.

He wanted to know why I had made the noise in the first place and I told him I was unconscious about it. He studied over that. He asked me if I was unconscious when I made the noise again after he had said to stop it. I told him that then I wasn't exactly unconscious but it happened before I thought at all. It was embarrassment, I said. It was a reflex, I said. He seemed to study over that, too.

"You make some of the most peculiar answers I've ever heard," he said. "They are pretty bright. Maybe they are just a little too bright. Do you make these answers up out of your own head? Or have you been exposed to some extraordinary knowledge somewhere?"

I knew that was making fun of my answers and so I didn't answer. Some of the students in the room laughed and old Elijah threw them a quick glance and laughed too, as if he had said something very funny.

"So you flatly disobeyed but at the same time you claim that you did not disobey. And the reason you give is that it was an unconscious reflex?"

"Yes, sir."

"You're quite a reader, aren't you? Do you remember when I assigned some Stevenson for outside reading? To show all of you that classics are not always dull? *Treasure Island.* And *Dr. Jekyll and Mr. Hyde.* Did you read them?"

"Yes, sir."

"I have often thought that if Mr. Hyde had been spelled h-i-d-e and could have been soundly spanked every time he appeared there wouldn't have been any Mr. Hyde for long."

"I thought the Hyde part of us is always there," I said. "It is what they call psychology."

He sat and thought about that for a minute and then he said, "Psychology. Humph! In my opinion it's only skin deep. To a great extent, that is. To a great extent."

He turned to me. "Willie," he said, "I think we shall experiment in this theory of mine in preventing Mr. Hydes. Will you aid me in the experiment?"

"I don't know what you mean," I said.

"It will become apparent," he said. He picked up his ruler. "Come here," he said.

So now I knew what he was going to do and so did everybody else. All the room had dropped their work and were watching. The boys in my crowd had stone faces, not looking at me but boring their hate into Elijah T. Bovee. There was dread in the eyes of the girls. I saw pity for me in the expressions of Addie Johnson and Salo Shultis. That was hard for me. Whatever happened, I didn't want these bigger girls to pity me.

But there wasn't much time to think about anything.

Elijah T. Bovee took hold of me with his big hands and pulled me between his knees with my face to his left. He lifted me over his left knee and put his right knee over the backs of mine. My short blue serge pants I had on went tight because they were last year's and a little too small. Then he whaled me with the ruler so long and so hard that my whole body stung from head to foot. If he had killed me I wouldn't have uttered a sound.

He set me on my feet, looked at me with a grin, and told me to go back to my seat. Before I did so I looked into his eyes and he couldn't have understood me any clearer if I could have nailed the words into his brain. I hated him with all my soul. I would hate him as long as I lived.

He started to lay the ruler down but it caught on the edge of the desk and clattered to the floor. He reached for a book but it dropped out of his hand. Then he tried to pick up some papers from his desk but some of the sheets slithered away. He knew and I knew and all the students knew that Mr. Hyde wasn't in me. He had proved it was in him.

⚘ The Big Secret at District School

. . . and scholarship raised to the nth degree

The thing that has all our fathers and mothers puzzled is the way that the district school has quieted down and how much the troublemakers who used to bedevil Elijah T. Bovee are learning. Folks are saying that it is all due to our new teacher, and of course it is. She is Blossom Teller. But there is a secret about it that our parents don't know and that you can be sure they will never find out. I didn't find it out myself until school had gone along quite a ways with our new teacher.

Even Roy Harder and Delancy Boice are studying hard. This is queerer than you think.

Roy Harder and Delancy Boice never did study too much when old Elijah T. Bovee was the teacher. That was because old Elijah beat them so much with his hickory stick that they spent all their time thinking up ways to get even. But no matter what they did I always thought that for pure cussedness they couldn't equal old Elijah. One recess after old Elijah had beat him, Delancy took some of us boys into the boys' backhouse on the edge of the school lot and took off his shirt and showed us his back. His welts were certainly bigger than his grades. And Roy, who is a comedian if there ever was one and had to take it from old Elijah too, wasn't learning enough to even go on the stage.

A good many of the older boys sided with Roy and Delancy and that didn't help teaching any. It got to be a feud.

The thing came to a head one day in the winter. We have an entrance hall in our district school where we all hang our wraps and where the water bucket with the dipper in it is kept if you can get permission to get a drink. Old Elijah kept his overcoat and mittens there, too, and he had this big fur coat and heavy mittens because he drove up from his home in Van Dale every morning. He kept his rig at Jimmie and Ceil Lasher's, across the road from the school. Well, in this entrance hall there isn't any stove. Water will freeze two or three inches in the water pail some days in the winter.

This winter day it was below zero and the snow was deep. Delancy had done something or other in the morning. It had got so it didn't make much difference what. And Old Elijah had taken him into the entrance hall and beat him. After school started in the afternoon, the water pail was empty and old Elijah asked Delancy to go to Jimmie Lasher's pump and fill it. But this is the way he asked him, "Mister Boice, if we may impose on your good nature and your valuable time, may we be so bold as to request you to get a pail of water?" That was the way old Elijah was.

Pretty soon Delancy came back, but he was quiet and he didn't cause any more trouble for the rest of the day. When school was dismissed and we went out to get our wraps we noticed that the outside door to the hall was standing wide open. This should have been closed on such a cold day. Old Elijah roared about it and then he remembered about Delancy going after water and he started for him. But Delancy did not linger.

Old Elijah put on his coat and then he reached for his mittens and then he roared again. Delancy had filled them full of water and hung them with their tops up and they were frozen full of solid ice. Then Elijah put his hands in his pockets—or tried to— but they were full of solid ice, too.

Next day he expelled Delancy from school and that raised a ruckus. The school board had to meet and Eulie Boice showed them the welts on Delancy's back. The upshot was that Delancy went back to school with a warning and the board told old Elijah that he could stay to the end of the term, but then he was through.

Delancy was a model student until the summer vacation and butter would not have melted in his mouth. But in the end I guess he came out ahead. On the last day of school he was sent for water again to Jimmie Lasher's pump and where old Elijah kept his rig. When old Elijah drove away from Lasher's after that last day at school and down the road at a spanking pace one of the wheels left the buggy and rolled off across the fields. Old Elijah was pitched out and could have killed himself. Delancy had taken off all the axle nuts that hold the wheels on.

That's how it was that the school board had to find a new teacher and they decided on Blossom Teller. She is a blossom all right. She is about twenty-four and is a graduate of New Paltz Normal School where they teach teachers how to teach. And she had been a teacher somewhere else a couple of years where she had got along pretty good, the board said. But folks had their doubts about her. They thought she was too pretty and too young to handle the big boys in our school, and they shook their heads. And there was something else that made them shake their heads. Miss

Teller had been to college, they said, and she was the new kind of girl. Folks said she was too advanced in style, like some of the city-boarder girls, to be teaching school in our Village. This was because she looked like a Gibson Girl. She rode a bicycle to school in a tight skirt that was about two inches out of the dust.

But here are Delancy Boice and Roy Harder and other boys beginning to study and even studying at night, and people are surprised that they were so wrong about Blossom Teller. But, of course, they don't know the big secret.

The reason I didn't get into it sooner was because we have a rule that when you get in the big room at district school you can pick where you want to sit by getting your books into the desk before anybody else does. The best place is in the single seats and desks along the inside partition that separates the little kids' room from the big room. You have everything to yourself there and a wall alongside you where you can hang paper pictures of the West Point cadets on parade, or the death of Wolfe at Quebec, or the battleship *Maine* before it was sunk in Havana harbor, or any other educational subject.

I took my books and went to the schoolhouse a week before school opened. I found a window I could raise on the side away from the road and got in and put my books in this back corner desk in the single row. So that's where my seat is—as far as possible from the long bench up front, on the other side of the room where classes sit in a row to recite. I can study better and I don't pay much attention to what is going on up there at recitation. That's why I didn't learn the study secret of our school sooner.

Miss Blossom Teller would do pretty good even if it wasn't for this secret; and more than that I am sure that she does not know for a minute what the secret is, though, I can't be too sure of that. Ed Harder who is good-looking and a fine dresser and lively, and who knows so much about girls and women, says that the things they will do sometimes to get your attention would raise your hair.

There never is any trouble with the younger boys, with their studies anyway, nor with the girls even if they are older. And there is never any trouble with such boys as I am. I am a natural-born student and I would study for any teacher, because I want to learn things and nothing pleases me so much as to be one of the best in school.

Right from the start Miss Blossom Teller didn't handle Roy and Delancy like old Elijah T. Bovee had, by taking them into the hall outside the room where all the hats and coats are hung and closing the door so that we could not see, and then beating them.

First came Roy. When he did his first comedy trick to try her out she didn't say anything. She just laughed along with the students and stopped a class reciting. She just strolled down the aisle toward Roy's seat and she was smiling at him as if she enjoyed his funniness as much as the rest of us. Boy, she looked good. She is about five feet and a half tall, pretty, pleasant, a waist you could span with your two hands, as the men say, and she walked like a queen. You could see that Roy was puzzled. This wasn't the way for a teacher to act. She ought to be mad.

She stopped at his desk right alongside of him and she was still smiling. "That was funny, Roy," she said. "I didn't see it all. Do it again, will you?"

Roy is kinda dried up for his age and not big like Delancy, and that's one reason he can be so funny. But now he got a stubborn look on his face and slumped down in his seat. All of a sudden Miss Teller changed. She grabbed hold of his shoulders and lifted him clear out of his seat so fast that one of his leather boots that always sagged halfway down to his ankles caught on the seat and flew halfway across the room. Then she dropped him back in his seat.

She turned and went back to her desk in the front of the room and rapped for order. Then she went on with the class recitation as if nothing had happened.

But everybody had laughed right out loud at Roy and his flying boot in spite of themselves. Roy's face was red as a beet. He sat there a minute without his boot and then went and got it and put it on. You could see he was trying to think up something he could do in a funny way but it was no use.

When Elijah T. Bovee used to take little Roy out and beat him, Roy was kind of a hero. This was different. Now all he felt like was a fool. At recess he talked it over with Delancy Boice while some of us boys stood around and listened. Delancy said Miss Teller couldn't do anything like that to him because he was too big to be yanked out of his seat.

"I'll bet I can get her to lick me," he said. "Wait till she tries to yank me out of my seat. I'll wrestle with her. Then she will have to lick me."

He got his chance the next day. He brought an apple to school and while Miss Teller was conducting the advanced class in English, Delancy took the apple out of his desk and began to eat it. While he was eating it he motioned to some of the big girls and held out the apple as if he would offer any of them a bite.

The big girls began to snicker and Blossom Teller looked away from her class to see what was going on. She spotted Delancy, who quit just a second after she looked up so she would catch him, and then made out as if he was studying hard.

This time, too, she looked around the room and at Delancy, and broke into a smile. Then she dismissed the class before the recitation was over and said they would go on from there the next day. Delancy expected her to get up now and come smiling down the aisle to his seat, and he got braced. But she just sat there behind her desk.

"Now," she said to Delancy, "you better dispose of the apple. You have had your fun and it isn't of any use to you any longer."

But Delancy was out to rile her if he could. He saw the window

across the room was open and he got to his feet and threw the rest
of the apple through it and then sat down.

The smile left the face of Miss Teller. But she didn't flare up.
She just looked at Delancy for a long time. She looked at his
head and at his hands and all over him for so long that Delancy
dropped his eyes and began to fidget. A look of pity came into her
eyes. And then she spoke.

"There are two things about you and me that you don't know,
Delancy," she said. "Before I agreed to teach here this year the
school directors warned me about you. They said that you would
ruin my teaching if you could, just as you ruined Mr. Bovee's. But
I have known your mother and father for a long time and they are
wonderful people. I have known you ever since your mother used
to carry you around as a baby. And I remember how proud she
was of you.

"I told the school directors that I had faith in you and that before this year is over they would have faith in you, too. You didn't
know that so many of us were worrying about you, did you?

"I have studied you a great deal, Delancy. There is no reason
why you should be a problem at school or anywhere else. You're
not crippled like some boys and girls who feel cheated and want
revenge. You are good-looking. You are not dull in your mind.
You are bright. Your eyes and hearing are perfect so that you do
not have to struggle against these failings as some boys and girls
have to do.

"You have a strong big body so that someday you are going to
look like a big man even if you do not have a big mind. Your
father and mother and I and everybody else know these things
about you, and it would please us very much if you had sense
enough to study and learn and cooperate so that some day you
will have a big mind to go with your strong body.

"Now, I don't expect you to become perfect all of a sudden.
One reason you are so mischievous is because you are so bright. But

there is one thing you should think about until you get it straight. When you make trouble you are holding me back and also holding back every boy and girl in this room and you are holding yourself back. That means the only fool is yourself."

Delancy had wilted long before she finished and at the end he was crying. I had never seen him cry before, not even when Elijah T. Bovee beat him so hard that he had red welts on his back. But Miss Teller had decided to put the welts on his spirit.

If she had been cranky or if she had creaked like old leather I don't think Delancy would have minded a bit. But Miss Teller is beautiful and graceful as the actresses in the pictures in packs of Sweet Caporal cigarettes, with their hair high on their heads and standing as if they had turned around and left the bottom of their skirts in front of them. She was the kind you couldn't take your eyes off of.

"All I ask," she ended, "is your cooperation, and I hope you will be a man and give it to me."

Then she smiled at all of us and called the next class.

But discipline is not all there is to teaching school. You can be as good as gold in school but if you don't like to study the whole thing is heavy and tedious and, of course, you can't lie down and go to sleep to pass the time the way older people out of school can, like some of them do in church.

Blossom Teller had a way to handle that, too, and it has worked wonders. She calls it incentive. Maybe it would work with a man teacher, too, if all he had were boys and girls who don't know anything else than that you go to school to study. But with Miss Teller as teacher it has made even the older boys study like thunder, which is a miracle. And that's where the secret in our school comes in.

When the classes had their first recitations Miss Teller had each member of each class draw a number out of a hat. These numbers ran one, two, three, four, and so on, up to the number in the class. Then the class took its place on the long bench along the side wall up front where it faced the side of the teacher's desk. The boy or girl with number one sat at the head of the class against the front wall, number two sat next, number three next and so on.

Miss Teller explained that she would start questions with number one. If number one did not know the answer he or she went to the foot of the class and number two had the next chance, and everybody else went one number ahead. If number two missed he or she went to the foot and number three was the head of the class. And so on with all the class recitations. Well, the ones who didn't study and didn't know all the answers just never got a chance to be at the head of the class. But if you did study hard you got a chance to be at the head of the class and to stay there.

Drawing the numbers alone got everybody more interested than usual. It was like a game you play at parties and at spelling bees. Almost everybody forgot how to say, "I don't know," and came up with some answer, even if it was a pure guess. A lot of these guesses were so strange that they got a lot of laughs. Miss Teller entered right into it that first day and made the questions pretty easy. But after that she was strict about it and the questions were tough ones. You just simply had to know if you didn't want to be at the foot of the class most of the time. That's why I think even a man teacher could do it if he had as much brains as Miss Teller.

My luck is never very good and it didn't amount to much this time. I didn't draw number one in any class and I had the highest number and was at the foot in a couple of them, and about halfway up in the rest.

Redheaded Roy Harder drew number one in history class and there was a lot of joking about the last shall be first, and king for a day, and a child shall lead them, and so forth. Roy never has studied much and he has always said that history is dead stuff. Everybody expected that it would be only a day or two until he was right down at the foot. And that's what happened. But then, to everybody's surprise, he began to study so that he could fight back up the line. And pretty soon he was in first place again at the head of the class. And the remarkable thing about it was he stayed there. There didn't seem to be a single thing about history lessons that Miss Teller could ask him that he didn't know.

This alone would have been amazing. But what else was going on was even more strange. Delancy Boice was fighting for first place in English. It was Egbert Boice in bookkeeping. Pete Reynolds was the top man at the head of the class next to the front wall in physiology. And my older brother, Harry, was head man in arithmetic. After two weeks, the older the boy the better the student. The more problem a boy had been, the more books he carried home at night.

Then one day in my class in grammar just after class had started we had a big shuffle. Nobody above me could give a sentence showing the proper use of a semicolon, but I could. I went to the head of the class. And then I found out the secret that was making the older boys study so hard.

Before this I had been sitting where I was looking at Miss Teller on an angle toward the front of her desk. All I saw of her was her pretty face and her shirtwaist and the little watch pinned to it. Now I was sitting where I saw all of her, even the part of her under the desk. Every once in awhile she changed her position. When she crossed her limbs and got really interested in the lesson her short bicycle skirt got so high that I could see her silk stocking clear up to her knee. It was a wonderful sight and one that you never see, of course, except in an accident, like when the hammock broke with Linnie on our front veranda.

If anybody gets me out of number-one position in grammar he is going to have to know the book by heart and then some more. But I guess I don't have much chance in the other classes. I could get past the girls who don't know about this, but I don't know as I want to be top man in more than one class anyhow. That's because I want to help Blossom Teller. If we can keep a different older boy as top man in each class, the scholarship in our district school is going to be something wonderful.

❧ The Last of Woodstock

. . . housing shortage and artistic customs

Ed Harder, my father's head clerk, rode up in front of the store on his bicycle after he had been to dinner up at his father's home in Rock City. That's where you begin to go up the mountain to Mead's Mountain Hotel, and it's all along the side of that part of the mountain where the artists have built cabins and shacks and the like among the trees. Ed was worrying about this.

The only trouble is that there are so many artists that they are beginning to edge down to the Village. I have overheard it said that some of them are well-to-do and don't have much regard for money, and so this kind will buy up a big patch of mountain land so as to have maybe a little waterfall in a brook on their place. But a lot of them seem to have to get along from day to day and they will take any kind of a place to live that they can. Besides, the artists coming to Woodstock have attracted a good many folks who are not artists, but think it is fine to live in a high, artistic place like Woodstock is getting to be. There's that man from the Waldorf Astoria Hotel in New York City. The way his name sounds it is Shirkey, but that may not be the way it is spelled. I have overheard the men in the store say he is French or Russian or something like that. Jim Plass says he is the chief cook and bottle washer at the Waldorf Astoria, but there again I think Jim Plass is just showing off and talking through his hat. Because this Mr. Shirkey must be very rich and how can a cook be rich? Anyway, he has bought most all of the Johnson acres on the right-hand side of the Bearsville road just above the Village, and he has built a fine home, and planted trees and bushes to hide him from the road, and he has a swan pond in his big yard and a paved road running up to the house, and pretty flashy rigs and things like that. He is just a sample of some of the richer folks who like to live in an arty place.

And these artists are not only the kind of artists who set up a piece of cloth on a board and put paint on it with a brush in all kinds of ways, some that you have to ask them what it is because they are the only ones who can tell. It seems that anybody who makes anything is an artist, just so long as what they make is different, like carving a piece of wood, or making jewelry, or finding old relics on the farms hereabouts, or inventing things, or writing stories, or writing anything else, especially poetry.

It takes a queer set to not care anything about a steady job, or farming, or money, or anything but art. A lot of them wear funny clothes and hats, or next to nothing, and quite often you see one of them with a beard or a cane he has cut in the woods and polished. Mostly they seem to roam around the Village with lots of time on their hands. They are great for talking and arguing, and sometimes a group of them will be standing right in the middle of the road when a farmer comes along with a team. But they don't move. The farmer will drive around them as the easiest way out. I see a lot of this and I overhear talk about it, and I overhear it said that a little work goes a long way with artists.

I was sitting on the step of the store when Ed rode up on his bicycle after dinner, because it was vacation time at school and I didn't have anything to do and was wondering what I would do next. None of the boys seemed to be around.

So I was glad to see Ed ride up to the store. You can follow Ed around and he will say something or do something that is interesting. He leaned his bicycle up against the front of the store and then looked a long time at a fat young woman artist who was coming from the Woodstock Hotel. She looked like she had cut off the legs of an old pair of Sweet Orr overalls just above her knees so that her limbs were bare, and she was in her bare feet. She had on a red blouse, and her belt to hold up the short pants was a wide one with a big brass buckle. When she walked her bottom wiggled. She had a bottle of Moxie that she must have got at the hotel barroom and she was taking swigs on it. She wasn't saying anything to anybody and was just walking along and Ed and I looked at her for a couple of minutes.

"My God," Ed said, as if he was thinking and I wasn't there. Then he leaned down and took the clips off the bottom of his pants and went in the store and I followed him in.

Nobody was in the store except my father and Grove, the hired man who looks after the barn and horses, because after dinner is a slow time at the store, and all the others were not back from dinner.

Ed walked in, and spotted my father and Grove together by the bookkeeper's cage and walked up to them and then he said, "Well, I've just heard the best one yet. Some of these artists don't go much for homes, and I guess a few of them will live any place that has a roof. Of course, I know that everybody that has any room has one of them boarding, and there's not much other place left. You can understand their taking barns and woodsheds and fixing them up a little if folks don't need them for themselves. But I've just heard the limit."

"Well, what is it?" said Grove.

"One of them is dickering for Hudler's backhouse."

My father looked up with a squint. "Hudler's backhouse? Do you mean his privy?"

"Well, yes," said Ed. "That's what it amounts to. You know where Hudler's privy is?"

"I never had the honor," said my father.

"Well, it's in that little structure on the mountain side of Chris Hudler's lot. Maybe two hundred feet from the house. On top of a bank, of course, so that it can be cleaned underneath. The privy is in one end of it, and the rest of the room is storage. This artist, he's a funny gink with a little goatee on his chin like a Frenchman, and he wears a green coat and yellow pants, and has a young wife, he wants to rent it. I told Chris Hudler if he let his backhouse go that will kind of dam up him and his wife, but he says the artist says no, they can all use it."

"Kind of chummy," said Grove.

"Chris said the artist told him it works all right. They're used to things like that in France where this artist comes from."

I didn't do anything but listen, but I thought that it just goes to show you how the old Woodstock has changed. Even to woodsheds and privies. And that is not all. Two or three little buildings have been built in the village that they call galleries, where paintings are for sale. Two houses are what they call gift shops but not because they give you anything, but so that the summer boarders can buy jewelry and painted cards and ashtrays and a lot of other stuff the artists make, but I overheard Jim Plass tell the men around the white-bellied stove in my father's store that he had been in these shops and it was a caution how many of these things are stamped on the bottom "Made in Japan" or China or Germany and you have to be on your guard if you want the genuine article made in Woodstock.

Things have changed so in Woodstock that a country road is not good enough any more. The county is building what the men call a MacAdam road all the way to Bearsville.

One of the old houses has been made into a library because these artists are great readers of books. Not just stories like Oliver Optic but a lot of dry stuff. Dominie Park says that this shows that the artists are high-minded and intellectual, but I overheard Jim Plass say right away that if they are so brainy it's a funny thing they don't know more like how to milk a cow, or shoe a horse, or grease a wagon. And when Dominie Park said, "Yes, those things are knowledge, but they are not intellectual," Jim Plass came right back and said, "Well, then, why don't they know enough to vote Republican, or to go to church, some of them, or to dress like sensible folks? Suppose all the women in town went around in short pants and bare legs," he said, "would that be intellectual?"

"It might be," said Dominie Park, "in hot weather. And they may, some day."

And Jim Plass went on and said that intellectual wasn't all the artists were interested in, some of them, and he could tell him some of the things he had seen around the barns and haymows, like kissing and even worse; but Dominie Park said he guessed they had better put an end to the argument, and that's all I overheard about that. Of course, everybody knows that Jim Plass is a great talker and bragger and claims to know a lot of things when he is showing off.

But I have overheard the men in the store talking about a lot of changes they expect in Woodstock around the white-bellied stove. They say my father won't have the post office in the store much longer because the mail is getting heavy and the government is getting a building that won't be anything but a post office and that somebody will be hired to run it and not do anything else. They say that the old district school with two rooms and stone walls down below the ruins of the old sawmill won't do much longer because of the big number of kids, and that it will be torn down and a bigger one built of boards. Nobody will take the time to lay up stone walls any more, they say.

And some changes I don't have to overhear about. I can see them for myself. They are turning the old gristmill and big water wheel of Hugo Dish into a house for a club, and they are going to have what they call a golf course on both sides of the Sawkill. And actors who come to Woodstock in summer are taking over the old quarry on a side road down toward West Hurley and they are putting on queer shows. They call it the Maverick Theatre. Folks say this is because Hervey White and Bolton Brown had a fight with Mr. Whitehead and the Mavericks is the result.

Us boys asked Brook Romer why they call it the Maverick Theatre. He said maverick is an old, old word, and that it was the name of a cattle owner away off in Texas who was born in 1803. He said that there are no fences in Texas and a hell of a lot of land, and cattle owners have so many of them that they burn some letter of the alphabet or some little sign into the hides of the cattle with a red-hot iron so that other folks will know who they belong to. They call these burned spots brands. Well, now, this man by the name of Maverick, Brook said, did not brand his cattle. And so as time went on anybody who came across a bull or a cow or a calf without a brand, called it a maverick. And as time went on farther, this word maverick came to mean a calf without a mother. Maybe the mother had died or been lost, and the calf had to go it alone. Then time went on some more and maverick became a word in our language. And so today it means anybody who is different and is stubborn about it, in about everything he does.

Then Brook laughed and he said he thought that naming the quarry theatre The Maverick was delicious, although not in the same way as eating a Red Astrakan apple or a Van Benschoten plum. It is the touch of genius, he said, because it tells in one word the whole story of how the artists are changing the old Holland Dutch village of Woodstock.

But it isn't going to make much difference to Abe Rose, and my mother, and Harry, and me and Clifford and Alvarez, although I suppose it will make a difference to Linnie Jewel. That's because of what I overheard in Larry Elwyn's barber shop in his barn across the road.

This happened after my mother told me to brush my hair and

then take a look at it. "I did not know your hair had grown so," she said.

"You look like a small edition of Robinson Crusoe," said Linnie.

My mother gave me ten cents and told me to go over and have Larry Elwyn cut my hair. You don't have to watch for Larry Elwyn to be in his barber shop since the artists came. In the old Woodstock you had to watch for him because he might be painting a house somewhere, or butchering their pig in the fall, or even out hunting foxes with his hound. But now he is in his barber shop all the time because of so many people in Woodstock, although some of the artists don't pay much attention to their hair one way or another. The ones that have beards now, that is a horse of another color. It's like they think their beards must be exactly right, but they do that themselves.

Well, Larry Elwyn was busy on the big fat man who runs the steam roller for the new hard road down from Bearsville, and who is jolly and whose name is Mister Stuben, and who gets five dollars a day and goes to Larry Elwyn every day for a shave because he gets so much money he can afford it, and so I sat down and waited. Pretty soon I pricked up my ears because they were talking about my father.

"How old do you suppose Mr. Rose is?" said Mr. Stuben.

"Abe Rose?" said Larry Elwyn. "Well, now, let me see. He looks about my age, about 45, but he may be a year or two younger. I remember when he come to Woodstock from down in Rondout on account of being sick and started in the store business with almost nothing. I recall it because there was a lot of talk at the time about his not having much chance against Ed Snyder's big store right on the best corner. Well, the only corner, you might say at that time. That must have been about 1880, twenty, twenty-one years ago."

"He fooled them, I guess."

"Yah, he fooled them."

"I hear he will get cash."

"Yah, cash on the barrelhead."

"The house, the two barns, the store."

"Yah."

"How much do you suppose?"

"Well. For cash, that makes a difference, you know. Oh, I don't know. $25,000 I guess, lock, stock, and barrel. But I suppose Abe Rose is worth all together, well, say $35,000. He's fixed for life if he lives to be a hundred." Then Larry turned to something else. "I see that you're almost down to the Village with the road. How much longer do you figure it will take?"

"Oh, two months maybe."

Larry Elwyn had slapped on some bay rum. He took the sheet away from Mister Stuben's neck, and Mr. Stuben paid him ten cents and went out.

Larry Elwyn does not do anything but think, and work with the comb and scissors when he cuts the hair of boys. He does it quick. I didn't dare let him know I had overheard and so I didn't learn anything more. But I would be dumb if I didn't know something was up.

I went up to the store to tell my father and there were two men with him. I overheard him call one of them Mister Whitney and the other Mister Beekman. My father and Mister Beekman were counting stock and Mister Whitney was writing what they counted down in a book. They were busy and I couldn't ask questions, but I overheard them say that they would go to see the lawyer they call Judge Alphonso T. Clearwater and a bank in Kingston the next day. They looked like nice men. Both of them had dress-up suits on with coats. Mr. Whitney was full-bodied and was older but Mr. Beekman was younger and slim.

I went down to the house and found my mother and Linnie. I told them about the barber shop and Mr. Whitney and Mr. Beekman and I said, "What's going on, anyway?"

"I hardly know myself," my mother said, and when she said that Linnie began to cry and went and sat down on a chair and lifted her apron up and put it over her face.

"There, there, Linnie," said my mother. "Let's hope for the best. But it does seem that things have changed so fast ever since the artists have come. I can't say anything about it, Willie. It's a secret."

"What do you mean, it's a secret," I said. "It can't be much of a secret when you hear about it in Larry Elwyn's barber shop."

"Yes, I know," she said. "But folks are just guessing. Maybe nothing will come of it."

"I hope," said Linnie. Then she started to sob again and put her apron back up to her face.

"Wait a couple of days and you can know, Willie," my mother said. Then she went and sat down by Linnie and looked miserable and tears started to run down her face.

It was too gloomy for me, and besides I could see that I was wasting my time, and so I went out.

But at supper two nights later the whole thing came out. My father asked the Blessing and took his napkin out of his napkin ring and spread it on his lap and started to pass the cold meat and the fried potatoes.

"Well?" my mother said.

"Well, the die is cast. It's settled," he said.

"Maybe it's for the best," said my mother. "But I was so hoping."

"I know," said my father. "But you have to guard against emotions in a thing like this. I talked with Dominie Park. I told him that a country-store business depends on what kind of a man the owner is. You have to study folks and know their whims and cater to them and yet keep a level head. You can't be too strict and you can't be too easygoing. And I told him that you only get a chance to sell a country store, and your home, and your store buildings and barns all in one lump once in a lifetime. Of course, I said, it means tearing up everything by the roots, and losing old friends and comfortable surroundings. But, after all, Woodstock has changed from what we loved. And maybe there are other changes coming in the world that won't be good for the country-store business. And it's not exactly like desertion because Whitney and Beekman from Shandaken look to me like fine men and they will be just as good for Woodstock, and maybe they will know how to handle things better than I would with the changes."

"But we have worked hard for this," said my mother. "And we are free and clear. It's hard to give it all up for less really than it's worth. And you are only forty-two, and at your age it would be a sin to just loaf and stop working."

"You know I wouldn't do that," said my father. "You know me. I can't loaf. I'd go crazy. My idea is that we will move to the county seat, Kingston. I've often thought I would like to be a drummer, and Mathews and Harrison, the wholesale grocers in Kingston, have told me, time and again, that if I ever quit they would like to put me on to travel through the Catskills for them. Come to think of it, moving to the county seat seems to be the dream of most country folks anyway."

"Your health," said my mother. "You came here because you were sick."

"That was from Rondout. It's low and down by the water. Kingston is on high ground."

"You said you talked it over with Dominie Park. What did he say?"

"He asked me if I knew Shakespeare. I allowed that I had heard of him. He said that Shakespeare was a great fellow for knowing what folks had ought to do. In fact, he knew so much that it was uncanny. He said Shakespeare is about the next best thing to the Bible. Dominie Park said that one of the things Shakespeare said was that there is a tide in the affairs of men and that if it is taken at the flood it leads on to fortune, but that if it is not taken, their lives are full of shallows and miseries. In other words, it just happens that things in Woodstock are on the up right now. That's why I happen to have a chance to sell lock, stock, and barrel; and as I say, once in a lifetime. Anyway, it's settled, and we can't back out. The thing to do now is to make plans."

"We have to believe that it's the Lord's will and that it's all for the best," my mother said.

"Well, I concur with the Lord," said my father. "It's my will, too."

"There are some other things," said my mother. "They make it easier. The boys can go to Kingston Academy and not have to board in Kingston or maybe travel back and forth to Woodstock. And it will be nice to be in the old First Dutch Church in Kingston. For the music and the dignity and for the boys. But I wish Linnie was going with us. It will be like losing one of the family."

Clifford and I both hollered at once. "What! Won't Linnie go with us?"

"Maybe later," said my father, "after we get settled. But that might not be the best thing for Linnie. If she didn't come with us, she would probably marry some nice young farmer here and that certainly would be a better life for her. I notice she wouldn't have much trouble. There's Grove, for instance. I notice him paying attention and it wouldn't be surprising if he is thinking things over. He's our barn man now, but he'll inherit a pretty fine farm from his father some day. How about it, Linnie?"

But he missed if he thought Linnie would come back with something cute. All she did was start to cry.

After that things began to move fast around our house.

My father and mother invited almost everybody to three big dinners and my mother and Linnie had to work like sixty. Different ones to each dinner, of course. There were so many friends that every time the big table in the dining room was stretched out to the limit and filled with people, but not any children, and afterward everybody played dominoes and authors and old maid in the living room and the parlor.

And next, after that, there was the big public auction that took all day and the Ladies' Aid helped my mother and Linnie run a lunch in the dining room for anybody who wanted it, for fifteen cents, and the money went to the Ladies' Aid.

There were only two things bad about the auction. There was a lot of manure and mud from the boots of some of the men left in the dining room on the hardwood floor that was varnished, and that had my mother and Linnie scrubbing most of the next day. And the other thing wrong was what my father said. It was because of the artists, he said. He said that stuff that he was ashamed to put up for sale because it was junk, and only did it because the auctioneer said once he was hired he was the boss and how about his commission, this stuff went for unholy prices. But on the other hand, good stuff went for a song. But he guessed the good stuff wasn't old enough or artistic enough, he said.

Pretty soon the day came when the big lumber wagon stood in front of the gate in our white picket fence, and it was loaded to the skies with furniture and bedding and dishes that we were taking along to Kingston. My father and mother and Harry and little Alvarez were going to ride in a rig that stood behind the lumber wagon, but Clifford and I asked if we could ride up on the seat of the lumber wagon above the tails of Jim and Carrie, and my father said we could. It was our last time to use Jim and Carrie and old Dick because now they belonged to Whitney and Beekman.

So we climbed up there. Linnie and Old Tom were staying with Mr. Whitney and Mr. Beekman. But Brownie was going with us, and I had him in my arms. My father said we were ready, and told Grove to start. We moved through the village street and around the corner between Snyder's store and the Woodstock Hotel.

I lifted Brownie up and said, "Take a good look, Brownie. Good old Woodstock is gone forever."